THE
Custom
Government
MODEL
Pistol

To Bill

With Best Wishes

[signature]

7-98

THE
Custom
Government
MODEL
Pistol

Layne Simpson

DISCLAIMER

Wolfe Publishing Company and the author
disclaims all possible liability for damages, including actual, incidental
and consequential, resulting from reader usage of information
or advice contained in this book. Use data and advice
at your own risk and with caution.

ISBN 1-879356-16-3

Wolfe Publishing Company
6471 Airpark Drive
Prescott, Arizona 86301

Dedication

This book is dedicated my father, Bailey,
who introduced me to guns and hunting,
and
to my lovely wife, Phyllis,
who does more unto others than she would have them do unto her.

CONTENTS

1   John Browning and His Autoloader 1
2   How the Government Model Works 33
    How Individual Components Work 38
3   Pistolsmiths and Custom Pistols 50
4   Planning Your Custom Pistol 80
5   Slide Modifications 98
    Tightening the Fit 98
    Mechanical Tighteners 101
    Squeezing, Peening, and Lapping 102
    The ACC-U-RAIL System 103
    The Caspian Alternative 104
    Spare Firing Pin Stop 107
    About Those Sight Slots 107
    Lowered and Flared Ejection Port 107
    Shortening and Lightening 110
    The Extractor 118
    Internal Polishing 118
    The Grasping Handle 119
6   The Frame 122
    The Beveled Magazine Well 122
    Magazine Well Funnels 123
    Mainspring Housings 130
    Extended Frontstrap 131
    Para-Ordnance Frame 133
    Aluminum Frame Recoil Block 133
    Squaring and Checkering the Trigger Guard 135
    Extended Magazine Release 137
    Custom Slide Stops 140
    Extended Slide Stop 143
    Ambidextrous Slide Stop 143
    The Weak Hand Thumb Rest .144
    Extended Ejector 144
    Pins 147
7   Metal Checkering and Serrating 148
8   Metal Preparation and Finishes 169
9   The Barrel 181
    Factory Barrels 181
    Custom Barrels 184

Bushing-Type Barrels 188
Sleeved Barrel...................................192
Heavy Barrel....................................193
Jim Stroh's Design 195
Centaur System's Quadra-Lok™ 196
Advantages and Disadvantages....................198
The Fully Supported Chamber 199
Locking Lug Engagement 203
Barrel Life.....................................204

10 **The Fire Control System** 209
Standard Trigger Designs 209
The Series 80 Trigger 213
The Pivoting Trigger............................217
Hammers 218
The Titanium Firing Pin 222
Beavertail Grip Safeties 225
Extended Thumb Safeties 227
Ambidextrous Thumb Safeties 231
The Thumbguard 233

11 **Open Sights** 240

12 **Optical Sights and Mounts** 264

13 **Magazines** 286

14 **About Those Coil Springs** 298

15 **Odds and Ends** 311
Full-Length Recoil Spring Guide 311
Recoil Spring Plugs.............................317
The Humble Shock Buffer 317
Grip Panels 322
Grip Panel Screws 333

16 **Compensators** 339

17 **The Switch-Top Guns** 372

18 **Complete Disassembly**.........................382

19 **Maintaining the Custom Gun**...................411
Removing the Gunk 413
Getting the Lead Out 415
Removing Copper Fouling 417
Magazine Cleaning 417
Lubricants 419
Long-Term Storage 422

Adjusting Extractor Tension 422
Spring Replacement 424
Electronic Sights.................................426
Spare Parts 427
The Shooter's Logbook 427
Thirty-Point Lubrication Plan.....................428

20 How Much Does It Weigh? 430

21 Government Model Cartridges 454

22 Handloading for the Government Model 486

23 Load Data 507
9x19mm Parabellum (Luger) 508
9x21mm +P 511
9x23mm Super +P...................................512
.38 Colt Super Auto 513
.40 Smith & Wesson 517
10mm Auto 522
.41 Avenger 525
.41 Action Express 526
.45 ACP 527

24 USPSA/IPSC Competition 535

25 The Practical Belt Holster 561

26 The Competition Rig 584

27 Into the Twenty-first Century 601

APPENDICES

  I   Contributing Pistolsmiths 620

 II   Other Contributors 623

III   Spring Rates 626

 IV   Factory Load Velocities..........................631
9mm Parabellum (Luger) 631
.38 Super 632
.40 Smith & Wesson 632
10mm Auto 633
.41 Action Express 634
.45 ACP...634

  V   Actual Jacketed Bullet Diameters 636

 VI   The Cover Gun 639

ACKNOWLEDGMENTS

Anyone who writes a book owes a lot to the many people who directly and indirectly shared their time, knowledge, opinions, and assistance. I am deeply indebted to many friends, both old and new. Thanks to Mark Harris, owner of Wolfe Publishing who thought this book was a good idea even during those moments when I had a doubt or two; Chuck Warner and Cecil Hare for their enthusiasm, assistance, and boundless energy; Bill Wilson, from whom I contracted that incurable ailment called the custom Government Model bug; Dave Stanford, president of the United States Practical Shooting Association for photos of all those competitors who first appeared in *Front Sight* magazine; Paul Thompson, of Browning, for the historical photos; various other friends and companies who contributed their time and assistance; and last, but most important, all the other pistolsmiths who supplied photos of their fine work. Without them, this project could not have progressed beyond the idea stage.

INTRODUCTION

With few exceptions, this is not a step-by-step, do-it-yourself book about working on the Government Model pistol. It is not intended as a guide that will enable the inexperienced to pick up a few tools at the local hardware store and magically transform a frame, a slide, and sack full of parts into a gorgeous tackdriver with a malfunction rate of zero per 5,000 rounds.

Producing such a book would be comparable to writing a handyman's guide on transforming the family station wagon into an Indy 500 winner. Even if such a book existed, most of us still couldn't win the race simply because the correct and proper transformation of a factory machine into a winner requires someone who has spent years dripping sweat and tears on a cold shop floor while slowly developing the necessary talent. Some really good pistolsmithing books are available, but primarily they are intended for those who seriously plan to become a pistolsmith. This book tells you what pistolsmiths do and how their work should look and work, rather than how they do it.

I'm not a pistolsmith, never wanted to be one, and have no plans to become one. If it is possible to drop in a custom part here, or bolt on something there, I'll do it. But when it comes to filing, scraping, drilling, milling, sanding, or any other modification that requires removal of metal or precise hand fitting, I want no part of it. This especially holds true for so critical an area as the fire control system. Given enough time, I can completely disassemble and reassemble a Government Model pistol while blindfolded, but modifying its component parts is not my cup of tea.

One does not have to be a pistolsmith to recognize craftsmanship. I am told that I have a keen eye for recognizing quality work, and for spotting the other kind from even greater distances. Whether or not this is entirely true, I can't honestly say, but I have examined many custom firearms over the years and if you look long enough, some of it is bound to sink in. The truth of the matter is, anyone can separate the superb from the mediocre and the good from the bad; all it takes is a knowledge of what to look for and where. So, in some respects, this is a how-to-do-it book.

As you read the pages ahead, you will notice that like most serious firearms enthusiasts, I have strong opinions about almost everything. If mine don't agree with yours, you're the boss because the money you'll probably spend after looking at some of the photos in this book is yours and not mine. By the same token, if my opinions don't agree with those of your pistolsmith, don't forget who is writing about it and who is actually doing the work on your gun.

This book is not about one-of-a-kind, gold-plated pistols covered with hand engraving and wearing genuine ivory grips. I have nothing against those types of guns, indeed I have the greatest admiration for artists capable of such work, and wouldn't mind owning at least a dozen, but my real interest lies in guns for shooting and not collecting. I like handsome guns with flawless workmanship, but they must still be reliable and accurate working guns before they will excite me. This book, then, is about working guns.

This book centers mainly on custom Government Model pistols and things pistolsmiths do to make them so. It also tells you where the Government Model originated, why it went on to become so popular, how it works, what is available for it, what to carry it in, how to make it last many years, how to take it apart, how to put it back together, how to handload for it, how to keep it running for many years, and, perhaps, where it is headed. It includes the strengths and weaknesses of the gun.

More importantly, this book is about working guns built by working men with dirt beneath their fingernails. It's about a group of master craftsmen who with keen eyes, steady hands, aching feet, and pride in their hearts undertake the often thankless job of making one of the world's greatest firearms even greater.

Enjoy.

Layne Simpson
Simpsonville, South Carolina
April 9, 1992

1

John Browning and His Autoloader

A S a rule, firearms inventors are remembered for their single greatest achievement. Peter Paul Mauser gave us what many consider the very best of bolt action rifle designs; Henry Deringer's little handgun was just the thing for a riverboat gambler to stow inside a boot or vest pocket; Arthur Savage was far ahead of his time in the lever-action sporting rifle field; a famous pistol still wears Georg Luger's name; and General Custer might have worn his hair a bit longer if he had arrived at a place called Little Big Horn with Dr. Gatling's multiple-barrel gun in tow. And, of course, everybody knows how Oliver Winchester, Sam Colt, and others helped take the wild out of the West. Other names such as Thompson, Schmeisser, Hotchkiss, Borchardt, Uzi, Garand, Johnson, Arisaka, and Maxim have become more or less synonymous with particular firearms.

John Browning is remembered not for one, but for dozens of accomplishments in the field of firearms design. He was the son of gunsmith and rifle inventor Jonathan Browning, who was a friend of Brigham Young. Jonathan had planned to make the Illinois to Utah exodus with Young and other Mormon followers in 1846, but was asked to remain behind where his skills were badly needed. In 1852, five years after Young gazed across the Great Salt Lake and stated, "This is the place," Jonathan Browning arrived in Utah.

John Moses Browning was born in Utah on January 23, 1855. He designed his first rifle, the Winchester Model 1895, at the age of 23. In 1923, three years before his death, Browning applied for design patents on his last major project, a new 9mm caliber semiautomatic pistol. It was introduced in 1935 by the Belgian firm, Fabrique Nationale (FN) and sold as the Model 1935,

John Browning *(Courtesy of* **Rifle***, No. 105)*

the Grand Pussiance, and the Hi-Power. Between those first and last designs, there were many other success stories, but unlike most firearms inventors, few of Browning's guns wore his name. In addition to the Hi-Power pistol, there were the Browning Superposed shotgun, the Baby Browning pistol, the Browning Automatic-5 shotgun, and the Browning .22 Automatic rifle, but most of his designs were manufactured under other names.

Browning didn't become rich by being a poor businessman. He insisted that his designs be marketed under the names of their manufacturers. He realized that household names such as Winchester, Colt, and Remington stamped on the barrels would sell far more guns than the name of an unknown Utah inventor. A few of his many creations included Winchester's models 1886, 1887, 1890, 1892, 1893, 1894, 1895, 1897, and 1900; Remington models 8, 11, 17, and 24; the Stevens Model 520; and the Colt Woodsman. Browning's more famous machine gun designs are the Colt Model 1895, the Browning Model 1917 .30 caliber water-cooled, and the Browning .50 caliber. One also must not overlook Browning's 37mm cannon and his Model 1917 .30 caliber BAR (Browning Automatic Rifle), the latter used by United States armed forces during World War I, World War II, and the Korean conflict.

Browning invented his first semiautomatic handgun in 1893 or 1894. He had been experimenting with various gas-operated rifles so it was only logical that his first pistol be designed to utilize propellant gas to operate it. Colt tested prototypes of the .38 caliber autoloader in 1896 and bought the manufacturing and sales rights for it throughout the western hemisphere, but never produced it for the commercial market. Browning's second pistol, also .38 caliber, was of blowback operation. It was tested the same year, but Colt decided not to produce it either. So, Browning sold the eastern hemisphere rights for that design to FN and it was manufactured by the hundreds of thousands for the European market.

Browning sold other designs to Colt, but the first one actually manufactured by that company for the commercial market was the Model 1900 Sporting. It was the first autoloading pistol to be introduced by a United States manufacturer. Chambered for the .38 ACP (Automatic Colt Pistol) cartridge, the Model 1900 was a recoil-operated, locked-breech autoloader with an exposed hammer. Its locking system was the parallel ruler type, which consisted of two pivoting links connecting the frame with the barrel at its chamber and muzzle ends. When the slide moved rearward during firing, the links lowered the barrel in a parallel fashion and in doing so disengaged its locking ribs from their recesses in the slide. As the slide returned to battery, the links raised the barrel to its locked position. Two later variations of the same pistol were the Pocket and Military models.

John Browning with his water-cooled machine gun.

Utah's top live-bird shooting team with their shotguns during the 1890's, from left to right: G. L. Becker, John M. Browning, A. P. Bigelow, and Matthew S. Browning. Becker used a Winchester Model 1901 lever action, the two Browning brothers are holding Winchester Model 1897 pump guns and Bigelow's double is not identifiable.

Interior of Browning shop at the turn of the century.

John Browning's first autoloading pistol design was gas operated. It never went into production.

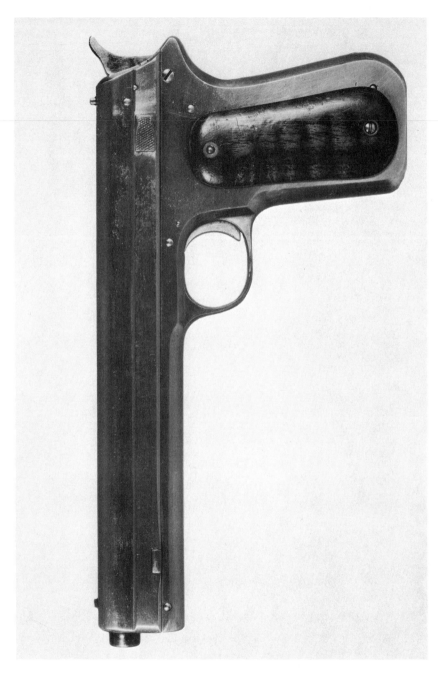

Browning's pilot model of a .38 caliber recoil-operated autoloader introduced by Colt in 1900.

The Browning storefront around 1882.

By the late 1890s it became evident to those in United States military circles that a semiautomatic was the sidearm of the future. Thus, in 1898 a group of army officers met at Springfield Armory to evaluate various designs. They included a prototype of the soon to be Browning/Colt Model 1900 in .38 ACP, as well as four autoloaders of European design, Mauser, Borchardt, Bergmann, and Mannlicher. None proved entirely satisfactory, but Browning's gun scored far more favorable points. A couple of years later another Model 1900 was tested and as a result, the United States Army and Navy purchased slightly over 200 for troop field testing.

Field tests of the Model 1900 prompted changes that evolved into the Model 1902. One modification was the addition of a stop on the left of the receiver, which locked the slide back when the last round was fired. Magazine capacity was increased from seven to eight rounds and a lanyard swivel was installed on the gripframe's left side. By this time tougher contenders had entered the ring, including 1,000 Lugers in 7.65mm caliber bought from Georg himself.

Next a decision was made that put all firearms manufacturers who had submitted guns for testing back at ground zero. Having decided that its service revolver in .38 Long Colt was less than effective on Moro warriors in the Philippines, the Ordnance Department decided to initiate stopping power tests to determine the caliber of its proposed new autoloader. In 1904 a board headed by Colonel Louis La Garde of the Medical Corps and Colonel John Thompson of the Ordnance Department performed various tests with revolvers and autoloaders. They decided that the larger calibers were more effective. As a result, the United States Army decided on a .45 caliber cartridge firing a 230-grain bullet at 800 feet per second (fps) as the minimum acceptable level of performance. Until a new autoloader could be adopted, the Army abandoned its .38 caliber service revolvers and issued (or reissued) .45 caliber Colt Frontier and New Service revolvers.

Colt and Browning already were experimenting with a 9.8mm caliber cartridge in a modified version of its 1902 Military Model pistol, so going up to .45 caliber probably was no big deal. Within a year after La Garde's "Gunshot Injuries" report was published, Colt modified its .38 caliber Model 1902 and introduced it as the 1905 Military Model. Like the 1902 pistol, the 1905 had the parallel-ruler lock/unlock system, an inertia-type firing pin, and a slide stop lever on the receiver's left side. Its cartridge was called the .45 Automatic Colt Pistol, or .45 ACP for short. Colt introduced the new cartridge with a 200-grain bullet at 900 fps, but in order to meet military specifications, the lower velocity 230-grain bullet was later substituted.

New tests were initiated at Springfield Armory in 1907 in which the Colt Model 1905 Military Model was pitted against several other .45 caliber autoloaders (e.g., the Savage, Luger, White-Merrill, Bergmann, and Knoble, the

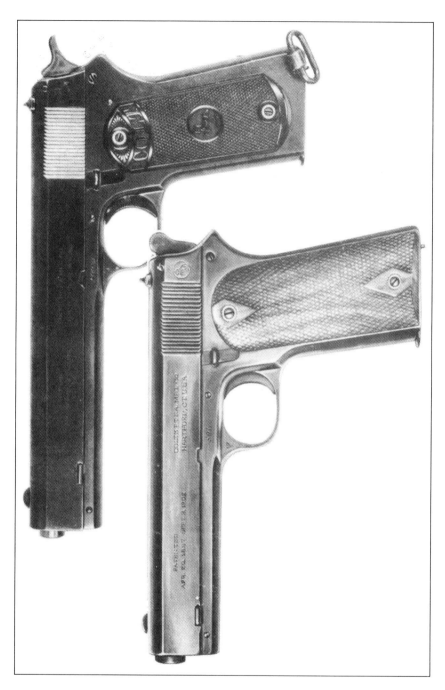

Left, Colt Model 1902; right, Colt Model 1905. *(Courtesy* Rifle, *No. 105)*

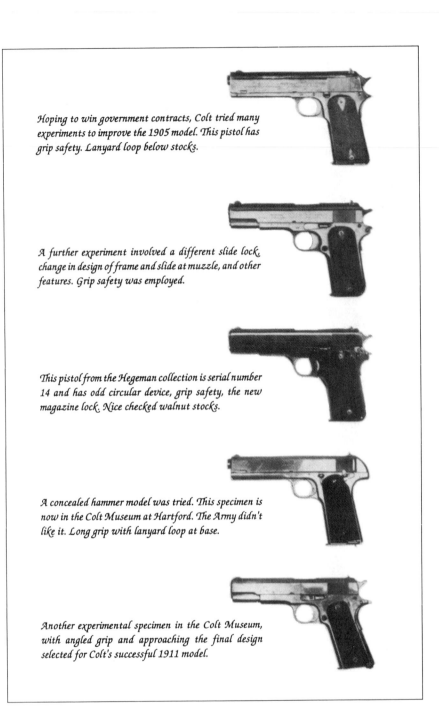

Hoping to win government contracts, Colt tried many experiments to improve the 1905 model. This pistol has grip safety. Lanyard loop below stocks.

A further experiment involved a different slide lock, change in design of frame and slide at muzzle, and other features. Grip safety was employed.

This pistol from the Hegeman collection is serial number 14 and has odd circular device, grip safety, the new magazine lock. Nice checked walnut stocks.

A concealed hammer model was tried. This specimen is now in the Colt Museum at Hartford. The Army didn't like it. Long grip with lanyard loop at base.

Another experimental specimen in the Colt Museum, with angled grip and approaching the final design selected for Colt's successful 1911 model.

(Courtesy Colt Firearms, James E. Serven, Wolfe Publishing Co.)

latter in both single and double action configurations). Also included in those tests were Colt and S&W .45 caliber revolvers and the Webley-Fosbery auto-revolver. The Colt and Savage semiautos won that contest with the Luger placing third. Colt and Savage then were invited to submit 200 additional pistols for testing, but the Army requested several changes in the Colt's design. These changes included a grip safety in the backstrap, a spur-type hammer in lieu of the rounded hammer, and a loaded chamber indicator. The latter feature eventually was deleted from the specifications. It also was specified that the extractor, ejector, and ejection port be modified so fired cases would be ejected in a more vertical direction, rather than to the side.

Cavalry troops were assigned the task of testing the modified Colt pistols and they performed their duty with great vigor. Slides stuck, frames cracked, sights fell off, firing pins shattered, and broken sears caused some guns to go full auto. On top of it all, troopers complained that the noise made by retracting and releasing the slide spooked their horses and since it was impossible to reload the magazine at full gallop, extra loaded magazines would have to be carried. The parallel-ruler lock/unlock system also made the gun difficult to field strip for cleaning.

John Browning returned to the drawing board and made several design changes. One consisted of eliminating the front barrel link and enclosing the barrel's muzzle in a removable lugged bushing which engaged notches machined inside the front of the slide. That converted its lockup operation from parallel-ruler to tipping breech. Rather than the barrel locking and unlocking by moving up and down in a parallel fashion, the chamber end moved up and down during the firing and reloading cycle. Other changes consisted of a new slide stop, relocating the magazine catch to the frame just behind the trigger, an improved grip angle, and a stronger firing pin. A new thumb safety on the receiver's left side locked the hammer and slide, and a lanyard loop on the floorplate of the magazine was optional for horse-mounted troops.

Browning and Colt still had a few miles to go. In late 1910, the military board once again met at Springfield Armory to put the latest versions of the Colt and Savage pistols through their paces to the tune of 6,000 rounds each. The Savage gun broke 13 parts during the test. The Colt broke four parts and ruptured a barrel.

In March of 1911 both guns were subjected to final endurance tests during which the Colt wore a barrel of stronger design. The Savage ate up parts and was plagued by numerous malfunctions. The Colt digested its entire 6,000 rounds with zero malfunctions or broken parts. The examining board had the following to say on March 11:

> The Board recommends that the Colt Caliber .45 Automatic Pistol
> of the design submitted to the Board for tests be adopted for use

By 1909, the design had evolved to a single-link system. Subsequent Army-requested changes resulted in the Model 1911 shown above. *(Courtesy* Rifle, *No. 105)*

by foot and mounted troops in the military service in consequence of its marked superiority to the present service revolvers, and to any pistol, of its extreme reliability and endurance, of its ease of disassembly, of its accuracy and of its fulfillment of all essential requirements.

On March 29, 1911, orders from the Secretary of War and the Chief of Ordnance of the General Staff enacted the official adoption of John Browning's pistol. The cost per unit to Uncle Sam was $15.60, which included a magazine and spare parts.

Incidentally, it cost American taxpayers a tidy sum to completely outfit a doughboy in those days. His battle gear consisted of a 1903 Springfield rifle ($19.50), bayonet and scabbard ($3.28), 100 cartridges and cartridge belt ($9.08), gas mask ($12), steel helmet ($3.00), three blankets and a bedsack ($19.83), and trenching tool (50 cents). When his clothing, 11 cooking utensils and other equipment were added, the tab ran $115.30.

Eventually other countries adopted Browning's pistol as well; Thailand, Argentina, Vietnam, and Norway to name but a few. The Model 1914 Norwegian version had an extended slide stop, a detail later offered by pistolsmiths in the United States. Mexico's version, the Obregon, had a rotating barrel and combination slide lock and thumb safety. The 1911 pistol chambered for the .455 Webley was adopted by the British Royal Navy during World War I. Of course, Colt wasted no time in offering its new military autoloader to the commercial market as the Government Model Automatic Pistol Cal. .45 with a "C" prefix in its serial number and a $20 price tag.

The Army's new .45 first drew serious blood in skirmishes along the Mexican border during 1913. It was on hand when the U.S. Marines seized Vera Cruz in early 1914, and again in March of 1916 when General John J. "Black Jack" Pershing led his mounted troops across the border in pursuit of Pancho Villa. However, bigger things loomed just around the corner in a faraway land.

When Pershing and his doughboys landed in France on June 27, 1917, the Army had approximately 75,000 of the new Colt pistols. When the Armistice was signed on November 11, 1918, Colt, Remington, and Springfield Armory had increased the inventory to over 375,000 with peak production at almost 2,000 units per day.

A little known fact about the Model 1911 was its use by aviators in the fledgling U.S. Air Corps. Before the machine gun was adopted for aerial warfare, pilots were armed with .45 caliber pistols with an extended 20-round magazine and a small wire cage attached to the righthand side of the grip. The cage collected spent cases as they were ejected from the gun to prevent them from striking the pilot or fragile parts of the airplane.

PROOF, Not Talk

You need an automatic pistol for home protection. You know you do. But you're not sure, after reading the different makers' claims, which pistol is the best. Good. Now listen to this:

The Colt was adopted by the U. S. Government because of its "marked superiority to any other known pistol."

The U. S. Ordnance Board made the most exhaustive and rigid tests before it decided on the Colt. It brushed claims aside—its experts decided on *results*.

Marked superiority! A strong statement—from the highest source in the country, too. Be guided by the Government's decision—get a Colt—the automatic pistol that

Fires the First Shot First

the pistol that is automatically safe—those two qualities so essential to a firearm for home protection.

Write for new booklet No. 85
on "How to Shoot."

COLT'S PATENT FIRE ARMS MFG. CO.
Hartford, Conn.

October 10, 1914

This Colt advertisement is dated October 10, 1914.

16

The Model of 1911 pistol fought its first world war with honors, but hard use by troops in the field pointed out a few needed refinements. As a result, the following modifications were made: the grip safety's tang was lengthened, the trigger was shortened and its surface serrated, relief cuts were added on the frame adjacent to the trigger, the mainspring housing was changed from flat to arched, nominal bore and groove diameters were slightly modified, and the width of the front and rear sight notches was increased. With those changes the gun was redesignated M1911M1 in 1924. In 1926 the designation was changed to M1911A1 and the old Model of 1911 redesignated as the M1911.

In 1929 Colt added the .38 Super chambering in its Government Model, calling it the Super .38 Automatic Pistol. Shortly thereafter other variations began to appear. The ACE .22 was introduced in 1931 and 1933 brought the .45 National Match and .38 Super Match. In 1937 the .22 caliber Service Model ACE was introduced. A floating chamber designed by David (Carbine) Williams, closely simulated the recoil of the .45 ACP. Prewar prices were $41.50 for the Super .38 and .45 caliber Government Model; $50 for the National Match, Super Match, and ACE .22; and $60 for the Service Model Ace. Available at $34 was a .22 conversion unit with slide, barrel, floating chamber, barrel bushing, ejector, slide stop, magazine, and recoil spring with guide and plug. About a year before the Japanese bombardment of Pearl Harbor, Colt discontinued production of all commercial models. Total respective production of the ACE 22 and 22 Service ACE was 10,935 and 13,800 units through 1940.

When the United States officially declared war on Japan on December 8, 1941, only Colt was producing the .45, but by the time the Enola Gay flew over Hiroshima on August 6, 1945, almost 2,000,000 units had been manufactured by Colt, Remington-Rand, Singer Sewing Machine, Union Switch & Signal, and Ithaca. Aesthetics suffered during wartime production. Plastic grip panels replaced checkered wood, the trigger was made entirely of stampings, the hammer spur was machined to the same width as the body of the hammer, and Parkerized steel replaced blued steel. Even so, the changes didn't stop the gun from working.

John Browning's big .45 autoloader is one of the most famous and recognizable handguns ever produced anywhere in the world, but it probably was better liked in the private sector than within the military establishment. Some soldiers considered the M1911A1 the finest battle pistol in the world, but common criticisms heard from both high and low ranks included an extremely heavy and rough trigger pull, poor accuracy, excessive weight and bulk, and far too much recoil for green troops. Lieutenant General George Patton reportedly hated the gun because it once discharged while holstered and the fat bullet had to be dug from his leg.

The Service Model ACE was introduced in 1937, discontinued shortly before World War II, and reintroduced in 1978, but was not being produced as this book was written.

Even before World War II ended, the Ordnance Corps had a new pistol on its list of future projects, so in 1945 Uncle Sam bought the last M1911A1 pistols from Colt, Remington-Rand, and Ithaca. Serial numbers assigned by the government to various manufacturers range from No. 1 to Colt in 1912 to No. 2693613 to Ithaca in 1945. Eventually it was decided that the new service autoloader had to be a lightweight double action chambered for the 9mm Parabellum (Luger) cartridge. High Standard, Smith & Wesson, and Colt jumped at the opportunity of a juicy new government contract, but the Army decided that replacing mountains of ammunition, spare parts, and .45 caliber pistols was too costly. Rather than watch development money spiral down the drain, Colt introduced its candidate to the commercial market as the Commander. Introduced in 1949 in calibers .45 ACP, .38 Super, and 9mm, the Commander had a rounded hammer spur quite similar to the one on Browning's Model 1905 pistol. With its "Coltalloy" frame and 4¼ inch barrel, the compact autoloader weighed 26½ ounces. Advertised weight was later increased to 27½ ounces.

During early 1957, firearms writers got their first peek at the revival of Colt's National Match pistol. Called National Match 45 Gold Cup, it would feed semiwadcutter bullets, had an overtravel adjustment in its extremely light and wide trigger, a flat integral sighting rib on its slide, and a new Elliason-designed adjustable rear sight. Its fire control system was identical to that of the Government Model with one exception. To prevent sear bounce with the light trigger, which could cause the hammer to follow the slide down when cycling, a small coil spring attached at the rear of the sear increased its engagement pressure against the hammer.

The Gold Cup initially was available only with the flat mainspring housing. During the early 1960s the .38 Special Wadcutter with a five-shot magazine was offered as an option, but eventually discontinued. Years later, 750 each of .38 Super Elite and Elite IX (9mm) Gold Cups were manufactured for a distributor by the name of Wammes. Some extra Gold Cup slides also were manufactured for those calibers and one rides atop the Warner high-capacity, optical-sighted gun in C.P. 9x23 Super featured on this book's cover. During 1992, Colt built 200 more Gold Cup pistols in .38 Super, calling it the El Dorado Custom. The standard production Gold Cup is available in 10mm and .45 ACP, in blued steel or stainless, with a flat or arched mainspring housing.

In 1970, Colt introduced its Series 70 Government Model with a slightly modified barrel contour and collet-type bushing. Probably not one of the better ideas in firearms design, the collet bushing gradually was replaced with the old solid bushing during the late 1980s.

The year 1972 brought the Combat Commander, a 36-ounce, steel-frame version of the Commander. The original aluminum-frame Commander

Colt reintroduced its National Match pistol in 1957. This is the later Series 70 model.

20

The Series 1970 gun introduced a slightly modified barrel contour and a collet-type bushing. Colt has since gone back to the old solid bushing.

eventually came to be called the Lightweight Commander and the Combat Commander eventually became just plain Commander. More recently, the Commander once again became the Combat Commander. Are you still with me?

The Service Model ACE was reintroduced in 1978 but eventually dropped from production due to poor sales. ACE conversion units also were reintroduced, but their availability has been on again, off again.

Colt made two modifications to the Government Model and its variations in 1983 and thus began the Series 80 pistols. A new passive safety mechanism in the slide and frame is designed to prevent the firing pin from traveling forward unless the trigger is pulled and a noncaptive half-cock notch on the hammer replaced the old captive notch. This latter change is why the hammer will move forward on a Series 80 when the trigger is pulled even when the sear is engaging what used to be called the half-cock notch of the hammer.

Introduced in 1985, the Officer's ACP is the smallest Colt autoloader to utilize John Browning's basic M1911/M1911A1 design format. With its 3½-inch barrel and six-round magazine, Colt's runt of the .45 caliber family weighs 34 ounces, 5 ounces less than its 5-inch papa, and 2 ounces less than the Combat Commander. The lightweight Officer's ACP with aluminum alloy frame weighs only 24 ounces, or 3½ ounces less than the Lightweight Commander. Like all Government Model variations, this one also is available in stainless steel. Except for a limited production run of El Capitan guns in .38 Super, the Officer's ACP has been available only in .45 ACP.

In 1986 the tenon of the front sight on all models and variations was increased in width from .055 to .125 inch.

A few of Colt's double action versions of its Government Model finally became available during late 1989, but it was scarce throughout most of 1990. Called the Double Eagle, its frame differs considerably from that of the Government Model, but with the exception of a disconnector timing groove milled into the sidewall of its slide, the two upper assemblies basically are the same. Originally available only in .45 ACP, Double Eagles also have been manufactured in 9mm Parabellum, .38 Super, .40 S&W, and 10mm Auto. Variations include standard (35 ounces) and lightweight (25 ounces) Officer's ACP, and a Double Eagle Combat Commander at 36 ounces. The standard five-inch version is rated at 39 ounces.

In 1991 Colt introduced a plain-Jane version of the Government Model called M1991A1. It is obviously aimed square at other companies who offer Government Model pistols at lower prices than the standard blued steel Colt. The M1991A1 has synthetic grip panels and a Parkerized finish. Serial numbers began where Colt left off with the last pistols built for Uncle Sam in 1945.

The steel-frame Combat Commander was introduced in 1972.

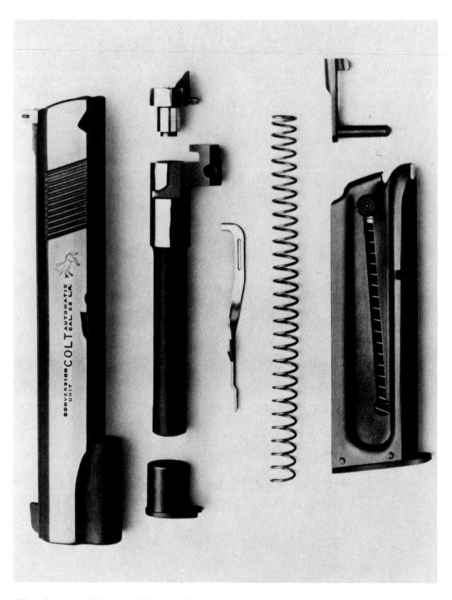

The Service Model ACE .22 Rimfire conversion unit was introduced during the 1930s and has since been available sporadically from Colt.

24

The Series 1980 gun introduced a new firing pin block and the non-captive half-cock notch replaced the old captive notch.

25

Introduced in 1985, the Officer's ACP is the smallest Colt autoloader to utilize John Browning's basic 1911 design format.

26

Colt's Double Eagle, a double-action version of the Government Model
was introduced in 1989.

Colt introduced the M1991A1 economy-grade version of the Series 80 Government Model in 1991. Serial numbers began where Colt left off with the last pistols sold to Uncle Sam in 1945.

Introduced by Colt during 1992 were enhanced upgradings of the Government Model, Delta Elite, Combat Elite, Commander, and Officer's ACP. The changes included a relief cut in the frame at the terminus of the trigger guard, a slightly longer grip safety, flared ejection port, long trigger, Commander-style hammer, and a flat-top slide.

Colt has produced other M1911A1 format autoloaders with different names, some limited in production numbers, but they are nothing more than a different stanza of the same tune. A few of these autoloaders include the Delta Elite, Combat Elite, Delta Gold Cup, Gold Cup Commander, El Commandante, El General, Ultimate Officer's ACP, El Capitan Officer's ACP, Tank Commander, Commanding Officer, Super Lite Commander, El Jefe Custom, and a number of guns introduced to commemorate various battles or other events in United States military history.

Dozens of copies, near copies, and numerous variations of John Browning's fine old pistol have been manufactured by companies in the United States and other countries, probably more so than for any other handgun. To name a few in no particular order: Auto-Ordnance, Federal Ordnance, Para-Ordnance, Llama, Caspian, Omega Defensive Industries (ODI), Coonan Arms, L.A.R. Manufacturing, Caspian, Safari Arms, Pachmayr, Springfield Armory, Detonics, New Detonics, Omega, Arminex Ltd., and Randall.

The M1911 remained an important part of United States military ordnance longer than any other firearm. Old slab sides, the gun everybody hated and nobody could shoot, outlasted the 1903 Springfield, the 1917 Enfield, the BAR, the Thompson submachine gun, the M1 Garand, the M1 Carbine, and the M14. The .45 was still alive and kicking long after a young whippersnapper called M16 first scrambled aboard ship. In 1985 the United States military came full circle by adopting the 9mm Parabellum, a cartridge it had rejected at the turn of the century. The big autoloader with the huge hole in its barrel lasted three quarters of a century, long enough for any old soldier to serve a country and its people with honor.

John Browning would be proud.

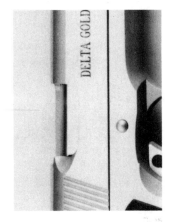

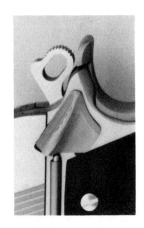

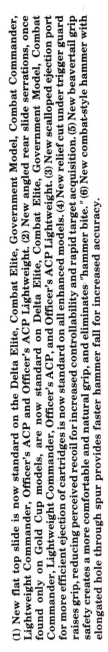

(1) New flat top slide is now standard on the Delta Elite, Combat Elite, Government Model, Combat Commander, Lightweight Commander, Officer's ACP and Officer's ACP Lightweight. (2) New angled rear slide serrations, once found only on Gold Cup models, are now standard on Delta Elite, Combat Elite, Government Model, Combat Commander, Lightweight Commander, Officer's ACP, and Officer's ACP Lightweight. (3) New scalloped ejection port for more efficient ejection of cartridges is now standard on all enhanced models. (4) New relief cut under trigger guard raises grip, reducing perceived recoil for increased controllability and rapid target acquisition. (5) New beavertail grip safety creates a more comfortable and natural grip, and eliminates "hammer bite." (6) New combat-style hammer with elongated hole through spur provides faster hammer fall for increased accuracy.

New enhancement features added by Colt to the Government Model and its variations during 1992.

This stainless steel Gold Cup is the enhanced version which was
introduced by Colt in 1992.

Gold Cup Commander, caliber: 45 ACP, stainless steel, Model No.
04070.

32

2

How the Government Model Works

THE following description of how the Government Model pistol functions is based on the assumption that the gun is intact with no missing or altered parts and is in safe operating condition. This is a description of how the gun was designed to operate, and not necessarily how individual guns will operate. This information is not intended to replace or contradict the instructions in owners' manuals printed by the various manufacturers.

Loading one or more cartridges into the magazine compresses its follower spring. Since the follower is now deep within the magazine, a flange located on its left side is unable to make contact with the slide lock when the magazine is inserted into the gun. When the loaded magazine is pushed into the gun, a notch on its right side engages the magazine catch which holds it in position.

(A) Retracting the slide fully to the rear

1. Pulls the barrel slightly rearward, causing its link to rotate to the extent of its travel and therefore draw the breech end of the barrel downward for disengagement of its locking lugs with their recesses in the slide's roof.

2. Forces the spring-loaded disconnector downward to disconnect the hammer from indirect contact with the sear.

3. Rotates the hammer rearward and downward to engage its full cocking notch with the sear.

4. Compresses the recoil spring.

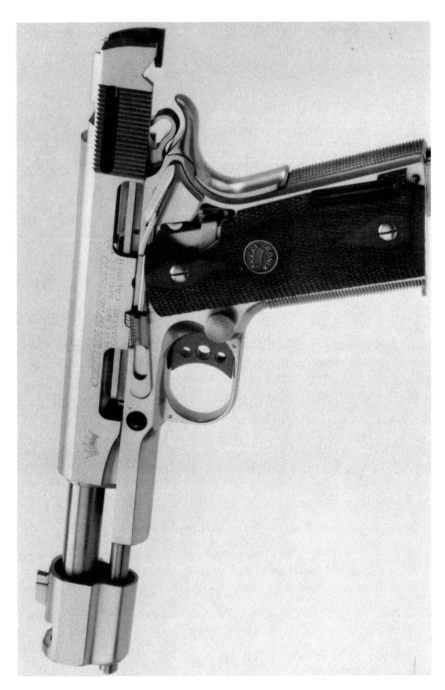

Cutaway of .45 Comp gun.

34

Merle Edington making a quick reload with his optical-sighted, high-capacity .38 Super during the Banker's Revenge stage of the 1992 USPSA Area VI Championships.

Match winner among lady shooters at the 1992 USPSA Area VI Championships, Sharon Kimbrell is shown here unleashing six rounds during the 40-yard kneeling stage of the Pyramid of Pain course.

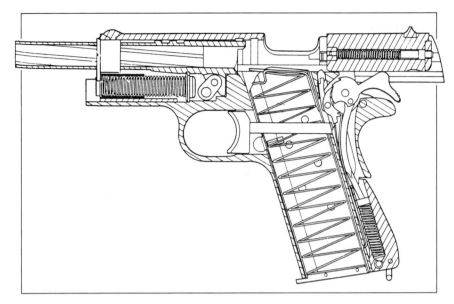

Slide fully retracted and held back by slide latch. Barrel link has
cammed rear of barrel down to disengage its locking lugs from their
recesses in the roof of the slide. (*Courtesy of* Gun Digest, *1980*)

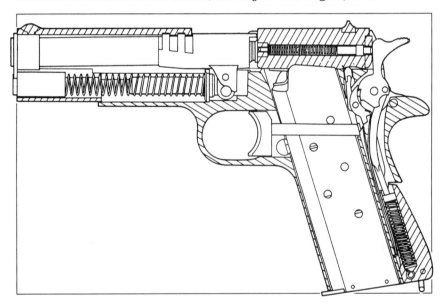

Government Model loaded and locked. Hammer is down, but inertia
firing pin is not contacting primer of cartridge in chamber. (*Courtesy
of* Gun Digest, *1980)*

(B) Releasing the slide allows the recoil spring to push it forward to

1. Strip a cartridge from the magazine.

2. Engage the rim of the cartridge with its extractor.

3. Push the cartridge into the chamber of the barrel.

4. Push the barrel forward to its locked position.

Note: If the trigger is held back during slide release, the disconnector will not allow the gun to fire until the trigger is released and then pulled for firing. If the trigger was not held back, the disconnector connects the sear with the trigger stirrup and allows the gun to be fired after the slide has moved forward to its fully locked position. If for some reason the slide does not return fully forward, the trigger and sear will remain disconnected until it does.

(C) When the trigger is pulled, the hammer strikes the firing pin, propelling it forward to strike the primer of the chambered cartridge. When the cartridge fires, rapidly expanding propellant gas pushes rearward on the interior surface of the head of the case. This rearward force pushes against the breechface of the slide and

1. The slide and barrel start moving rearward in a locked-together relationship.

2. The barrel link reaches the limit of its travel and pulls the breech end of the barrel downward, disengaging its locking lugs from their recesses in the slide.

3. Free of constraint from the barrel, the slide continues moving rearward, extracts the spent case from the chamber, rams its head into the nose of a fixed ejector in the frame, and presses the disconnecter downward to disconnect the trigger from the sear.

4. The case is ejected out through the open port in the slide.

5. Step (C) is repeated and subsequent pulls on the trigger continue to cause the gun to fire until its magazine is empty.

When the last round is stripped from the magazine, the follower reaches its full upward travel and a flange on its left side applies upward pressure against the bottom of the slide lock. When the last cartridge fires, the slide travels backward and then starts moving forward, but the lock engages a notch in the bottom edge of its left wall and prevents it from forward travel. Manually pressing down on the latch releases the slide.

How Individual Components Work

The Sear Spring

The name of this leaf spring is a bit misleading as it performs three duties more than implied. It has a bent tab at the bottom that fits inside a slot in the frame. This tab, in conjunction with inward pressure exerted by the inner surface of the mainspring housing, holds it in position and causes its three fingers to apply pressure to other important parts.

The left finger of the sear spring bears on the rear of the sear and disconnector (which bears on the trigger stirrup), and returns the trigger to its forward position after it has been pulled. The same finger also pushes the bottom end of the sear forward, causing its upper end to pivot backward to engagement with the full cock (or half cock) notch in the hammer's front surface. The center finger bears on the beveled end of the disconnector and cams it to its upward or connected position. The right finger pushes against the grip safety and keeps it in its rearward (or safe) position until it is depressed.

Custom sear springs with four fingers are sometimes installed by pistolsmiths when an extremely light trigger pull is desired. Its extra finger (third from the left) bears directly on the rear of the trigger stirrup. This prevents the trigger from bouncing against the disconnector and causing the hammer to follow the slide during a firing cycle rather than remaining in a cocked position.

The Grip Safety

The grip safety pivots at its top end on the transverse shaft of the thumb safety and is retained at the bottom by the mainspring housing. Pressure from the righthand finger of the sear spring pushes the safety to its extreme rearward position. This positions a forward-projecting arm on its inner surface directly behind the trigger's stirrup, preventing it from traveling rearward. Gripping the gun with the hand forces the safety forward, causing its arm to pivot up and out of the path of the trigger stirrup.

The Thumb Safety

The thumb safety is retained in its on (safe) and off (fire) positions by a spring-loaded, dual-opposed plunger that projects from a housing fastened to the frame just above the left grip panel. When pushed to its uppermost position (safety on), the safety engages a notch in the slide on the outside while an interference surface on its transverse shaft blocks the sear on the

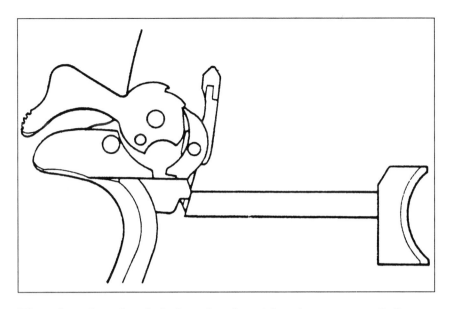

When the grip safety is in its relaxed position, its arm extends forward to block the trigger stirrup from rearward travel. *(Courtesy of Gun Digest, 1980)*

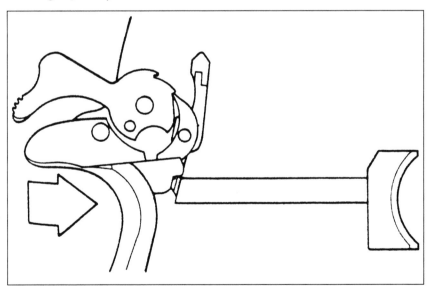

Grasping the grip of the gun with the hand causes the top of the grip safety to pivot on transverse pin of the thumb safety. This pivots its arm upward and out of the trigger stirrup's path. *(Courtesy of Gun Digest, 1980)*

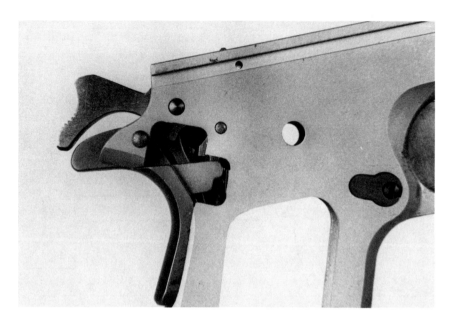

When the grip safety is in its relaxed position, a forward-projecting arm on its front surface blocks the trigger's stirrup from rearward travel.

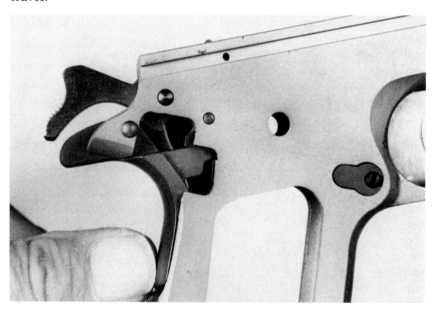

When the grip safety is pushed inward, its blocking arm pivots above the path of the trigger stirrup.

inside. With the sear blocked from forward movement, it cannot be pushed from the full cock notch of the hammer by the trigger. Pushing the safety to its down position (safety off), frees the slide and rotates its interference surface from the sear's path.

The Trigger

The Government Model trigger consists of a finger piece and stirrup joined together by various means during manufacture. The finger piece projects through the frame and inside the trigger guard. Extending from its rear surface, the stirrup rests in raceways cut into both sides of the interior surface of the magazine housing or grip of the frame and reaches back to make contact with the bottom end of the disconnector. Pulling the trigger transfers rearward force indirectly to the sear through the disconnector.

The Sear

The sear and disconnector are held in their proper vertical positions and relationship with each other by a transverse pin through the frame. Forward pressure applied to the bottom of the sear by a finger on the sear spring causes its top end to pivot rearward and against the front surface of the hammer to engage its full- or half-cock notch. The bottom end of the sear is too short to extend into the path of the trigger stirrup so the two must be connected by the disconnector. Pulling the trigger forces the bottom end of the disconnector rearward and it in turn transfers the same directional force to the bottom end of the sear. As the top end of the sear pivots forward, it disengages from the notch in the hammer, thus allowing it to travel forward to strike the firing pin.

The sear in Colt's Gold Cup differs from that used in other guns. A tiny coil spring projecting rearward and located just above its bottom end presses against another part called the sear depressor lever. The Gold Cup is the only Government Model variation with these two parts. The coil spring acts along with a finger of the regular leaf-type sear spring to increase engagement pressure between the sear and its notch in the hammer. It is designed to prevent the sear from bouncing from engagement with the hammer as the slide slams forward during the firing cycle. This was once a common problem among custom target pistols with their light trigger pulls and minimum sear engagement. The introduction of aftermarket triggers made of extremely light materials such as aluminum, titanium, and carbon fiber seems to have made the design obsolete for use in custom Government Model pistols.

41

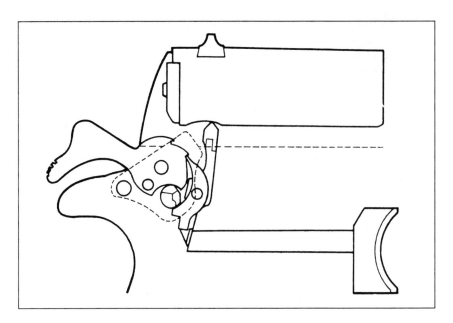

When the thumb safety is in its up or "safe" position, the hammer is
blocked from forward movement. *(Courtesy of* Gun Digest, *1980)*

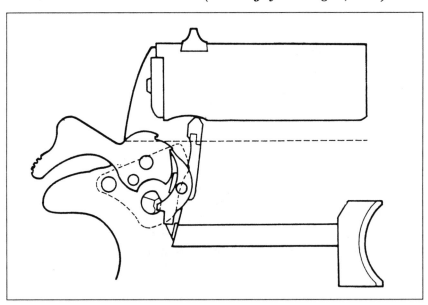

Pushing the thumb safety to its down or "fire" position, allows the
hammer to move forward to strike the firing pin. *(Courtesy of* Gun
Digest, *1980)*

The Disconnector

This ingenious little part actually should have been named a connector/disconnector since it serves both purposes in the trigger to sear relationship. The disconnector rests vertically in the frame on the same transverse pin as the sear. The pin passes through a vertical slot in the body of the disconnector which enables it to travel upward and downward. When pushed and held in its full upward position by pressure on its beveled bottom end by the middle finger of the sear spring, the top end of the disconnector protrudes slightly through the frame's top. When the slide is fully forward, a timing recess at the rear end of its center rail allows the disconnector to assume its full upward position. When in that position, a tab at its bottom end bridges the gap between the bottom end of the sear and the rear of the trigger stirrup. The trigger and sear now are connected. A pull on the trigger pushes on the tab of the disconnector which serves to transfer the pressure to the bottom end of the sear. This pivots the top end of the sear forward and out of engagement with the full-cock notch of the hammer, allowing it to travel forward to strike the firing pin.

When the gun fires and the slide travels to the rear, the disconnector is pushed downward by the timing rail. This positions the connecting tab on its bottom end below the bottom end of the sear where it is retained until

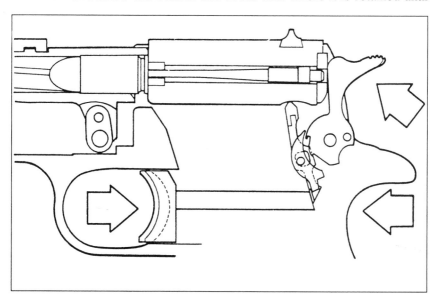

A pull on the trigger disengages the sear from the hammer, enabling it to move forward and strike the inertia-type firing pin. *(Courtesy of* Gun Digest, *1980)*

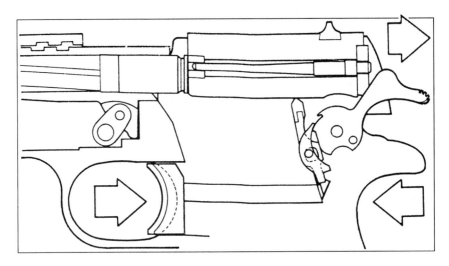

Cartridge has fired and slide is beginning to move rearward. Hammer is being cocked by the slide and timing notch in bottom of slide has moved to the rear of the disconnector. Disconnector is pushed to its downward position by the slide, causing its bottom end to move below the end of the sear to disconnect it from the trigger stirrup. *(Courtesy of* Gun Digest, *1980)*

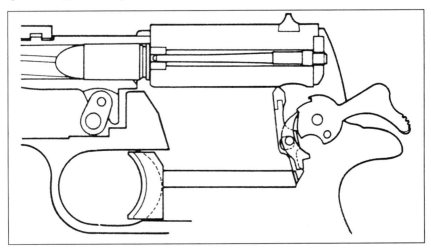

Slide has moved forward, but not far enough for complete lockup. Even though trigger has been released, slide has not moved far enough forward to allow the end of the disconnector to move upward into its timing recess in the bottom of the slide. This prevents the disconnector from moving upward to bridge the gap between the sear and trigger stirrup until the slide is pushed completely forward to full lockup. *(Courtesy of* Gun Digest, *1980)*

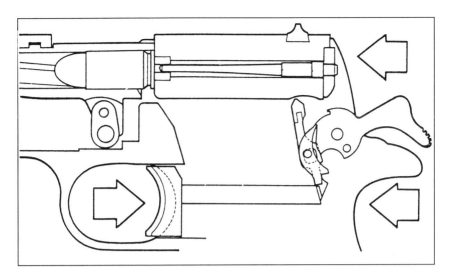

Slide has returned to battery and loaded another cartridge in the
chamber. Hammer is cocked, but gun cannot be fired until trigger is
released to enable the disconnector to move upward to bridge the gap
between sear and trigger stirrup. *(Courtesy of* Gun Digest, *1980)*

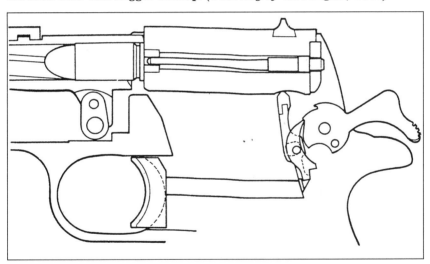

Chamber of gun loaded and barrel in its locked position. Cocked hammer is held back by the top end of the sear; top end of disconnector is
in the timing groove in slide, allowing its bottom end to bridge the
gap between the bottom end of the sear and the trigger stirrup. A
pull on the trigger disengages the sear from the hammer, enabling it
to move forward and strike the inertia-type firing pin. *(Courtesy of*
Gun Digest, *1980)*

the trigger is released. If the slide travels forward but stops short of complete lockup, its timing rail continues to hold the disconnector in its downward position even if the trigger is released and then pulled. If the slide travels fully forward while the trigger is held to the rear, the recess at the rear of its timing rail is positioned over the disconnector, but it is still held downward until the trigger is released. Releasing the trigger allows the disconnector to return to its upward or connecting position.

The two different relationships between the timing rail and its recess with the disconnector prevent the gun from firing unless the slide is fully forward in its locked position. The two relationships between the trigger, disconnector, and sear prevent the Government Model from firing in the fully automatic mode by requiring that the trigger be released and then pulled for each shot.

The Hammer Strut

Contained within its housing at the bottom of the frame's backstrap is a strong coil spring called the mainspring. It also is commonly referred to as the hammer spring. A rod-shaped part called the hammer strut connects the mainspring with the hammer. When the hammer is cocked, the spring is compressed by the strut. Pulling the trigger releases the hammer to be driven forward by the mainspring to strike the firing pin. The Gold Cup hammer strut is a bit shorter than the one in the standard Government Model and Commander, a dimension after which some aftermarket struts are patterned.

Inertia-Type Firing Pin

The inertia-type firing pin of the Government Model pistol is shorter than its tunnel in the slide. For this reason, when the hammer is gently lowered on a chambered round, the firing pin is too short to reach the primer. When the hammer is cocked and the trigger pulled, the hammer strikes the firing pin with enough force for its inertia or momentum to enable it to travel far enough to strike the primer of a cartridge. As the firing pin travels forward, it compresses its return spring. After the firing pin has struck the primer of a cartridge in the chamber, or has reached the limit of its travel when the chamber is empty, the spring returns it to its rearward position.

If a pre-Series 80 Government Model pistol with a live round in its chamber is dropped muzzle down on a hard surface with considerable force, the firing pin conceivably can fly forward and strike the primer. This is more likely to happen with guns that have an extremely weak firing pin spring. Colt introduced a firing pin block mechanism on its Series 80 gun for just that reason.

The Firing Pin Stop

Also commonly referred to as the firing pin retainer plate, the firing pin stop retains the firing pin and extractor in the slide. The plate is retained on both sides by grooves in the slide, and by the rear of the firing pin protruding through a hole in its center. A Series 80 stop can be used in earlier guns, but not vice versa. The Series 80 version has a wider notch cut into its lower righthand corner for greater clearance with the upper firing pin block lever in the frame.

Series 80 Firing Pin Block

Introduced by Colt on its Series 80 guns, a passive safety feature commonly described as a firing pin block is designed to prevent the firing pin from moving forward unless the trigger is pulled. It consists of four parts—two levers, a plunger, and a plunger spring. Located in the frame, the lower operating lever pivots on the same crosspin as the sear and disconnector. The upper lever pivots on the hammer crosspin.

When the trigger is pulled, its stirrup pushes the bottom of the lower lever to the rear. This pivots a short arm at its top end against the bottom of the upper lever, causing that lever to depress the spring-loaded firing pin lock plunger in the slide.

The blocking plunger rests adjacent to the firing pin and is retained in the slide by the extractor. It is shaped somewhat like a barbell with a small diameter center section and larger diameter ends. The upper cupped end bears against a coil spring and the lower end protrudes from the bottom surface of the slide. When the plunger is held in its downward position by the return spring, its top end rests inside a groove in the body of the firing pin. This blocks the firing pin from forward travel. When the trigger is pulled and the top lever in the frame pushes the plunger upward, its thin center section is aligned with the groove in the firing pin. This frees the firing pin to travel forward when struck by the hammer.

The Slide Lock

Also called the slide release and slide latch, the slide lock performs several duties; it locks back the slide and a transverse shaft at its front end extends through the frame to serve as a pivot point for the barrel link. Also, as the bottom lug of a handfitted barrel rides over the shaft, the barrel is cammed upward to its locked position with the slide. At the rear of the latch is a short channel that engages the bottom of the slide rail to retain it against the frame's side. The latch can be removed from the frame only when aligned with an

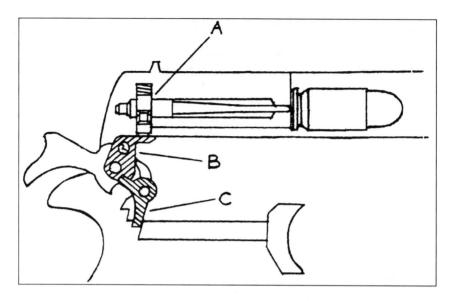

The Colt Series 80 firing pin block. Rearward force is transmitted from the trigger to the spring-loaded firing pin block plunger "A" through the lower "C" and upper "B" levers. *(Courtesy of Rifle, No. 105)*

escape notch in the slide. Adjacent to the channel is a lug that projects through the frame's side. When the magazine contains one or more cartridges, its follower is unable to contact the lug. When the magazine is empty, its follower applies upward pressure on the lug and when the slide is retracted, the latch engages its front locking notch. A spring-loaded plunger located in its housing on the side of the frame prevents the latch from bouncing upward during the firing cycle and locking the slide back while cartridges are in the magazine.

Slide stops vary a bit among the various calibers and should not be interchanged. For example, the slide stop made for the 9mm Luger and .38 Super should not be used in a gun chambered for the .45 ACP and vice versa.

Ejector

The fixed ejector is attached to the top of the frame with a transverse driven pin. During the firing cycle, the slide grasps the rim of a fired case with its extractor and pulls it from the chamber as it travels to the rear. During its rearward journey, the slide rams the head of the case into the nose of the ejector. The impact causes the case to twist away from the extractor's grip and fly out through the slide's ejection port.

Barrel Bushing

The barrel bushing is held to the muzzle of the slide by an integral locking lug on its body that engages a recess inside the slide. Its purpose is to maintain an aligned relationship between the barrel and the sights and to retain the recoil spring within the slide. The three common sizes of factory bushings are long for standard size guns, medium for the Commander, and short for the Officer's ACP. The shorter barrels require a shorter bushing to prevent binding between barrel and bushing because they tilt down at a sharper angle during unlocking than the standard five-inch barrel.

Recoil Spring, Guide, and Plug

The recoil spring and its guide are retained in the slide by the spring plug. The recoil spring plug is retained by a flange on the bottom of the barrel bushing. When the gun fires and its slide travels rearward, the recoil spring is compressed. Force exerted on the recoil spring plug by the spring causes the slide to move forward.

Magazine Catch

Also called the magazine release, few words are required to describe how the magazine catch works. Pushing the magazine catch (or release) button inward compresses its return spring and moves its lug outward from engagement with a slot in the righthand side of the magazine. When a magazine is inserted, the beveled lug is pushed outward and then snaps into engagement when the slot in the wall of the magazine becomes aligned with it.

3

Pistolsmiths and Custom Pistols

CONSIDERING the number of pistolsmiths who specialize in building custom Government Model pistols, I believe it is safe to say that no other autoloader or revolver ranks anywhere near its popularity as the basis for a custom handgun. The demand for custom pistols has created companies and suppliers of all sizes that thrive and survive on nothing but the manufacture and sale of aftermarket parts for John Browning's old gun. One chap who started a pistolsmithing business on little more than a shoestring during the late 1970s recently reported sales of close to $3 million per year for custom parts alone. He is but one of several shops that cater almost exclusively to other pistolsmiths and do-it-themselvers who work on the Government Model and its variations.

Private sector gunsmiths probably first started fine-tuning the Government Model for bullseye competition back in the 1930s. J. D. Buchanan of Los Angeles was one of the better known pioneers and as the years passed others began to specialize in transforming a war pistol into a target pistol. Among many champions of yesteryear whose names will long be synonymous with the sport are Toney, Reeves, Lea, Hebard, Guiette, Backstrom, Chow, Defino, and Blankenship.

Seldom are pistolsmiths given the credit they deserve for leading Colt and other companies down the road to certain improvements, modifications, innovations, and variations of the basic Model 1911 design. Before Colt introduced its National Match during the 1930s, military armorers already had made great strides in accuracy.

Steve Nastoff classic .45 ACP wadcutter gun with Springfield Armory slide and frame. *(ACRI Studio photo)*

Don Fraley's .38 Super Colt Commander carry gun.

Among the many Government Model ideas and modifications that have originated in small shops rather than a big factory are

- Closer barrel to slide fit
- Tighter slide to frame fit
- Lowered and flared ejection port
- Polished and throated barrel
- Squared trigger guard
- Double-action conversions
- Metal checkering
- Lowered and melted rear sight
- Grip-attached scope mounts
- Frame-attached scope mounts
- Reduced-power springs
- Extra-power springs
- Variable-power springs
- Full-length recoil spring guide rod
- Beavertail grip safety
- Extended thumb safety
- Ambidextrous thumb safety
- Beveled magazine well
- Magazine well funnel
- Genuine match-grade barrel
- Titanium hammer
- Titanium firing pin
- Titanium hammer strut
- Carbon fiber/titanium trigger
- Throwaway shock buffer
- Improved design sears
- Ambidextrous magazine release
- Barrel with a full-support chamber and integral feed ramp.

A few more interesting stories follow.

Government Model target pistols were once plagued by a problem called sear or trigger bounce. Simply described, when trigger pull weight was reduced for target shooting, the hammer often would follow the slide down during the firing cycle. The problem was solved by adding a fourth finger on the sear spring to increase engagement pressure. Colt took the hint and added a depressor spring to the back of the Gold Cup's sear when it was introduced in 1957.

When Colt introduced its aluminum-frame Commander in 1949, its slide and barrel were not made available to pistolsmiths. So, those innovative chaps simply shortened the slide and barrel of the 5-inch gun and started offering

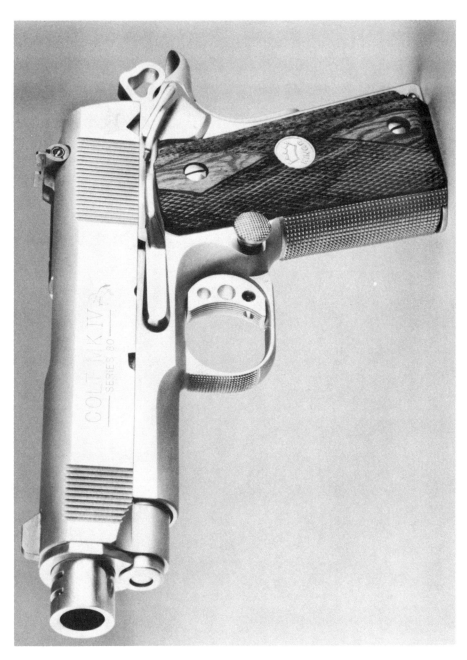

Al Capone; Colt Officer's ACP with Smith & Wesson rear sight and King's extended magazine release, slide release, and thumb safety.

Classic Colt Combat Commander carry gun in .45 ACP (Kim Ahrends).

.45 ACP compensated Colt Series 80 (Bill Laughridge).

the Combat .45 to customers. Its steel frame was heavier than Colt's version, but just as compact. In 1972, Colt introduced a steel-frame version of its earlier gun called the Combat Commander.

A number of attempts were made to come up with a passive firing pin safety for the Government Model. One, designed by William L. Swartz (patented in 1939) was actuated by the grip safety. Colt greatly improved on the idea and introduced its trigger-actuated firing pin block on the Series 80 gun in 1983.

After being liberally sprinkled with magic dust by a good pistolsmith, the Officer's ACP is my favorite carry gun. A super compact .45, however, was not exactly a brand new idea when Colt introduced its version in 1985. As far back as the 1960s gunsmiths like Armand Swenson and Austin Behlert were shortening the grip of the frame, the barrel, and the slide of the standard five-inch gun and offering them to customers under catchy names such as the Bobcat conversion.

Something else various pistolsmiths had tried to perfect was a way of converting the Government Model's single-action trigger to double-action. Then a pistolsmith by the name of Larry Seecamp got it right. Seecamp offered his conversion for years and hundreds of guns so modified are still floating around, mostly in the hands of collectors. The story doesn't end there. During the early 1980s a New Jersey company by the name of Omega Defensive Industries (ODI) incorporated the Seecamp design into the first factory-made double-action Government Model pistol. Called the Viking Combat, it was available with a 4¼- or 5-inch barrel in 9mm or .45 ACP. Another model, the Combat II, had a thumb-operated firing pin safety in its slide. The 5-inch model weighed 39 ounces and the shorter Commander version tipped the scales at 3 ounces less. It was only slightly more expensive than Colt's single-action autoloader.

In 1989, Colt slightly modified the Seecamp double-action design and incorporated it into the Double Eagle. It's a nice pistol, but there are those who believe it is inferior in design to the ODI gun in two ways. First, the exterior shape and dimensions of the ODI gun are identical to those of the old Government Model. In fact, that's exactly what it was—a double action version of the old single-action pistol. Secondly, the trigger mechanism at the righthand side of the ODI frame is protected by a removable steel plate which rests beneath the grip panel. On the Colt gun, the trigger drawbar is held in place only by the grip panel.

Some developments probably will be remembered as poor ideas by historians. Many years ago pistolsmith Irv Stone (who also makes Bar-Sto barrels) introduced the collet-type barrel bushing. Stone eventually abandoned the design because its fingers had a tendency to break off. Colt picked up the

Introduced during the early 1980's, this ODI Viking was the first factory Government Model pistol to utilize the Seecamp double-action trigger.

Basic Government Model carry gun in .45 ACP with Brown hammer and thumb safety (Ed Brown).

International Grade compensated Caspian in .45 ACP (Al Dichiara).

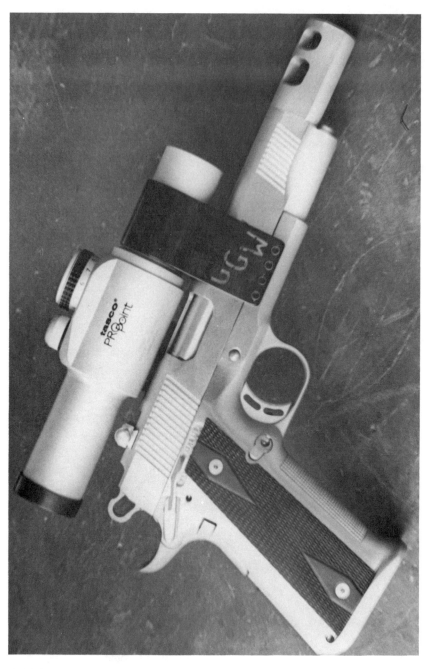

A high-capacity .38 Super built by Wayne Bergquist around the
Caspian frame.

Richard Heinie's .45 ACP Springfield Armory carry gun with Heinie
sights and hammer.

idea and introduced it on the Series 70 gun in the 1970s, but after discovering what Stone and hundreds of shooters already knew, they began to phase it out during the late 1980s.

An idea that never managed to fly at all was a conversion called the Double Ace. Introduced by the California Firm of Caraville Arms, it was a drop-in unit designed to replace several of the pistol's factory parts. When the gun was grasped by the hand, the replacememt grip safety cocked the hammer through a series of cranks, levers, and rollers. The trigger could then be pulled in the usual fashion. Since the unit allowed the hammer to be carried down and then quickly cocked by pressure on the grip, it was a great idea but failed as a commercial venture because its installation increased the girth of the Government Model's grip too much for small- to medium-size hands.

About three decades ago, a famous firearms writer opined that once the small handful of talented pistolsmiths of his era had gone on to their rewards, the world would never again see their equals. As a youngster I read a lot of his stuff and considered him right more often than wrong, but if he were alive today, he would have to reach for the salt shaker and begin nibbling on those words. No doubt about it, there were some great pistolsmiths in the old days, but a new generation has taken the craft to levels of quality, precision, and aesthetics that were virtually unheard of in the distant past.

Just as the passing of time has seen a change in pistolsmiths there has been an even more drastic change in customer preference. There was once a time when the typical customer was satisfied if his new custom pistol was accurate and worked the majority of times its trigger was pulled. Although some beautiful guns were built back then, aesthetics often were low priority. That won't cut it in today's competitive market.

An ever-increasing number of people who have custom guns built today demand everything. If they can't have it all, they don't want it. Today's custom gun must first and foremost be 100 percent reliable, not for 100 rounds, nor for 1,000 rounds, but for many thousands of rounds. The gun also has to be exceptionally accurate, and I'm not talking about an occasional two-inch, two-shot group at 25 yards. If a custom Government Model pistol won't consistently put 10 shots inside two or three inches at twice that distance, more than a few customers will yawn and try another pistolsmith. Last but certainly not least in importance to a growing number of customers, anything less than absolutely flawless workmanship simply will not do.

What is a custom gun? I have a shooting pal who is of the opinion that in order for a gun to qualify as a custom job, its modifications must include virtually everything under the sun. I disagree. A custom gun is one that a customer has modified to his/her specifications. This may include nothing more

Colt's Double Eagle is a relatively new gun, but the idea of converting the Government Model pistol for double-action fire is old.

Steve Woods' Limited class Springfield Armory carry/competition in
.45 ACP with Gun Craft mag well funnel, checkered frontstrap, and
extra grasping serrations at front of slide. *(Stephen Longley photo)*

Jim Stroh's .22 Rimfire ACE top assembly on Caspian frame, with Bo-Mar rear sight, Stroh mag well funnel and Videki trigger.

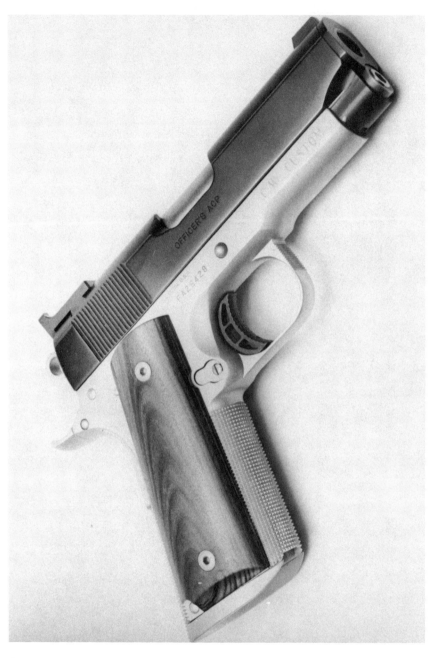

Chuck Warner's Officer's ACP with Heinie sights and hammer, Wilson sleeved barrel, SASA mag well funnel, and accent cut along top of slide.

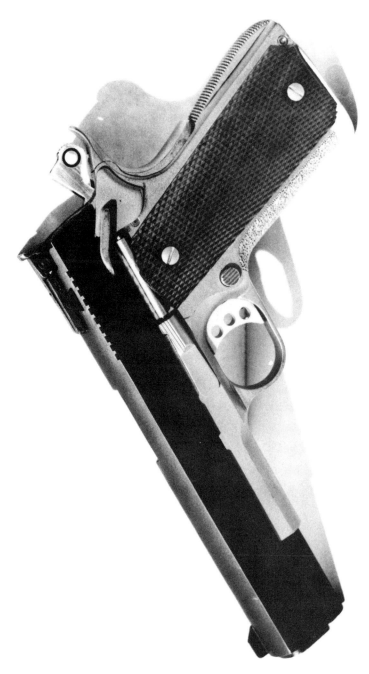

Glenn Martin's Caspian carry gun in .45 ACP with Bo-Mar sight and stippled frontstrap.

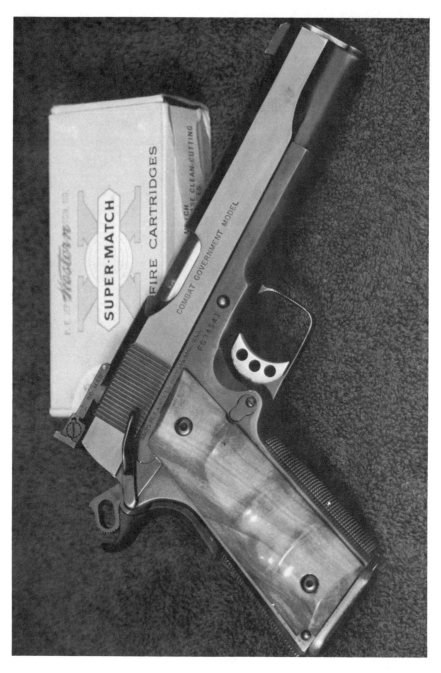

Neil Wiggans' carry/competition Colt Government Model in .45 ACP with squared trigger guard.

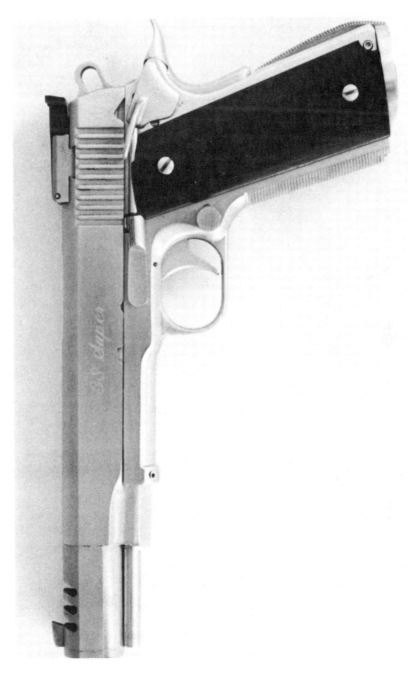

Bob Cogan's Caspian in .38 Super with pivoting trigger and half-profile compensator.

The author has just gotten up from the park bench, wheeled around, drawn his .38 Super, and is about to engage the first series of targets in the How Ya Makin' Out stage of the 1992 USPSA Area VI Championships.

than a basic trigger and accuracy job, and new sights. In my book, it is a custom gun if it is exactly the way its owner wants it to be and he or she is happy with it. People have different tastes in custom Government Model pistols and that's as it should be. I tend to be conservative when ordering a carry gun while others want all the options. Conversely, some folks prefer to stick with the basics on a gun built for practical pistol competition while it's the wilder the better and bring on all the bells and whistles when I start thinking about having one built.

Another question is what is a pistolsmith? A colleague of mine once classified all but a very small minority of people who refer to themselves as pistolsmiths as nothing more than parts installers with business cards. As he put it, they simply buy parts from various sources, put them together and call them a custom gun. I don't believe he was entirely fair. I know of no pistolsmith who actually manufactures all the parts used in a custom gun. Most of the parts bearing the names of various pistolsmiths may have been designed by them, but many actually are manufactured by outside subcontractors.

My definition of a parts-installer is someone like myself who can put all the pieces of the puzzle together but they don't work. A pistolsmith is

70

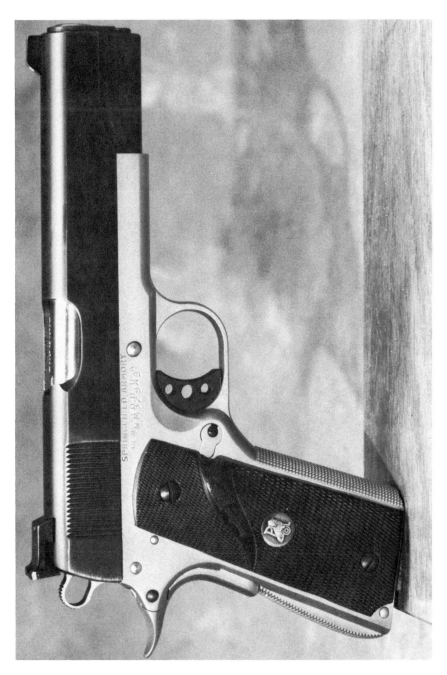

.45 ACP Springfield Armory carry gun with tritium sights (Nelson Ford).

Jim Garthwaite's Colt Government Model in .38 Super with
Garthwaite full-profile compensator.

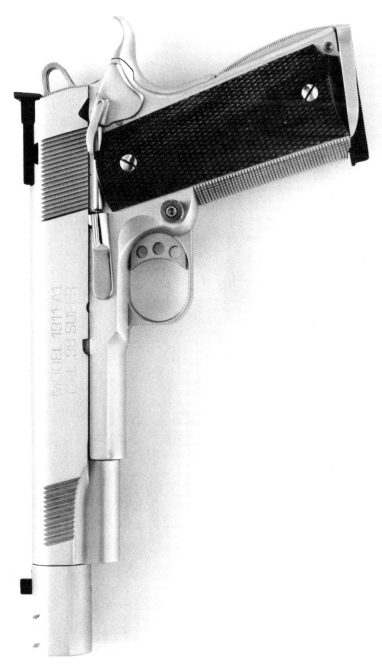

.38 Super Distinguished Model compensated gun (Springfield Armory
Custom Shop).

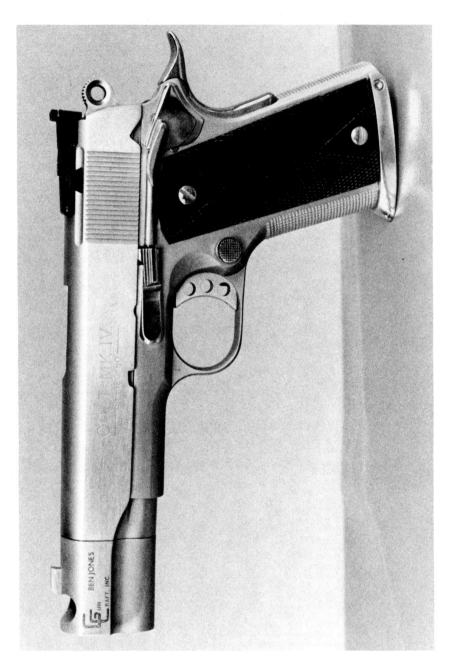

Ben Jones / Kim Stroud compensated Colt Officer's ACP with Gun Craft mag well funnel, Videki short trigger, and Swenson ambidextrous safety.

Dave Lauck's Limited class Colt competition gun in .45 ACP with Lauck thumbguard and extra grasping grooves at front of slide. *(Mike McCoy photo)*

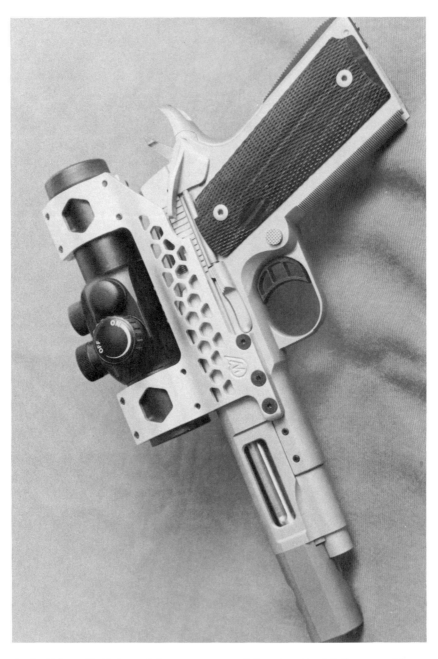

Jack Weigand's lightweight compensated Caspian in .38 Super, with
Weigand Stabilizer scope mount, lightening cuts in slide, fluted barrel,
contoured slide latch, and Quick-Lock hammer.

Bill Wilson's Super Grade compensated Colt (left) in .38 Super and (right) Tactical Special Colt in .45 ACP.

anyone who rounds up all the parts and then has the talent to produce an accurate gun that works every time its trigger is squeezed. A master pistolsmith is someone who has those two bases covered, is capable of flawless cosmetics, and won't let a gun out the door until it is as perfect as human hands can make it.

I'm quick to admit, however, that there are pistolsmiths and then there are pistolsmiths. I used to get a real kick out of a local used car dealer who starred in his own television commercials. His favorite slogan was, "I got some good ones, some not so good ones, and some pretty darned bad ones, but you'll always get what you pay for." And so it goes with people who work on guns. Depending on the individual, the quality of work can range from superb to not so good to pretty darned bad. I suppose the best rule to remember is that you seldom find really good work down in the basement. As it is with used cars and everything else in life, one gets exactly what one pays for. Relatively speaking, good work is inexpensive while cheap work can end up costing you an arm and a leg.

Perhaps pistolsmiths will someday institute a classification system among their ranks. Then the customer would know what to expect and when. A proposal for how it might work follows.

A Class D pistolsmith would be someone who (1) gathers up a bunch of aftermarket parts, (2) installs them in a gun, (3) discovers that the gun is ugly and doesn't work, and (4) pays a qualified pistolsmith to make the gun work and be handsome.

A Class C pistolsmith would be the same as a Class D pistolsmith except people pay him for steps (1), (2), and (3).

A Class B pistolsmith would be an individual who is capable of turning out master class work and most often does, but his workmanship sometimes suffers when he yields to the pressures of life. Also, he never meets a delivery date.

A Class A pistolsmith would be the person who knows how to build a totally reliable and exceptionally accurate custom pistol. From a practical point of view, he builds excellent guns that are well worth the money, but they are a bit off the mark in overall aesthetics. He is, however, totally honest when describing his work and his delivery capability to a potential customer.

A Master Class pistolsmith has all bases covered and is the cream of the crop. He (or she) almost always delivers on time and no power on earth will cause a custom gun to leave the shop until it is totally reliable, exceptionally accurate, and its workmanship is beyond compare. When the customer opens the box he knows the gun is a bargain regardless of how long he had to wait or how much he had to pay.

Of course, if pistolsmiths should decide to self-impose such a classification system, it would be only fair for customers to do the same.

A Class B customer would be the chap who never cleans a gun, is a sloppy handloader, knows more about pistolsmithing than pistolsmiths (and readily admits it), and will never admit that shooter ability or lack of same has as much influence on the accuracy of a gun as the way it was built. He doesn't pay his bills on time, scratches himself in public places, calls twice each week to inquire about his gun, writes rubber checks, has bad breath, changes his mind twice a day, and blames someone else for problems he created. On top of all that, he complains a lot. Except for those few shortcomings, he is a really nice guy.

Class A customers would be those who are guilty of none of the above and who buy this book.

4

Planning Your Custom Pistol

L IKE many things in life, the planning and anticipation of having a custom Government Model built is almost as much fun as the day you rip open the shipping carton and see your dream resting there in all its splendor. It may even be more fun.

Having a custom gun built is a bit like the old chicken and egg adage; which do you decide on first, the pistol or the pistolsmith? If you already own the gun and want it rebuilt, the question is answered, but buying a gun to be rebuilt is a horse of another color. In that case, I believe it's best to decide on the pistolsmith first. One reason for doing so is because some of those fellows will only work on certain brands of guns.

Believe it or not, a good pistolsmith actually can help a customer save money by steering him in the right direction when choosing a gun to be transformed. A few examples follow.

Some guns cost less than others for a variety of reasons, one being the quality of their metal finishes. Some have deep machine marks on their slide and frame. One brand of frame sometimes suffers from acute metal acne on its surface and hidden air pockets as a result of the casting process. The pits often are too deep or too costly to remove from the surface. The internal air pockets do no harm until the pistolsmith's checkering file suddenly drops into one, or the cutter on his milling machine does the same when the frame is being mortised for a full-support barrel. If you want a no-nonsense, rough-duty gun and are not overly concerned about aesthetics, a rough metal finish would obviously be of no concern. On the other hand, if a gorgeous

Steve Woods' Government Model bullseye gun with adjustable grip and Officer's ACP carry gun.

The author's wife, Phyllis, with her favorite security blanket.

finish is high on your priority list, the pistolsmith may charge more for transforming the ugly duckling than the difference you would have paid for a gun or frame with a better factory finish.

Here's another example of choosing between the right and wrong gun for custom modifications. Colt's Gold Cup costs almost 30 percent more than the standard Government Model. This may come as a shock, but I find little to no difference in their mechanical accuracy. I've shot some factory-stock Government Models that would shoot rings around any Gold Cup made today and the most inaccurate gun in .45 ACP I have ever worked with was a Gold Cup. This was not the case years ago, but I find it to be true of guns being made by Colt today. Typically, the additional 30 percent buys, not a higher level of accuracy, but a better trigger, better sights, a more handsome gun (in the eyes of some at least), and a gun that will feed ammunition with a greater variety of bullet shapes.

When the two are compared in their factory-original condition, the Gold Cup is worth the extra money. It also is a good buy if the plan is to have very few modifications made. The Gold Cup is not the way to go if it is purchased with the intention of having it transformed into a custom gun. When building a fullhouse custom job, the pistolsmith usually replaces every factory

Many pistolsmiths consider Colt guns the best while others believe a Springfield Armory gun is equal in quality except for its metal finish.

83

part except the frame and slide and it makes no sense to pay an additional 30 percent for those two items in the beginning. It is best to start with the standard plain-Jane Government Model and spend the cash saved by doing so on custom labor and parts.

Moving on down to even less initial investment, the Colt M1991A1 with its Parkerized finish is a bit less expensive than the standard blued version. Is it the way to go? It depends. If you want a bead-blasted finish, either blued or hard chromed, this least expensive of the Colt models is an excellent choice for a custom gun. On the other hand, if a high-gloss blue job is your cup of tea, the factory rollmarks on the sides of the slide may almost disappear by the time the pistolsmith completes the metal polishing. In addition, the job will take more time and what they say about time being money is absolutely true.

Then we have stainless steel. Staying with Colt's Government Model for another example, the stainless version costs about $100 more than its blued steel mate. It's a great idea and worth its price to those of us who sweat on factory guns and tote them in humid country, but as custom guns go, I prefer regular steel with a hard chrome skin for three reasons. First, due to stainless steel's reputation for galling, some gunsmiths don't tighten the slide to frame fit as closely as they do with standard guns. Secondly, the surface hardness of stainless is lower than that of hard chrome, making its wear quality lower. For this reason, I believe a stainless gun will shoot loose quicker. Thirdly (and this is purely personal), stainless steel is not as handsome as hard chrome to my eyes. If I was having a custom gun built, I would buy the blued steel and spend the $100 saved on a hard chrome skin for it. If I decided to go for a stainless gun, I would ask Bill Krieger to install his Acc-U-Rail system in it.

There are many cases where starting from scratch with all custom parts is far more economical than having a factory gun modified. When building a fullhouse custom gun whether it be for carry or competition, most pistolsmiths replace all parts of the gun except the slide and frame. If you paid, say, $625 for a factory gun, that's basically what the frame and slide alone of your new custom gun will cost you. On top of that, you can add the cost of tightening the sloppy fit between those two parts. In comparison, a Caspian frame and slide costs about one-third as much to buy and when purchased together, they have a match-grade fit that requires only hand-lapping.

It becomes even less cost efficient to modify a factory gun when building a custom job around one of the high-capacity aftermarket frames. The least expensive way to travel that route is to have the pistolsmith utilize a Caspian, Colt, or Springfield Armory slide which is available as a separate part from those companies.

Colt's M1991A1 is a good buy for out-of-box use, but a poor choice
for a custom gun if a high-gloss blued finish is desired.

Some pistolsmiths don't like to work on a gun such as this Colt Delta
Gold Cup because of stainless steel's tendency to gall.

86

Christie Rogers mowing them down in the A Head for Trouble course at the 1992 USPSA Area VI Championships.

I'm not saying all of this to put down certain guns, nor to say that I'm right about everything and everybody else is right about nothing. I delved into the subject of gun choices as a way of pointing out that what appears to be black and white or cut and dried doesn't always turn out so. If in doubt, ask your friendly pistolsmith.

Some pistolsmiths offer standard custom packages and prefer not to make changes or substitutions of their component parts and custom details. Some flatly refuse to do so. Others offer package deals, but allow the customer to make certain changes if desired. For example, if brand A barrel is standard for his Master Grade package and you prefer brand B, he (or she) usually will substitute your choice if it is considered equal in quality. Other pistolsmiths simply have a menu of custom parts and modifications from which the customer designs his pistol through the picking and choosing process.

There are pistolsmiths who refuse piecework orders and will build only fullhouse guns with all the bells, whistles, and trimmings. Others offer build-as-the-budget-allows plans which enable the customer to have certain parts of the overall package completed during different time frames. Perhaps it's new sights and a trigger job the first time; the gun returns a year later for a new barrel, then back again in another six months for metal checkering and finishing. Before you know it you're the owner of a custom gun.

Some pistolsmiths prefer the series 70 Colt over the Series 80 because the latter has a firing pin block that adds a few ounces to a custom trigger pull.

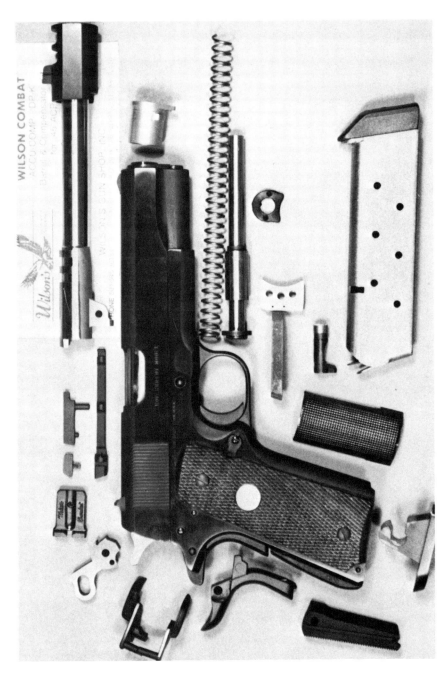

A Colt Government Model pistol surrounded by Wilson aftermarket custom parts which will replace its factory parts.

When having a custom pistol built, each shooter should decide what works best for him.

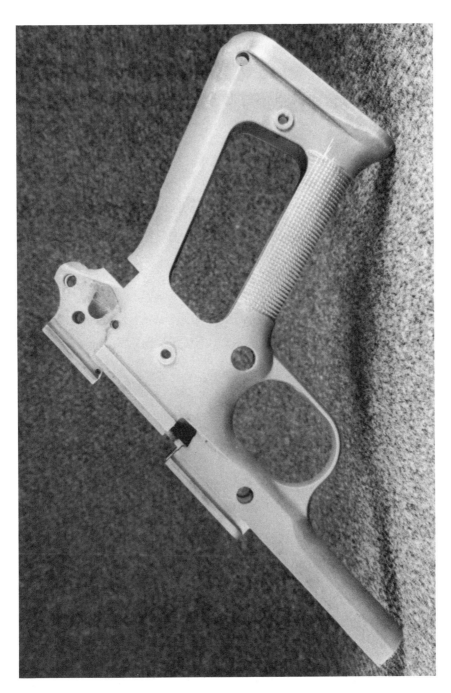

Caspian high-capacity frame.

Custom Handgun Accessories

If I've learned anything about dealing with reputable pistolsmiths, it's the fact that they know more about the quality of various custom parts than the typical customer. So, if you want a brand B barrel and the chap who is building your gun insists on using brand A, it's probably best not to argue the point since he is the one who must satisfy you in the accuracy department.

When planning a custom gun, look as far down the road as possible before deciding on its features. Few of us own a really accurate crystal ball, but what you think you want now may be quite different than what you wish you had ordered six months into the future. Taking the custom plunge without putting a great deal of thought and research into a gun is a story that can have a sad ending. The following hypothetical example illustrates my point.

Let us suppose that a fictitious chap by the name of Joe Brainfade decides to have the custom pistol of his dreams built. Joe has read a magazine article or two on the subject and thinks he knows exactly what he wants. He spends maybe 15 minutes writing the specifications while chatting with his wife and screaming at the kids as an Archie Bunker rerun plays on TV. Ted Twelvethumbs, a local boy who made good in the pistolsmithing trade can transform any Government Model pistol into a totally reliable, uncommonly accurate thing of beauty, so he is commissioned to perform the work. Ted disagrees with many of Joe's ideas, especially the caliber, but Joe's mind is made up and, after all, he is the paying customer.

A year or so later, Ted completes the gun and Joe drops by the bank to mortgage his pickup truck before taking delivery of his lifelong dream. Joe's new custom gun is truly remarkable. Old Ted has built many custom guns for Texas oil men, Arab sheiks, Indian maharajahs, used car dealers, and gun magazine editors, and even he is a bit surprised at how well Ted's job turned out. The flawless handfitting of each part would turn a Swiss watchmaker green with envy. Not a single blemish can be found on its surface, even with a jeweler's loupe. The checkering is more perfect than humanly possible. Dropping the slide on a loaded magazine feels like closing the door on a bank vault full of new money. During final tuning, the gun gobbled up every load Ted tried without missing a beat and kept all but one bullet on a spot the size of a dime at 50 paces. Its beauty is beyond compare. Men who gaze upon it are struck speechless. Women smile. Children hush. Dogs bark. Joe is sitting on a cloud.

Joe heads for the range to shoot his new gun. When drawing it from his new Disneyland holster, sharp corners on its Roll-Bar rear sight rip his brand new T-shirt to shreds. The sharp 10-line checkering on its frontstrap takes the hide off of his tender fingers like a wood rasp. The blaze orange Millipede front sight fades out in the sunshine and makes Joe squint. The long McDonald titanium trigger makes him shoot left and the Jones & Jones arched mainspring housing makes him shoot high. The Greene high-sweep beaver-tail grip safety looks trick, but is so high that Joe's hand won't disengage it when gripping the gun naturally. The overhanging rear sight makes the Commander-style hammer difficult to cock. The Behrends grip panels are too thick. The slightest touch on the Fanny extended magazine latch with its reduced-power spring makes the magazine go bombs away even when Joe doesn't want it to. The righthand lever of the Wilkinson ambi thumb safety digs bits and chunks from Joe's chubby knuckle. His hand keeps bumping the Quasi-Luck super-extended slide latch and locking back the slide with rounds still in the magazine. Light glinting from the bumper-shiny, chrome-plated slide hurts Joe's eyes, sunburns his face, and annoys overflying air-plane pilots.

On top of all that, Joe is out of 9mm Nambu ammunition, has no idea where to find more, suffers from dandruff and indigestion, his wife snores in her sleep, and his best bird dog steals eggs from the hen house.

Admittedly, this is an exaggerated story and I doubt if many custom gun projects turn out as disastrous as Joe's. However, it does serve to empha-size the importance of a bit of planning and research prior to ordering a custom gun. Reading about the subject helps and the newsstands usually are stacked with magazines full of what's new and interesting. Some pistolsmiths have catalogs and brochures with photos of the work they offer. Perhaps this book also will assist in some way.

The pistolsmith you decide on may be of valuable assistance when choosing custom parts and modifications. If he has been in business for awhile, he will have built enough guns to know what works for some people and what doesn't for others. Simply tell him for what purpose the gun is to be built and ask for his advice on various and sundry details. If you need a carry gun, he'll have good ideas on sights and other options. On a gun built for practical pistol or bullseye competition, he'll have the latest information on what most competitors are using and can help you avoid an option that will be obsolete before the gun is completed.

Even with all this said, you can't beat hands-on examinations of other cus-tom guns when trying to decide in what direction to go with yours. Handling several different guns tells you how various custom modifications feel and look. Most gunshop owners know someone in town who owns a custom Government Model or two and they may be happy to show them to you. He may even know of a nearby pistolsmith who specializes in Government Model work. If practical pistol competition is popular in your area, go to a few matches and you're likely to see more custom Government Model pistols than you thought existed. Even better, join the USPSA in the United States, or other IPSC-affiliated organization if you live in another country, and start

The Colt Officer's Model ACP is one of the most popular candidates among various pistolsmiths for building a custom carry gun.

competing. Most club-level competitors will be flattered when you show interest in their custom gun and will gladly allow you to examine it in a safe area after the match. Ask lots of questions about the guns you handle, feel, and examine. Take notes on which custom modifications feel best in your hand and look best to your eye. Who built the gun? What brand of beavertail grip safety is that? What size is the checkering on the frontstrap? How heavy is the trigger pull? Who makes the trigger? What brand of extended thumb safety does the gun wear? How much does it weigh?

When placing an order for a custom gun, everything should be in writing, including detailed specifications. Some pistolsmiths furnish custom order blanks to be filled out by the customer while others don't. Either way, the entire transaction should be in written form. This includes the guaranteed price of the work. Some pistolsmiths with a backlog that extends for as long as three or four years include an escalation clause in their quotation. In other words, the eventual price charged upon delivery may be greater than the original quoted price. This is OK as long as you understand what you're agreeing to and want a gun built by a particular pistolsmith badly enough to accept such a condition.

When writing the specifications, include everything you want on or done to the gun and clearly spell out each detail. Most pistolsmiths will accept no more than one or two changes once the original order is placed and if more are made, additional inconvenience fees are added to the original quotation even if the work hasn't started. This will, however, often depend on the change requested. For example, if you ordered a comp gun with open sights before the red dots invaded the action shooting game and want to make that change, any pistolsmith worth his salt would do so without additional charge if he hasn't already started working on your gun or bought the parts for it.

Regardless of the circumstances, if you decide to make a change in your specifications, write the pistolsmith rather than call as the time you use from his work schedule can affect the delivery of your gun as well as those of other customers. Besides, he may write it down on his apron and then forget it. Having everything in writing is for the benefit of both parties.

A firearm should be securely packaged when shipped to a pistolsmith. I prefer to place it inside a hard plastic case and then pack it in a heavy cardboard carton. If the pistolsmith's business name refers to guns (like Ted Twelvethumbs Steal-Me Custom Guns, Inc.) ask him about deleting the company name when you fill out the address label. It also is a good idea to include his telephone number at the bottom of the address label. When shipping, insure for the replacement cost of the gun and the case. Equally important, tell the pistolsmith to insure for replacement cost when returning the gun.

If the shipment is to be made by UPS, sending it 1st or 2nd Day Air is money well spent toward peace of mind. The package gets there quicker and is more easily traced if it should go astray.

You should also obtain a written statement that guarantees your gun is insured by the pistolsmith during the entire time it is in his shop. If not, the price you paid for the gun when purchasing it can go up in smoke should his shop be destroyed by fire or burglarized.

Historically, people who work on guns have a terrible reputation for missing promised delivery dates. In some cases it is the pistolsmith's fault. At other times, a missed delivery date is caused by a circumstance or event over which the pistolsmith has absolutely no control. I know this to be true because on a number of occasions I have looked behind the scenes and observed some things that cause pistolsmiths' hair to turn gray at an early age. Perhaps this is why I'm a bit more sympathetic and understanding when I am told my new custom gun won't be ready until next year.

When placing an order for a custom gun, you must keep in mind that no pistolsmith can afford to keep every available brand and variation of after-market parts in stock. If he had that kind of money he probably wouldn't be a pistolsmith. Just to stock all brands and styles of beavertail grip safeties would represent a major investment. For this reason, most pistolsmiths don't round up custom parts for a gun until the customer's order is received. Also, some aren't set up to apply the final blueing or plating on a gun. Therein lies another wrench in the works. The pistolsmith is dependent on the delivery of parts or services from outside sources. If the delivery dates for those items slip, his delivery to the customer will probably do likewise. One pistol-smith tells me it is not unusual to send a gun off for its coat of hard chrome plating and not see it again for several months.

5

Slide Modifications

Tightening the Fit

Most pistolsmiths emphasize that barrel quality and proper fitting of the barrel contribute more to increasing the accuracy of a Government Model pistol than all other mechanical factors combined. To what degree tightening the sloppy fit between the slide and frame improves accuracy is difficult to say and probably varies from gun to gun. Some say it represents as little as 10 percent of the improvement. Even so, I believe this modification prolongs the life of an accuracy job and should be a standard part of any fullhouse custom package. It may not help accuracy a lot, but it certainly doesn't hurt anything, either.

Some folks believe tightening slide to frame fit makes a gun less reliable while others think the modification makes it more so. I believe it depends on the conditions and who owns the gun. John Browning designed the Model 1911 to function under extreme battlefield conditions in the hands of soldiers who were sometimes too busy to be bothered with firearms maintenance. For this reason, the fit between its moving component parts was intentionally designed to be extremely loose. If we retrieve a loose factory gun and a custom gun with closely fitted parts from a bucket of mud and then attempt to fire them, my money will be riding on the former as most likely to go bang more than a time or two. If both guns are owned by someone who never cleans them, my wager stays on the same horse.

On the other hand, very few individuals within the civilian sector subject their guns to such harsh treatment. So, if both guns are fired under more

Two Wilson Super Grade Colts in .38 Super. The lower gun has two lightening cuts at the rear of its slide.

As Dave Lauck is prone to prove, his custom Government Model
pistols are dependable under the worst of conditions.

100

normal conditions by someone who maintains them properly, I'll bet 10 to one against the factory gun as being more reliable. The reason for more reliability with a properly built custom gun is simple to understand. Loose fitting parts inside a factory gun don't return to the same relationship with one another between shots. With a good custom gun, everything happens the same from shot to shot. An exaggerated comparison of the two might best be described as dumping a handful of parts from a sack between shots with one and carefully repositioning each part to the same relationship between shots with the other.

Under the worst of conditions and in the hands of someone who neglects proper maintenance, a loose factory gun has a lot going for it. For more common conditions and in the hands of someone who keeps his guns properly maintained, the custom gun is the clear winner. Incidentally, various manufacturers continue to build loose Government Model pistols because it's the only way to stay alive in a highly competitive market. It is done so parts will interchange, but it will not make them more reliable.

Slide-to-frame tightening simply involves removing some of the horizontal and vertical play between the rails of the two. In other words, the empty spaces between the slide and frame rails are reduced in size. Grasp the grip of your unloaded Government Model in one hand, twist the top of its slide from side to side and up and down with the other, and you'll feel both lateral and vertical play.

Mechanical Tighteners

Reducing the loose fit between the slide and frame has been and still is accomplished either by adding a part to the gun or modifying its slide and frame. Years ago, Frank Pachmayr introduced a device called the Slide Tightener. It wrapped around the bottom of the frame and was held in place by the slide stop's lengthened crosspin. Turning the point of an adjustment screw against the front of the trigger guard pivoted the device upward to place pressure on the underside of both slide rails. It probably worked but wasn't exactly a winner in the aesthetics department and cost more than most pistolsmiths charged for accomplishing the same thing by more conventional means.

Possibly the all time best of the mechanical slide-to-frame fit tighteners is the Wilson Group Gripper. It will drop into most guns but may require minor fitting in some. The device simply replaces the factory recoil spring guide and is available in three styles, short, full-length one-piece, and full-length two-piece. A spring-loaded plunger in the head of the guide engages a shelf in a special barrel link and in doing so pushes the breech end of the barrel into tighter battery.

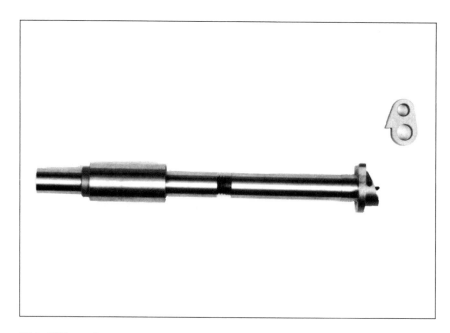

**This Wilson Group Gripper is an economical way to decrease the
sloppy fit between slide and frame.**

The effect the Group Gripper has on accuracy can vary considerably from
gun to gun. Of the guns in which I have tried it, accuracy improved from
a low of 20 percent to over 50 percent. I installed one in a Gold Cup and
50-yard groups measured the same as those fired with the gun without the
Group Gripper at 25 yards. One of my factory-original Commanders aver-
ages slightly over 2 inches at 25 yards with it and close to 6 inches without
it. A Colt Delta Elite averaged 8 inches at 50 yards without it and 6 inches
with it. The Group Gripper eventually will wear out and need replacing, but
if its head is lubricated each time the gun is field stripped for cleaning, it
should go at least 12,000 rounds with relatively light loads. Like all such
mechanical devices it is no substitute for permanently tightening slide to frame
fit, but is much better than nothing at all.

Squeezing, Peening, and Lapping

A more common method used for tightening slide to frame fit is called,
squeezing, peening, and lapping. The reduction of some lateral play is
accomplished by squeezing the bottom of the slide walls inward, although
some pistolsmiths prefer not to do this. Vertical and horizontal looseness is
reduced by carefully upsetting the metal in the slide rail with light taps from

a small hammer (i.e., peening the rail). After those two operations are performed the slide usually won't go completely on the frame or if it does, the fit is too tight for functioning of the gun. So, the pistolsmith applies an abrasive compound to the rails and forces the slide to and fro along the frame until it moves freely. The slide then travels like grease on glass with minimal lateral or vertical looseness.

The operation can be a bit more complicated than I have described and I've probably left out a minor detail or two, but now you should basically understand what a pistolsmith means when he says the slide to frame fit on your gun needs to be tightened. The job can be time-consuming and those who do a lot of this work usually have one arm about twice as big as the other and an elbow that creaks. It is an entirely satisfactory way of solving a problem and thousands of superbly accurate Government Model pistols have undergone this operation with great success.

The ACC-U-RAIL System

An excellent way to skin the same cat in a different manner is to utilize Bob Krieger's patented ACC-U-RAIL conversion. Bob machines a longitudinal semicircular groove down the bottom corner of the left and right rails of the frame and slide and then installs a .075-inch hardened tool-steel rod in each groove. The top half of each rod mates with a groove in the slide's rail and the bottom half rests in a groove in the frame's rail. The extremely hard rods run the full length of the frame rails. In addition to eliminating slop between frame and slide, the Krieger system reduces friction between the slide and frame to an absolute minimum. It also eliminates galling which can be a problem with stainless steel slides and frames and is the best thing going for reducing wear in guns with aluminum frames.

The advantages of using Krieger's system don't stop there. The steel rods are available with diameters in .001-inch increments. If the slide to frame fit eventually loosens after, say, 50,000 rounds or so have been fired in the gun, Bob simply replaces the old rails with new ones of larger diameter. I have ACC-U-RAILS in a Chuck Warner-built Gold Cup/Para-Ordnance comp gun in 9x23mm Super and consider it one of the better ideas in Government Model modifications. It also is an excellent way to tighten up an older gun that has shot loose and lost its original accuracy.

I'll never forget the first time I pulled back the slide of a gun that rode on ACC-U-RAILS. Like all guns with this system, the slide had absolutely zero vertical and lateral looseness and felt like it was on roller bearings. I believe it was Richard Heinie who compared the feeling with moving the table on a milling machine. If I could have only four modifications to a Government

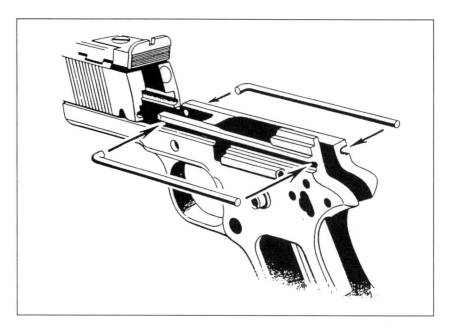

Bob Krieger's ACC-U-RAIL system is one of the best Government Model ideas to come along during this century.

Model pistol, they would be new sights, a trigger job, a handfitted barrel, and the ACC-U-RAIL system. Once you try Krieger's great idea, you won't want to own a gun without it.

The Caspian Alternative

When starting from scratch with all new component parts rather than rebuilding a factory gun, another option is to simply forego the previously described modifications and use a frame and slide made by Caspian. When the frame and slide are ordered together, the dimensions of their rails are oversized to the point where the two won't fit together until the rails are hand-lapped. This eliminates the bending and peening required on other slides and frames before their rails can be lapped, same as with old Colt National Match frames and slides of yesteryear. As one pistolsmith aptly put it, when Caspian parts are machined at the factory, their tolerances are intentionally held to a closer fit because they are made to be used in building a custom close-tolerance, match-grade gun rather than a factory loose-tolerance field-grade gun. Some pistolsmiths even go so far as to contend that the extremely uniform, end-to-end fit attainable between the rails of the Caspian frame and slide results in a gun that maintains its initial level of accuracy longer than when the rails

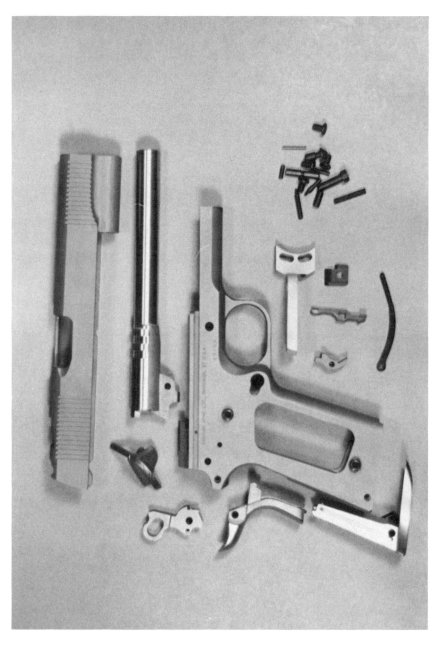

Beginning with a Caspian frame and slide and choosing among the numerous brands and styles of other component parts available from various sources can be less expensive than having a factory gun rebuilt.

The slide on Dave Lauck's custom Officer's ACP has three grasping grooves machined on both sides at the front of its slide. *(Mike McCoy photo)*

on other brands of frames are peened and lapped. Combine this characteristic with the Krieger ACC-U-RAIL system and a hard chrome finish on the rails of the slide and frame and you should have a gun that will keep on ticking long after the others have succumbed to the licking.

Spare Firing Pin Stop

I've covered milling out the slide for the low mounting of rear sights in the chapter on sights, but a few other details need covering and perhaps even repeating. When the rear of the slide is machined for some sights, the firing pin stop plate is shortened. This modification has no affect on the gun's functioning, but if the stop should ever need replacing, the factory version is too long. For this reason, it's best to specify that a spare be shipped with a gun so modified. It is not uncommon for those who are serious about the action shooting games to dryfire their guns dozens of times daily. For those individuals, two or more spare firing pin stops is not a bad idea as dryfiring can eventually batter them severely. I like to have three on hand for a competition gun, one for dryfiring, another used during practice and in matches, and a spare.

About Those Sight Slots

When the front sight on a comp gun is mounted out on the compensator, the sight on the slide must be eliminated. Consequently, the sight slot in the top of the slide has to be filled. Well, it doesn't have to be, but since I'm talking high-grade custom guns here, it will be. Some pistolsmiths can make the slot absolutely vanish while others never seem to master it. Using a Caspian slide which is available with no front sight slot is a good idea for those who have a problem with this modification. Toughest by far is the Gold Cup. As with any other slide, its slot can be filled with weld or the sight can be ground and filed flush, but matching those extremely fine grooves on the surface of the integral rib is a job I would hate to ask anyone to tackle. Of course, if the slide is to be chopped off for a light-slide gun, the problem is solved. The same goes if lightening cuts are made in the slide.

Lowered and Flared Ejection Port

Combine a properly tuned and adjusted extractor with an extended ejector and you've got reliable ejection of spent cases from most pistols being manufactured today. Older Government Models have relatively narrow ejection ports which work fine with the standard 230-grain hardball loads. The use of higher-velocity loads, especially those with the lighter bullets in compensated guns with their relatively slow cycle time has been responsible for

Old style Government Model ejection port before Colt introduced the
new enhanced version in 1992.

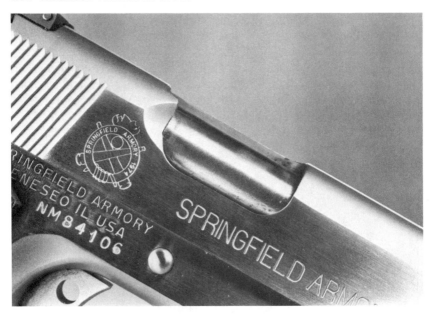

The ejection port on this Springfield Armory slide has been lowered
and flared. *(C. W. Custom photo)*

Kerry Lathwell burned up this course because she's fast and her custom compensated gun worked each time she squeezed its trigger. (Front Sight *photo*)

an increase in popularity of a slide modification called lowering and flaring the ejection port. On some older guns I've checked, the distance from the bottom of the slide to the bottom of the ejection port runs as much as .600 inch. I've heard of them being even higher. Reducing the sidewall height by 100 to .125 inch is usually all it takes for clean ejection of a gun with open sights.

Most manufacturers have lowered the ejection port on guns of current production. Here's how four unmodified slides I recently checked compared: Delta Elite (.470″), Gold Cup (.470″), Commander (.480″), and Caspian (.485″). In comparison, the same measurement on the slides of five custom guns read as follows: Wilson Combat .45 (.465″), Wilson Super Grade .38 (.470″), Warner Double Eagle Plus .45 (.470″), Warner Officer's ACP .45 (.475″), and Warner Signature Grade .38 (.480″). Since those guns are totally reliable, we can safely assume that a slide measuring anywhere between .460 to .480 inch from its rail to the bottom of the ejection port does not require lowering. Conservatively speaking, a good maximum is around .470 inch.

What you have just read applies to guns with open sights, but extremely low frame-attached scope mounts can change the rules considerably. With a low mount, ejected cases can ricochet off the edge of the ejection port, strike the bottom of the scope, and bounce back into the gun to tie up the works. Getting hammered by speeding cases also is rough on scopes and caused many to fail until pistolsmiths came to the rescue with their trusty files and milling machines. Incidentally, ejection problems with scope-mounted guns should come as no surprise since the Government Model was originally designed to eject spent cases almost vertically.

Lowering the ejection port even more than for open sights is part of the solution, but tuning the ejector and extractor for a lower trajectory arch of spent cases is equally important. How narrow the righthand wall of the port must be for reliable ejection varies from gun to gun, but I've been told anywhere from .400 to .450 inch by various pistolsmiths. The Warner .38 Super previously mentioned never missed a beat with its .480-inch port while wearing open sights. When Dave Pegram installed a Propoint on the gun with one of his mounts, he had to lower its port to .420 inch for 100 percent ejection of cases. Most pistolsmiths also lightly bevel the inside edge of the ejection port wall.

When the slide speeds rapidly to the rear and rams the head of a fired case against the ejector, the case starts turning cartwheels as it heads for daylight. During its journey, the spent case often bangs against the edge of the ejection port and either exits the gun or hangs around to cause a stove-pipe jam. Machining a bevel into the slide adjacent to its breechface and at the rear of the ejection port (i.e., flaring as the cut is commonly called) gives the case more of an unobstructed path to the outside world. Even if it does bang into the slide, the beveled edge (or rollover clearance notch as some pistolsmiths call it) has more of a tendency to flip the case east rather than west. Also, the flared port usually will reduce the number of dinged cases to a minimum, something greatly appreciated by most handloaders. Looks good, too. Colt's Gold Cup has long had it and you seldom see a fullhouse custom gun without it. Colt added this touch to the new enhanced version of its Government Model and variations during 1992.

Shortening and Lightening

There was a time when custom long-slide Government Model pistols enjoyed some popularity. Lengthening the slide an inch or two added weight out front and increased sight radius. Originally intended for bullseye competition, a few long-slides were used by practical pistol competitors of yesteryear before compensated gun became a household term. They are now the dinosaurs of practical pistols, and for good reason. The extra heft did dampen recoil, but all the extra weight racing back and forth had a tendency to increase muzzle jump.

Some of today's competitors often go in the opposite direction by using guns with shortened or lightened slides. Some slides are both shortened and lightened. This is done on competition guns to decrease the cycle time of the slide, or the time it takes the slide to make a complete fro and to trip during the firing cycle. Top-level competitors are convinced that the faster the slide completes its round trip, the less time the muzzle of the gun has to rise during recoil. This enables practical pistol shooters to double-tap targets faster in their game and speeds up target acquisition for those who specialize in steel plate competition.

When trimming the weight of a slide with lightening cuts, pistolsmiths concentrate their milling machines on areas that are not subjected to high levels of stress during firing. When maximum weight reduction is the goal, the cuts are quite large and often actually expose the barrel and other internal parts. Some pistolsmiths remove tiny bits of metal here and there inside the slide. It looks better than cuts all the way through, but the weight reduction often is so small the person spending the money will have to decide if it's worthwhile. It takes a lot of trimming and whittling to remove an ounce from the Government Model slide. The most drastic skeletonizing is seen in steel plate competition where the shooters use relatively light loads in guns chambered to .38 Super, 9mm Parabellum, 9x21mm, and others. As a rule, less metal

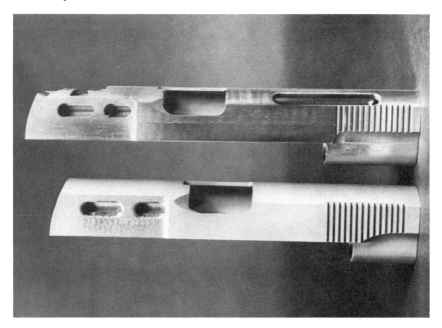

Two lightened Government Model slides in the rough. Slide on bottom has also been shortened one-half inch. (*C.W. Custom photo*)

111

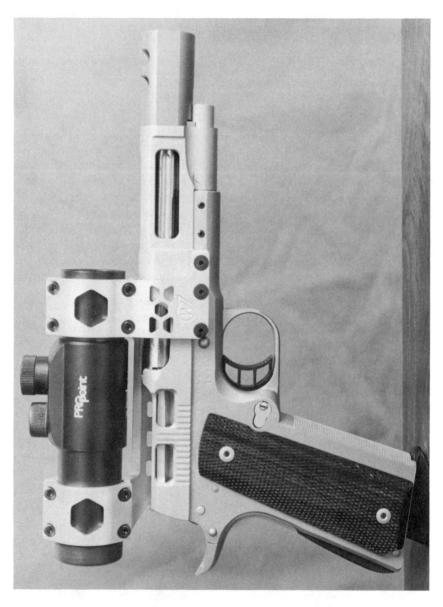

Jack Weigand reduced the weight of this optical-sighted gun by utilizing his lightweight aluminum scope mount, and by milling lightening cuts at the front and rear of the slide.

Close-up of lightening cuts in the slide of the Jack Weigand gun. Note the fluted barrel.

is removed from guns used in USPSA/IPSC competition due to the heavy Major power loads fired in them.

How much weight can be removed from the Government Model slide without drastically weakening it depends on which pistolsmith you ask, but it can be considerable. I have an old Government Model comp gun in .45 ACP built around 1980 by George Vais with, believe it or not, his version of a linkless barrel. It has a lightened slide, full-length recoil spring guide, a relatively short single-chamber compensator, and a fat .700-inch diameter bull barrel. The gun weighs 34 ounces with an empty magazine. A skinnier barrel, shortened slide, and synthetic spring guide would bring its heft down a few more ounces.

Shortening the standard Government Model slide by about ¾ inch to Commander-length is a popular modification for the lightweights, and probably reduces the heft of the gun by as much as, if not more than, the various lightening cuts. Of course, both operations are performed on some guns. I classify these highly refined exotics as more suitable for professional shooters than for the average guy who shoots a match or two each month at his local gun club. I fit into the latter category and have tried both types. Without exception, my scores in practical pistol matches are higher when I use a relatively heavy gun. I've shot my highest scores to date with a red-dot sighted

This Bob Cogan compensated gun has three lightening cuts in the lefthand side of its slide.

Three lightening cuts in a Colt slide by Steve Woods. *(Stephen Longley photo)*

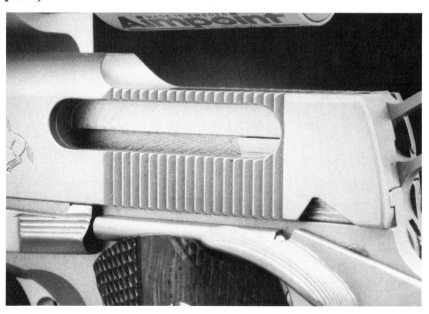

Lightening cuts in lefthand side and top of Colt slide by Steve Woods. *(Stephen Longley photo)*

The lightening cuts in the slide on George Vais' Warp Speed Government Model has reduced total weight to 34 ounces and yet the gun is still quite accurate.

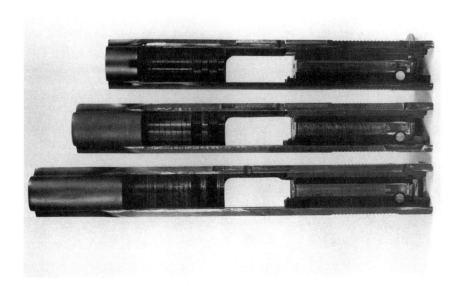

Three Colt slides illustrate the differences in their overall lengths and the lengths of their recoil spring tunnels at the front. From bottom: 1. Government Model, 2. Commander, 3. Officer's ACP.

Like Brian Enos, shown here filling the air with spent cases from his .38 Super, many shooters believe a lightened slide decreases the cycle time of the Government Model pistol. (*Zediker Publishing photo*)

.38 Super with a 6¾ inch barrel (including compensator) and weighing a whopping 53 ounces. To one of today's professional speedsters who rides on the edge of being quicker than fast, my gun would be like drawing and firing a boat anchor, but it works better for me than one of the flyweights.

The Extractor

In Chapter 7 I give a reason for ordering at least one spare extractor with a custom gun. Another reason is due to the fact that most pistolsmiths tune an extractor for its specific gun. This involves polishing and sometimes modifying its claw and even changing several of its angles. In the higher grade guns, especially those used for competitive shooting, the factory extractor usually is replaced with a heavy duty type. When properly cared for, the Government Model's extractor is not prone to breakage, but it can happen. When it does it's nice to have another ready to go. Some pistolsmiths include a spare with their fullhouse guns whether requested to do so or not.

Internal Polishing

Regardless of the manufacturer, some slides are considerably rougher on the inside than others. Two of my factory-original Colt Commander slides are good examples. All interior surfaces of one are quite smooth, but the other is extremely rough with deep tool marks on its breechface and disconnector timing rail.

The head of a cartridge slides hard across the breechface as it slips beneath the extractor during feeding. For this reason the surface of the breechface should be relatively smooth for reliable functioning of the gun. Also, any burrs around the firing pin orifice should be removed. If a good pistolsmith were to use my rough Colt slide on a custom gun, one of the first things he would do is attack its breechface. There are times, however, when an extremely rough example cannot be polished completely smooth as doing so would increase headspace excessively. An example would be a factory barrel with a headspace dimension that borders on maximum.

As the slide travels fro and to, the exposed nose of the disconnector rides against the bottom of its timing rail. The rail also rides over the nose of the hammer and pushes it to its cocked position. Even when the surface of the rail is extremely rough with deep tool marks, the gun will function perfectly, but on a custom gun it should be polished as smoothly as possible. In addition to improving the looks of the gun's innards, it also makes the slide easier to retract. This is an extremely critical operation, one that should not be attempted by anyone except an experienced pistolsmith. The removal of too much metal can render the disconnector dangerously inoperative.

The Grasping Handle

When an optical sight is mounted as low as possible on the Government Model, the grasping grooves on the rear of the slide can be reached, but they are not as accessible as on a gun with open sights. Install a safety thumbguard (described in Chapter 10) on one or both sides of the gun and grasping the slide to retract it becomes extremely difficult. If the guards extend upward fairly close to the top of the slide, the grasping grooves are completely covered. Installing a handle in the top of the slide solves the problem.

Two styles of handles are available. One is made to fit the factory rear sight dovetail in the slide and the other is shaped to fill a custom machine cut that was made for a low-mount installation of the Bo-Mar rear sight. In other words, both types simply replace the rear sight. The former works fine when simply pushed into the factory dovetail slot and secured with its setscrew, but looks much better on a fullhouse custom gun when it is lowered into the slide.

Several slide handle designs are available, some with wings that extend beyond the sides of the slide. The winged-type is inconvenient because it won't clear a frame-attached scope mount when the slide is removed and has to be detached each time the gun is field stripped for cleaning. Those

Richard Heinie's slide grasping handle on an optical-sighted C. W. Custom .38 Super.

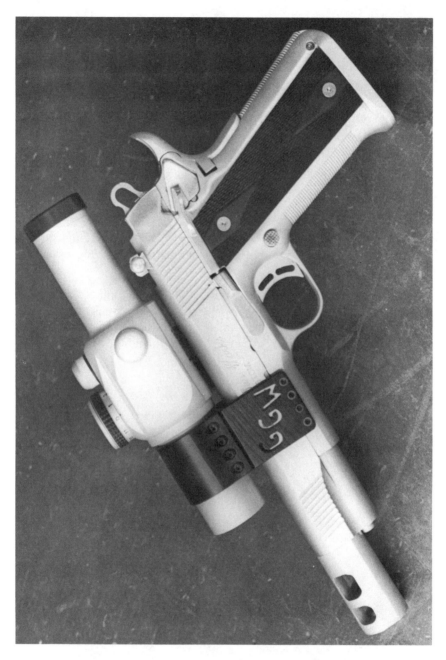

Built by Wayne Bergquist, owner of Glades Gun Works, this high-capacity .38 Super on the Caspian frame has, among other things, his Slide Racker slide grasping handle.

with extremely long wings make me a bit nervous when I visualize what might happen should a thumb wander up into the path of the speeding slide handle while the gun is being fired. Good-bye thumbnail—if you're lucky. I'm sure others will eventually come along, but as this is written, the T-Bone handle from C. W. Custom is tough to beat for an optical-sighted gun. A really neat one available from that shop is made for the Gold Cup slide. It replaces the Elliason sight and fills its factory cutout in the slide perfectly. The Heinie slide handle is a good one for a gun with open sights. Bill Wilson also has a good design.

Other modifications pistolsmiths commonly make to the Government Model slide are covered elsewhere in Chapters 7 and 11.

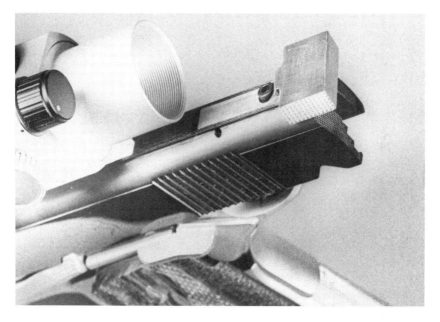

Chuck Warner's T-Bone slide grasping handle on a Colt Gold Cup slide.

6

The Frame

The Beveled Magazine Well

Government Model frame modification options range from something as simple as beveling the mouth of the magazine well to a major reshaping of certain areas and replacing all of its components with custom parts. One of the more popular is filing or machining a beveled edge on the inner surface of the magazine well's mouth. Some manufacturers are now doing this at the factory while others stick with the original shape. On guns without it, it's an important modification for two reasons. First, it allows smoother insertion of a loaded magazine, especially during a stressful situation. Secondly, anyone who hasn't pinched the skin of his/her hand between the magazine and frame when shoving a fresh supply of cartridges home hasn't shot the Government Model pistol very much or always wears gloves. A beveled magazine well eliminates the pain and blood blisters during quick reloads.

Many shooters handle this modification themselves and I've seen some home-performed jobs that appeared to be done by a professional. Sadly though, I've seen far more modifications that looked like their owners hogged out the metal with a dull chain saw. That's OK by me; these guns are theirs and whatever makes them happy is what's important. I make it a point to never criticize another fellow's wife, gun, or hound dog. On the negative side, when someone decides to sell a gun so butchered, the buyer won't be a bit bashful in stating how much its value was depreciated by such a seemingly insignificant modification. The problem with metal is that once it is removed it can never be put back. At least, it can't be put back economically.

The mouth of the magazine well on a custom carry gun beveled by Steve Woods. *(Stephen Longley photo)*

Magazine Well Funnels

On some guns, particularly those built for competition, the magazine well modification goes beyond a simple bevel job with the installation of a funnel which gives the shooter a bigger target for speedy reloads. This custom feature also is mildly popular on carry guns and it works out fine when one of the less bulky designs is installed. Many shapes, types, and styles are available. The Wilson and SA Shooting Accessories (SASA) require little to no fitting when installed. The SASA is probably worn by more custom guns than all the others combined for four reasons; it is relatively inexpensive, it looks good (when properly fitted), it is easy to install, and its integral checkered mainspring housing kills a second bird with the same stone. It is available for the Government Model and clones as well as the Officer's ACP and Para-Ordnance, with flat or arched mainspring housing. I have SASAs on several custom guns, including an Officer's ACP. It increases the length of that .45's backstrap just enough to make it more controllable with heavy loads, yet it does not defeat the compact gun concept.

Other styles of magazine well funnels are attached by welding or soldering, with some requiring shortening of the grip frame during installation. The

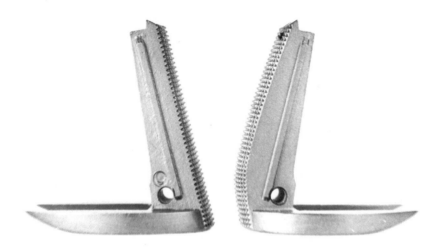

The SA Shooting Accessories magazine well funnel is available with (left) flat or (right) arched integral mainspring housing.

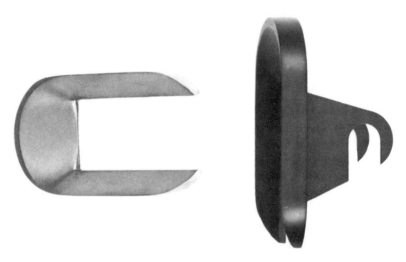

Requiring no modification to the frame for installation, the Wilson lightweight magazine well funnel is held in place by the grip panels.

124

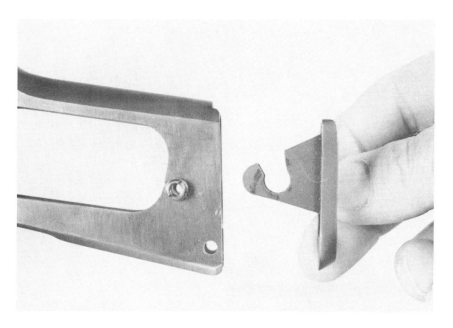

The Wilson magazine well funnel hooks over the grip panel bushings in the frame and is held in place by the grip panels.

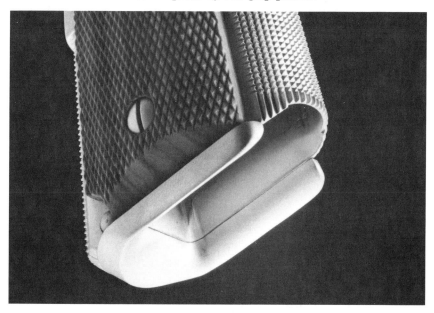

Steve Woods' installation of a Wilson magazine well funnel. *(Stephen Longley photo)*

Extending the frontstrap and installing an SA Shooting Accessories magazine well funnel on this C. W. Custom Officer's ACP lengthened its grip for better control with heavy loads, but did not defeat the compact gun concept.

126

one available from Gun Craft is a good example. It looks quite racy on a competition gun and when properly installed it appears to be an integral part of the frame because that's exactly what it becomes after installation. I have the Gun Craft funnel on an optical-sighted Para-Ordnance gun in 9x23mm Super and wouldn't leave home without it. Any time I miss its cavernous opening during a fast reload, I know who to blame. This type of magazine well funnel obviously is too large and bulky for a carry gun, but on a race gun it is the cat's meow. The smaller Wilson version is a better choice for a carry gun.

Some pistolsmiths heat the mouth of the magazine well and reshape it to form an integral funnel rather than installing one of the aftermarket types. Jim Stroh and Glenn Martin skin the same cat a different way by building up a strip of metal around the mouth of the well with TIG welding and then shaping it by hand to match the profile of the grip panels. Its edges do not extend beyond the outer surfaces of the grip panels and yet it increases the size of the opening by about 150 percent. The Martin and Stroh designs also rank right up there with the Gun Craft in aesthetics.

Incidentally, all magazines used with a gun that has an extended magazine well must have an extension or bumper attached to their floorplate. This item is covered in the chapter on magazines and is doubly important for a carry gun.

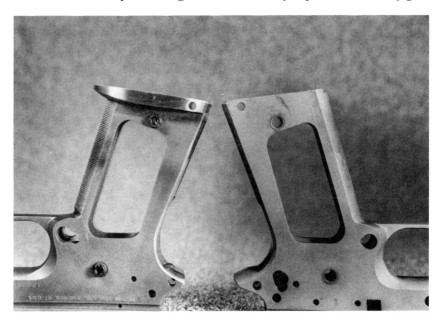

The Caspian frame on left has been shortened and a Gun Craft magazine well funnel soldered into place. *(C. W. Custom photo)*

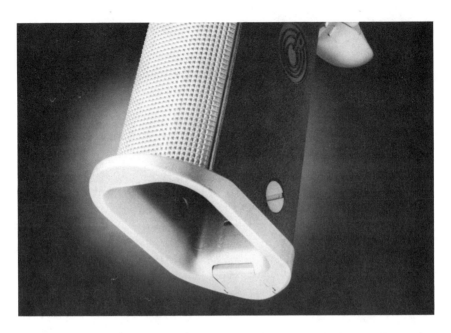

Gun Craft magazine well funnel installed on a Para-Ordnance frame by
Steve Woods. *(Stephen Longley photo)*

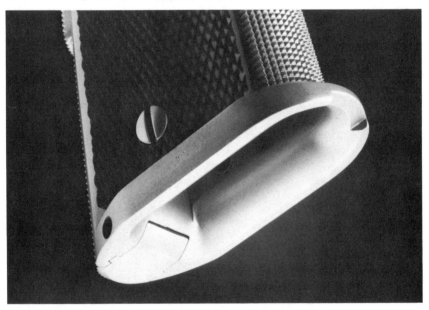

Steve Woods' installation of the Brown Maxi-Well magazine well
funnel. *(Stephen Longley photo)*

Mike Morris dropping an empty magazine and reaching for a fresh one for a fast reload during a practical pistol match.

Bob Bailey makes a quick reload while racing to the next group of targets during a USPSA practical pistol match.

129

Recognizing that those who have comp guns built always want a mag well funnel, some manufacturers of Government Model frames are responding to the demand by including a flared mouth on the magazine well. This eliminates the expense involved in having the aftermarket variety installed. The Caspian high-capacity frame with its integral funnel is a good example.

Mainspring Housings

A checkered mainspring housing greatly improves the gripping area of the Government Model, especially if the checkering extends across the adjacent surfaces of the backstrap. The synthetic housing Colt installs in its frames sometimes is retained when an optical-sighted gun is built for practical pistol competition in order to keep weight down. It is almost always replaced by a steel housing on other types of custom gun. Most pistolsmiths hand checker the steel housing or use those already so modified from Wilson, SASA and Brownells. On higher-grade guns, the machine-cut checkering on the after-market housing almost always is pointed up by hand. When modifying a flat mainspring housing, Jim Garthwaite adds a very nice touch. He drawfiles its rear surface to match the frame and when it is checkered, the points of the sharp pyramids are actually a bit below the adjacent surface of the backstrap. It offers a greatly improved gripping surface and yet the outer rows of checkering don't dig into the hand. When installing an arched housing, Garthwaite removes its abrupt curve for a more rounded shape.

Shooters with small hands usually specify a flat mainspring housing combined with a short trigger while those with large hands often opt for an arched housing and long trigger. Those of us with average-size hands can live happily ever after with either. I've tried both combinations in competition and can tell no difference in my performance as long as I practice a few hours with one or the other before a match. Some shooters claim the arched housing makes them shoot low while others say the flat housing causes them to shoot high. That's not true for me if I practice a bit.

The arched housing does have one advantage. When some shooters position their hand high up on the grip of a gun with a high-sweep grip safety, they often find that the flat housing prevents the palm of their hand from depressing the safety enough to disengage it. The arched housing changes the angle of the palm just enough to eliminate this problem. It doesn't work for everybody, but I know those who swear by it. From a practical and personal point of view, I would just as soon have one style as the other, but won't argue with those who say the flat housing looks better on a top-grade custom gun.

Extended Frontstrap

Extending the straight line of the frontstrap on the frame upward, or removing metal from the frame at the rear terminus of the trigger guard is a common modification, especially on guns built for the action shooting games. I like it just as well on a carry gun. This modification, along with a high-sweep beavertail grip safety, positions the shooting hand a bit higher and therefore closer to the bore's axis. The resultant high hold directs recoil closer to the center of the hand and improves control of the gun during rapid-fire. Pistolsmiths have offered this option for many years and Colt followed suit with its enhanced versions of the Government Model, Gold Cup, Delta Gold Cup, Combat Elite, Delta Elite, Commander, and Officer's ACP in 1992. Once a shooter tries a custom gun with an extended frontstrap, he usually would rather fight than switch, especially if its surface is checkered.

The extremely short gripframe of Colt's Officer's ACP, the Springfield Armory Compact, and others like them benefit even more from the frontstrap modification than larger guns. This especially holds true for those with medium to large hands. An extended and checkered frontstrap along with a high-sweep grip safety makes those small guns much easier to control as

Like most practical pistol competitors, Jim Buckner prefers an extremely high two-hand hold on the Government Model for maximum control during rapid-fire shooting.

Extended and checkered frontstrap by Steve Woods. *(Stephen Longley photo)*

they gobble up heavy loads. Installing a mag well funnel increases the length of the backstrap, .225 inch for the SASA, and .200 inch for the Wilson. The backstrap length on my custom Officer's ACP with the SASA funnel measures 3.25 inches to the bottom of its Brown grip safety. The extended frontstrap is 2.20 inches long. Compare those dimensions to your factory gun and you'll have a better idea of what the modifications represent.

Incidentally, even with all those modifications plus Heinie sights, a full-length recoil spring guide, a Wilson sleeved barrel, and an empty magazine, my little snubnose .45 weighs 35 ounces, a mere ounce more than it weighed fresh from the factory. Its mag well funnel does tend to defeat the compact concept by a small degree, but the sacrifice pales to insignificance when the Remington and Cor-Bon +P loads are fired in the gun. It is much easier to control than when in its factory original form.

Para-Ordnance Frame

The high-capacity Para-Ordnance pistol has been quite successful despite the fact that its extremely wide gripframe replete with squared frontstrap is too much of a handful for many shooters. Recontouring the frontstrap and rounding off its square corners helps a lot, but the grip is still too wide, even for those of us with average size hands. This particular problem is being solved in a number of ways. Gun Craft, combines the recontoured frontstrap with aluminum inserts that reduce the width of the grip by about ¼ inch. At C. W. Custom, a lot of metal is shaved away and extremely thin aluminum grip panels with a sharply checkered surface are installed. Glenn Martin of Shooter's World eliminates the grip panels entirely, fills the lightening holes in the sides of the gripframe, and wraps 20- or 30-line checkering completely around the frontstrap, mainspring housing, and sides of the grip. The thickness or width of the grip ends up at about 1.30 inches which is close to the same as the standard Government Model with grip panels.

Aluminum Frame Recoil Block

Choosing an aluminum frame over steel for a competition gun trims a lot of weight from one of the high-capacity rigs. Aluminum is fine on a gun built for light Steel Challenge-type loads, but it may not stand up to the pounding dished out by thousands of heavy Major power IPSC loads. You can have your cake and nibble on it too by selecting aluminum and installing a steel recoil block. I am not sure who originated this particular idea, but Richard Heinie was the first to describe to me how he does it on the Para-Ordnance frame. In my opinion, installing the recoil block and Bob Krieger's ACC-U-RAIL system (described in Chapter 5) is the only way to go with an aluminum-framed competition gun.

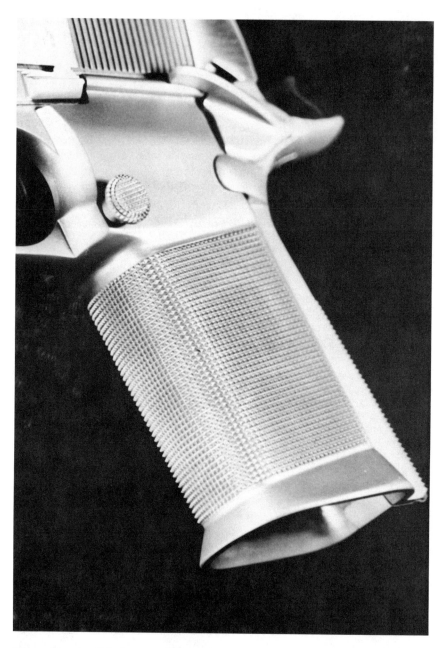

Glenn Martin filled the lightening cuts in the sides of this Para-Ordnance steel frame, extended the frontstrap by removing metal from the terminus of the trigger bow and frame, and eliminated the grip panels with wraparound checkering coverage.

Squaring and Checkering the Trigger Guard

Squaring the trigger guard or changing its front surface from curved to flat has long been a common modification on the Government Model pistol. The operation can range from a simple flattening of the guard's front with a file to more extensive work which involves heating and reshaping or building up its surface by welding and then recontouring by hand. On some competition guns the front bowed section of the guard is extensively modified to extend forward in the form of a hooked or concaved shape. Sometimes the factory trigger guard is completely removed and replaced by a custom guard carved to the desired profile from a block of steel.

These modifications were introduced when shooters began to adopt the two-hand hold with the weak hand wrapped around the strong hand. Those who preferred to wrap the index finger of their weak hand around the front of the trigger guard complained about its curved surface so the flattened or concave modification was born. The front surface often is serrated or checkered which is fine on competition guns as well as carry guns used with most types of holsters. It is not a desirable feature to have serrations on a gun to be carried in a Bianchi holster with the PRD retention device as in no time flat the sharp checkering will chew up the synthetic insert that grips the front of the trigger guard.

Extremely exotic reshaping or complete replacement of the trigger guard has pretty much died out and for this reason few pistolsmiths offer it in their standard custom packages. All pistolsmiths still offer a simple squaring of the guard and many customers consider a custom gun incomplete without it. The truth of the matter is that only a tiny percentage of shooters wrap a finger around the trigger guard when firing the gun and this particular modification is most often specified because many like the way it looks or it is the fashionable thing to do. This is, however, an extremely popular option and probably 50 percent or more of today's custom guns have it. Some pistolsmiths remove metal from the frame at the upper terminus of the guard to form a 90 degree angle in that area. Others leave the area slightly radiused. Some will do it either way. Take your pick.

From a practical point of view, I don't care for checkering on the front of the trigger guard. I am, however, quite fond of 40-line checkering on its bottom surface simply because it feels good to the finger of my weak hand when shooting a gun with the two-hand hold. Incidentally, checkering on this area is not compatible with the gun-retaining insert in some Safariland holsters as it wears out the synthetic trigger guard gripper in short order. The Final Option competition holster is a good example. On the other hand, checkering the front of the trigger guard does not harm the plastic retainer.

Squared and checkered trigger guard and pivoting trigger on a compensated gun built by Bob Cogan.

Extended Magazine Release

The location of a couple of controls on the Government Model pistol have led some to believe John Browning was left-handed. Watch a southpaw who really knows how to make the gun sing its pretty song in competition and you're likely to see his trigger finger performing triple duty by also operating the slide lock and magazine release. I have my doubts about Browning being a lefty, but unless a shooter has a thumb like an orangutan, it won't reach the factory magazine release when the gun is held in a natural shooting position. Speeding up reloads by enabling the competitor to dump an empty magazine without greatly shifting his grip is the purpose of various styles of extended releases.

The simplest design consists of a slightly oversized extension or button with a sharply checkered surface. This style is available from a number of sources, including Wilson, Heinie, King's, Brown, and Gun Craft. The latter company also offers a steel replacement for the plastic unit on the Para-Ordnance gun. On other guns, the extended button is attached by drilling and tapping the factory magazine catch and securing it with a hexhead screw. This modification makes the button easier to reach with the thumb, but those with small- to medium-size hands may still have to shift their grip slightly in order to do so. I personally don't consider a little grip-shifting a big deal. By the time my weak hand has stripped a fresh magazine from its belt pouch and is speeding toward the gun, my strong hand already has dumped the empty and reassumed its natural grip. Install a Wolff or Heinie reduced-power spring in the magazine catch and you're ready for competition at minimum cost.

Other types of buttons extend rearward, some to such an extreme that the front of the grip panel has to be mortised or notched out for clearance. The button made by Jack Weigand is this type. It is a good design, but some shooters have a tendency to depress the button with the thumb of their weak hand and make the gun go bombs away at the wrong time. Others swear by them and wouldn't dream of using anything else.

For those who don't want to shift their grip at all, there is the Wilson First Grip. Easily installed without modification to the gun, it consists of a replacement magazine latch and a thin steel plate which extends upward from beneath the grip panel, over the plunger housing, and up beside the slide. The top section serves as a thumb guard. Attached to the plate is a pivoting slide release lever. The lever engages the magazine latch and curves back over the front of the grip panel where it ends with a sharply checkered tab. Also included in the kit is a pair of checkered nylon grip panels with the underside of the lefthand panel inletted for the lever. Operating the First Grip requires absolutely no change in hold. Simply punch its tab with the thumb and the magazine exits the gun.

Extended magazine release installed by Steve Woods. *(Stephen Longley photo)*

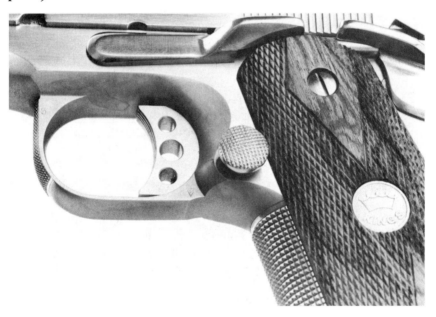

Extended magazine release, slide latch, and thumb safety by Al Capone.

138

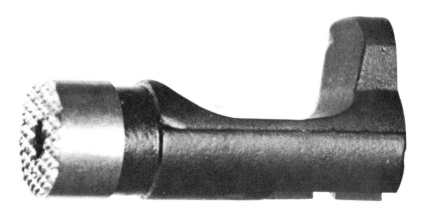

Wilson extended magazine catch or release.

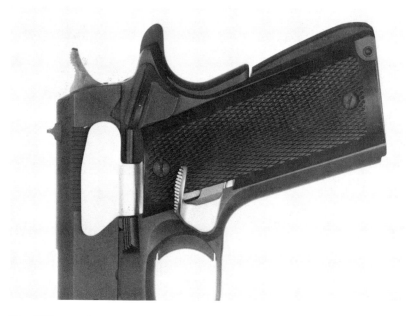

The Wilson First Grip is the fastest magazine release available for competition guns. It also features a thumbguard that extends from beneath the top of the grip panel.

When initially installing a First Grip on one of my comp guns, I figured the massive lever would rule out weak hand shooting. I also figured I would bump the lever with my weak hand in the two-hand hold and dump the magazine before I actually wanted to. It didn't happen. After becoming accustomed to its presence, I didn't even notice it. A righthanded shooter can jab the button with the strong hand thumb, or it can be bumped with the weak hand as it starts to move for a fresh magazine. It's fast. A more appropriate name would be the Lightning Grip. This is a neat trick for competitive shooting, but as with all extended magazine releases, it should never be installed on a defense gun.

My vote for the most ingenious Government Model magazine release of the century goes to SA Shooting Accessories for its ambidextrous design. It is as fast as the Wilson First Grip and even faster than all the rest. The SASA ambi consists of a slightly extended release button on the left side with a twin of about the same size on the other side. A righthanded shooter can operate the left-side button with his thumb in the traditional manner or he can punch the right-side button with his trigger finger as lefthanded shooters have been doing for decades. When a pistolsmith installs the SASA unit, a tiny bit of metal must be removed from inside the frame, but the modification does not prevent replacing it with the factory magazine catch should the need to do so arise. I've tried the SASA ambi release on Government Model, Double Eagle, and Para-Ordnance pistols and consider it one of the all-time great ideas in custom parts for competition guns.

There are those who will disagree, but I don't think a carry gun should wear any type of extended magazine release. I feel even more strongly about the use of a reduced-power spring for this application. They're great on competition guns; if a full magazine is accidentally ejected at the wrong time during a match, you still have the option of going back the next weekend for another try. This may not prove to be true if the same thing happens while a defense gun is being used for its intended purpose. I believe the factory version with good sharp checkering on its surface is the way to go in this department.

Custom Slide Stops

Radiusing the sharp corners of the slide stop adds a touch of class to a custom gun, as does 40-line checkering on its thumb tab. Both modifications also are practical. With its sharp corners removed, the stop is more comfortable for shooters who lay the thumb of their weak hand alongside the frame. The sharp checkering offers more of a no-slip surface than the coarse factory serrations. Jack Weigand goes a step farther by recontouring the stop's body. Al Capone does that, plus he mills an oval-shaped lightening cut through

Built by Chuck Warner of C. W. Custom, this Colt Double Eagle has an SA Shooting Accessories ambidextrous magazine release.

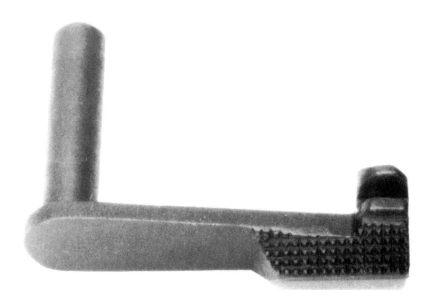

Al Capone checkered the thumb tab on this slide latch.

Jack Weigand's lightweight slide stop.

142

the stop. Both styles are nice. Moving on to less cost, the Wilson slide stop comes with a checkered tab only.

The most novel custom slide stop I have seen is made by Ben Jones and Kim Stroud at Gun Craft. On the factory stop, its transverse pin is an integral part of the exterior body. When the custom stop made by Gun Craft is installed on the gun, the transverse pin remains stationary while the body swings freely. This decreases the amount of tension required of the magazine follower to push the latch up to engagement with its notch in the slide. This is an especially good idea for guns with magazines that have weak or reduced-power follower springs, and for those who want something on their custom gun that everybody else doesn't have.

Extended Slide Stop

I have seen and examined dozens upon dozens of custom Government Model pistols owned by people of various walks of life. They included practical pistol competitors of all levels, lawmen, and weekend plinkers. After looking at all those guns, I have decided that very few people use an extended slide stop. Someone somewhere must be buying them, though, because they are still available from several sources.

According to this particular theory, an extended slide stop enables the right-handed shooter to release the slide from its locked back position with the thumb of his strong hand without shifting his grip on the gun. This may be true for those who by necessity or choice shoot the gun with one hand only. Today's shooters most often use a two-hand hold and for these individuals it is just as quick for a righthander to hit the stop with the thumb of the weak hand as the hold is resumed after a quick reload.

The problem I (and all others I know who have tried it) have with the extended slide stop is it will lock the slide back in the middle of a string if it is only lightly bumped by the thumb. Believe me, whether you shoot with one hand or two, it will happen and usually at the worst possible time. Conversely, it is a great idea for a right-handed handicapped shooter who doesn't have a left hand.

Ambidextrous Slide Stop

I have examined one custom Government Model that had an ambidextrous slide stop. The pistolsmith had welded an extension onto the transverse shaft of a factory stop and then cut four square shoulders into its end somewhat like those on a socket wrench. A custom lever was then fitted to the end of the shaft and held in place with a small hexhead screw. Of course, the lever had to be removed each time the gun was field stripped for cleaning.

The Weak Hand Thumb Rest

When firing a gun with the two-hand hold, most experienced shooters extend the thumb of the weak hand more or less parallel with the barrel and pointed in the target's general direction. A few in the action shooting games prefer to rest the thumb on an extension or shelf projecting from the frame's side. They feel that by doing so they are better able to reduce muzzle jump during rapidfire shooting. It doesn't work for me and I wouldn't want it on a gun, but obviously it works for them. I've seen several custom modifications designed for this purpose. One thumb rest was built for righthanded shooters; it consisted of a combination shelf and thumbguard welded to the front of the slide catch. Another type of thumb rest consisted of an extension soldered to the frame forward of the slide stop.

Extended Ejector

The use of an extra long or extended ejector in the Government Model originated with the introduction by Colt of its 1949 Commander version. Since cycle time with the shorter and lighter slide was quicker, the extended ejector caused a spent case to exit the gun with a bit more haste. The Officer's

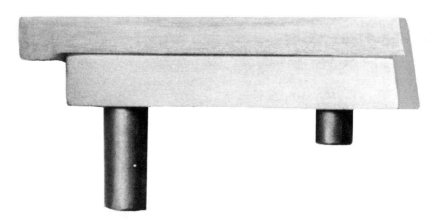

The installation of this Kings extended ejector starts a fired case on its journey from the gun a bit earlier than when a standard-length ejector is used.

ACP, with its even faster cycle time, also has an extended ejector. When you consider that the standard Government Model (with its heavier slide) fires and reloads a fresh cartridge before most shooters can release the trigger, it becomes obvious that a spent case doesn't have a lot of time to laze around inside before heading for daylight.

The use of an extended ejector in standard-size guns was introduced by competitors in the action shooting games as a way of improving reliability with heavy loads. Simply explained, when the slide speeds to the rear and rams the head of a case against the nose of an extended ejector, it starts exiting the gun a bit quicker than when struck by the shorter version. The change in ejection timing decreases the possibility of the slide returning before the spent case has cleared the gun. Even when booted in the rump by an extended ejector, the case may still get bumped by the slide. However, if the ejection port in the slide is low enough and has been flared, the case is likely to bounce out.

Installing an extended ejector is a popular option among those who have custom guns built, but its importance might be a tad overrated. I believe it is a high-priority item on a compensated gun, but less important on one without a compensator. I also believe an extended ejector improves the reliability of light-slide guns, but often makes no difference in some guns with slides of standard weight. My switch-top, switch-barrel Gold Cup is a good example of the latter statement. It has the standard short ejector and has never missed a beat even when its Commander slide and barrel are installed. I can't say whether or not that gun is simply an exception to the rule.

The extended ejector has one disadvantage. When a cartridge loaded to maximum overall length is manually removed from the chamber by retracting the slide, the ejector contacts the head of the cartridge before the nose of its bullet is completely clear of the front edge of the ejection port. This prevents the cartridge from being manually ejected in the usual manner by exiting the ejection port. This happens only with long cartridges, namely the .45 ACP, .38 Super, 9x23 Super, and 10mm Auto. Seldom is it a problem with the 9mm Luger and .40 S&W.

The best way to unload one of those guns is to point its muzzle in a safe direction, remove the magazine, slowly retract the slide, and allow the cartridge to drop through the magazine well and onto the ground. Some guns will eject a loaded round out through the ejection port if they are held right-side down as the slide is retracted, but I find them to be exceptions. Smooth manual ejection of a loaded round is something IPSC shooters are happy to sacrifice for increased reliability with comp guns, but most pistolsmiths don't recommend it for other applications.

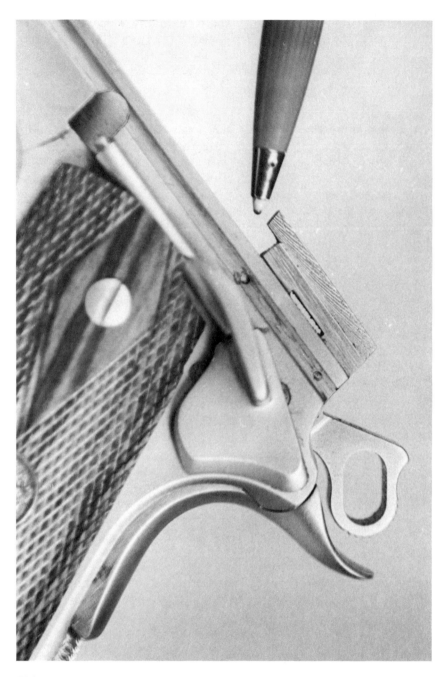

This extended ejector on a Wilson Super Grade in .38 Super causes a fired case to exit the gun a bit quicker than a standard length ejector.

Eric Stafford shoots, scoots, and reloads on the run during a match.

Pins

Pins in the Government Model are the driven and push types. The driven pin holds such parts as the ejector, barrel link, and rear sight (Gold Cup) in place semipermanently. Push pins are used to retain parts like the sear and mainspring housing. Push pins allow easy disassembly of the pistol. In most factory guns, their fit is loose. When building a high-grade custom gun, some pistolsmiths install slightly oversized pins for a better fit, yet they remain loose enough for easy removal. Caspian is one of the primary sources for those custom pins.

7

Metal Checkering and Serrating

CHECKERING

Consisting of intersecting V-shaped grooves cut into a material, checkering is quite decorative and provides a nonslip surface to various parts of a firearm. When properly executed by the steady hand and keen eye of an experienced craftsman who takes pride in his work, it is a thing of beauty and one of the more popular modifications offered by pistolsmiths. A full-house custom Government Model pistol without at least some checkering looks unfinished to some eyes.

The style of checkering commonly seen on rifles and shotguns has grooves intersecting at 30 to 45 degrees to form diamonds with pointed tops. With the exception of its grip panels, checkering on a custom Government Model pistol is almost always the old English style with grooves cut at right angles to form pointed squares or pyramids. I once thought this rather odd until examining a custom Gold Cup the frontstrap of which was covered with the diamond-style checkering. Even though the work was perfectly executed, something didn't seem exactly right. A close look at the shape or profile of the Government Model revealed the answer. Most of its lines were either parallel or reasonably perpendicular to each other. Thus, lines cut into relatively narrow areas of its frame and slide in the form of checkering, grooving, or serrating, must be parallel or perpendicular to existing lines in order to blend with the gun's natural form. The old English style of checkering is most often seen on the Government Model pistol. On the other hand, the diamond style of checkering looks fine on the extremely wide and relatively flat surface areas of the grip panels.

148

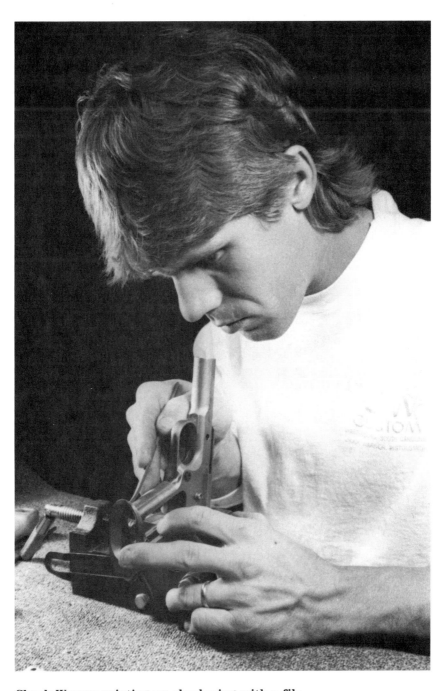

Chuck Warner pointing up checkering with a file.

Dave Lauck's checkering on the frontstrap and serrations on the trigger guard of a .45 caliber Colt carry gun. *(Mike McCoy photo)*

150

Pointing up the checkering on a frontstrap after a Gun Craft magazine well funnel was attached. *(C. W. Custom photo)*

The distance between the parallel rows of pyramids in a checkered area is commonly referred to as line count. When a checkering pattern is described as having 20-line coverage, it consists of 20 grooves or rows of pyramids per linear inch. Density or line count will vary, depending on customer preference and the part of the gun that is being checkered, but the most commonly seen consist of the following lines per inch: 20 (coarse), 30 (medium-coarse), 40 (fine), and 50 (extremely fine).

As aesthetics go, coarse and medium-coarse checkering are best suited for larger surface areas such as the frontstrap and mainspring housing. Finer checkering looks as good on those areas, but scores lower as a functional gripping surface. Finer checkering looks much better than coarse on small areas such as the bottom and front of the trigger guard, the heel of the slide, the hammer spur, the slide stop, and the magazine catch button. As a rule, 20- or 30-line checkering goes on the frontstrap and mainspring housing, with 40- or 50-line on smaller surface areas.

I personally prefer 20-line checkering on the gripping areas, but my hands stay reasonably tough from a lot of shooting. Those with more tender hands find the big pointed squares a bit uncomfortable and prefer 30-line on those areas. Some even go with 40-line; if the tiny squares are quite sharp they

151

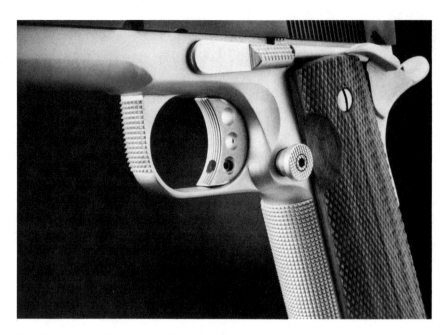

Checkering on the extended frontstrap, magazine release button, trigger guard, and slide latch tab by Steve Woods. *(Stephen Longley photo)*

offer a reasonably good gripping surface. Although it doesn't look as good, a workable compromise is to have the pistolsmith cut 20-line checkering and then carefully remove a tiny bit of the sharp points with a fine file. Most prefer finer checkering over that alternative.

Many pistolsmiths are capable of doing an excellent job on 20-line checkering and most have no problem with 30-line, but some have problems with finer checkering because its execution is so unforgiving. When coarse checkering is being cut, a minor slip of the file often can be corrected. The same tiny slip can be disastrous with 40-line or finer and result in several hours of eye-straining work spiraling down the drain. Fine checkering also highlights imperfections much more than coarser cuts. A pyramid or two not precisely the same height as their mates will often go unnoticed in 20-line coverage, but will look like a pinball machine with only two lights burning in a 40- or 50-line pattern.

Metal thickness in the frontstrap can vary from gun to gun even among those from the same manufacturer. This seems to hold true more often for Colt frames than for some of the others. For this reason, the frontstraps of some guns are too thin for the deep grooves of 20-line checkering. All

Fifty-line checkering on the heel of a slide by Jim Stroh.

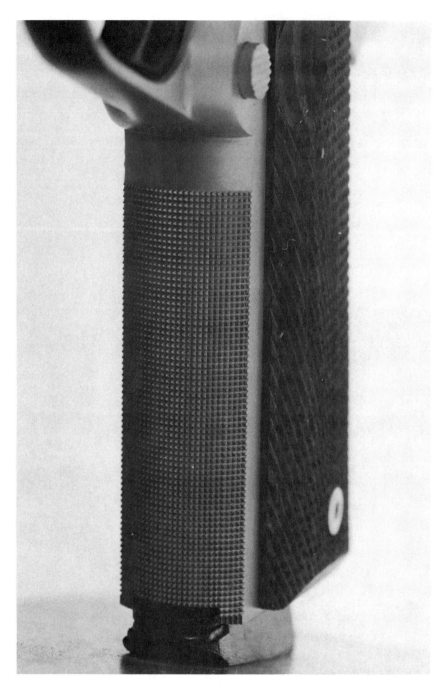

Thirty-line frontstrap checkering by Jack Weigand.

Para-Ordnance frames I've examined are too thin at the bottom of their front-strap for 20-line checkering, but most will take 30-line. If the Para-Ord grip is shortened for the installation of a mag well funnel available from Gun Craft and others, the thin section usually is eliminated.

Whether checkering is purely ornamental or both decorative and functional depends on what part of the gun it is applied to and whose opinion has center stage at the moment. In the function department, I classify a checkered front-strap as most important with checkering on the mainspring housing running a close second place. Once you have wrapped your hand around and fired a gun with those custom touches, you're spoiled forever. If I had to pick a third most functional area for checkering it is on the flat surface of the magazine catch button. Number four is on the bottom surface of the trigger guard. These four personal preferences apply to carry guns as well as those used for practical pistol competition.

Good checkering on other areas is attractive, but less functional. Years ago, pistolsmiths began to checker the front surface of the trigger guard for shooters who wanted to rest the index finger of their weak hand there with the two-hand hold. The idea caught on to the point where many customers now specify it on a new gun even though they never use it for its intended purpose. Since more shooters don't ride the front of the trigger guard with a finger than do, checkering is most often applied there for decoration rather than practicality. Even so, about one-half the orders for custom guns specify that feature, probably because it looks so nice.

Checkering or serrating is commonly seen on the rear surfaces of the slide and extractor. If during its firing cycle the slide is pushing a cartridge into the chamber and balks just short of lockup, a quick nudge in the rear often will send it the rest of the way home. Checkering on the slide's heel decreases the possibility of one's thumb slipping. There is, however, a potentially negative side. When the slide is checkered, the rear of the extractor also is checkered. If the extractor has to be replaced, the smooth surface of its replacement will stick out like a muskrat swimming in the Governor's punch bowl. Having the pistolsmith fit and checker an extra extractor or two while he has the gun is not a bad idea. If one breaks you still have spares. Checkering on the rear of the slide and extractor obviously is not an absolute necessity, but it does give a custom gun an extra touch of class.

Standard checkering coverage on certain areas varies among pistolsmiths, but most are happy to comply with individual customer preferences. If the front of the trigger guard has been flattened, the entire surface of the flat should be covered, with the pattern extending upward and close to the bottom of the frame, aft of the dust cover. It doesn't have to end hard against the frame and often doesn't, but many people think it looks better when it does.

This 40-line checkering on the heel of the slide is by Steve Woods. *(Stephen Longley photo)*

Steve Woods cut the serrations on the heel of this slide to match those on the leaf of the Wichita rear sight. *(Stephen Longley photo)*

Merle Edington at warp speed with his .38 Super comp gun.

I perfer checkering on the bottom of the trigger guard to start hard against the gripframe and extend toward the front at least one inch, which is about as far forward as the index finger of my weak hand extends along the bottom of the trigger guard with the two-hand hold. Checkering on this area of a carry gun works fine with some holster designs, but eventually it will eat away the synthetic retaining device in the Bianchi pinch type. It works fine on a competition gun when it is used with Ernie Hill's Fas-Trac holster, but the sharp checkering will quickly chew up the synthetic trigger guard lock in the Safariland Final Option. On a more positive note, that part of the Final Option is easily replaced.

How far the checkering extends up the frontstrap depends on customer preference and whether it is in its factory-original or modified form. On the former, the pattern usually ends at the bottom of the radius between the gripframe and rear of the trigger guard. If the frontstrap is lengthened by removal of metal just aft of the trigger guard/gripframe juncture, the pattern can extend upward and terminate against the bottom of the frame just below the magazine catch. Many shooters (including myself) like to see the checkering coverage extend as high as possible. There are those, however, who prefer the extended frontstrap but want the top border of the pattern to stop about one-half inch below the bottom of the trigger guard because they consider it more comfortable to the hand. This application puts checkering beneath two gripping fingers and a smooth surface beneath the third. Both can look good when properly executed.

The rounded front surface of the frontstrap on most Government Model frames terminates at a flat surface on the grip which starts just in front of the edge of the grip panels. It was once customary to simply cut the border of the checkering pattern along the transition line between the rounded and flat surfaces. It is now quite common among pistolsmiths to recontour both edges of the frontstrap so its radius extends a bit beneath the edge of the grip panels. This is one of the more attractive custom touches because it enables the craftsman to extend the vertical borders of the checkering pattern to the edges of the grip panels. An even nicer touch is what I call full-plus coverage where the checkering wraps completely around the frontstrap and disappears beneath the grip panels on both sides. With 20-line checkering, an extra line on either side of the pattern usually is all it takes.

Another popular option is full-coverage checkering on the exposed surface of the mainspring housing. The synthetic mainspring housing on Colt guns of current manufacture is replaced with old-fashioned steel. Those that come from their makers with the checkering formed during the casting process often are sharpened up by hand when installed on the higher grade custom guns. In addition to being attractive, checkering on the mainspring housing

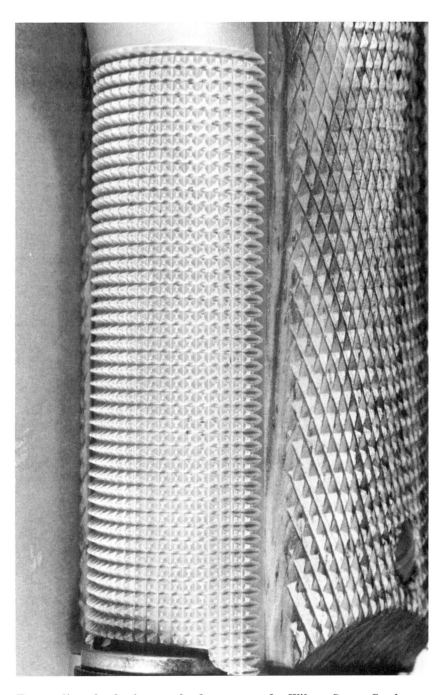

Twenty-line checkering on the frontstrap of a Wilson Super Grade.

The frontstrap on this Colt Gold Cup by Chuck Warner has been extended, but the checkering stops short of full coverage, as per the customer's specifications.

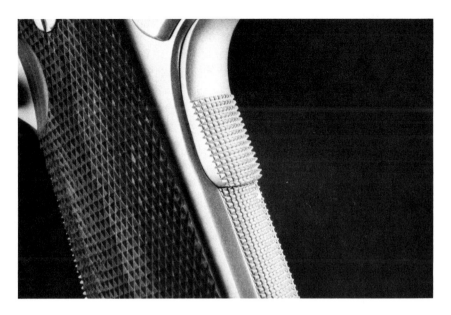

Steve Woods has extended the mainspring housing checkering to the surface of the grip safety on this gun. *(Stephen Longley photo)*

is practical as it really makes a gun stick in the hand for better control during handling and firing. Extending the same size checkering over adjacent metal on the backstrap amounts to taking a good thing one step further if a flat mainspring housing is used. In order for the job to look good, however, the backstrap checkering must be the same size and in perfect alignment with that on the mainspring housing. To some eyes, checkering the backstrap doesn't look as nice when an arched mainspring housing is used due to its elevated surface.

The quality of checkering seen on custom guns varies for several reasons. For one, some pistolsmiths either won't take the time to execute it properly, or they have yet to develop the knack for doing so. Some pistolsmiths are capable of checkering with such perfection that close scrutiny with a jeweler's loupe reveals no slip of hand, but their clientele can't afford or refuse to pay the price, preferring to have less than the best at less cost. That's certainly acceptable as some people would rather spend their money on other areas of the gun. Then there are pistolsmiths with long backlogs of work who are capable of top-notch checkering and won't do it any other way regardless of how much the customer complains about the price. In other words, take it and pay for it or leave it. Unfortunately, all pistolsmiths aren't in such a comfortable position.

The easily recognized characteristics of top-quality checkering are low in number but high in difficulty. First of all, each line is perfectly straight and exactly parallel or perpendicular to its mates. All tiny pyramids are exactly the same width and height and all are pointed up exactly the same, without a single one screaming for a final caress of the file. Where possible, the borders of the checkering pattern run precisely parallel or perpendicular with adjacent lines of the gun. Good checkering has absolutely no runovers; each line of grooves and pyramids marches straight forward and then halts precisely at the border with their leaders standing shoulder to shoulder in perfect alignment.

One controversy that threatens to rage on into the twenty-first century is hand-cut vs. machine-cut checkering. I've seen checkering cut by machine that was leaps and bounds ahead of some hand-cut checkering in quality. In fact the frontstrap on one of my comp guns has it and of the dozens of people who have examined the gun, not one realized how its checkering was applied until he was told. On the opposite side of the trail, I've seen some of the machined variety that wouldn't hold a candle to a good man with blood racing through his veins, pride in his heart, and a file in his hand. So, on this subject I'll leave you with the following as food for thought. Being a bit old fashioned, I like the idea of a craftsman spending long tedious hours standing over my custom gun with his trusty hand tools, but will take good machined checkering over poor hand checkering any day of the week. If the checkering is top drawer in quality, I could care less how it was cut. I believe we should be more concerned with how functional checkering is and what it looks like rather than how it got there. On the other hand, it would sadden me greatly to see the art of hand checkering die.

Incidentally, it's easy to spot a pistolsmith who does a lot of metal checkering in any crowd. He'll always be the grumpy one with squinty eyes and checkerer's elbow. If he doesn't have much hair, you can safely bet that he does a lot of 40- and 50-line work.

STIPPLING

I won't use up a lot of space on metal stippling simply because very few pistolsmiths offer it anymore and I'm told that with the exception of an occasional bullseye shooter, very few customers ask for it. Back when very few craftsmen offered checkering on the frontstrap, stippling was in demand, but since its cost often runs a third to one-half of a good checkering job, it appears it is rapidly becoming an obsolete feature on custom guns. There also are those who consider it unattractive even when properly executed.

A stippled frontstrap by Glenn Martin.

1991 National champion and match winner of the 1992 USPSA Area VI Championships, Todd Jarrett unleashes his high-capacity, optical-sighted .38 Super on the Twist and Shout stage.

Those who prefer to not have the frontstrap stippled or hand checkered have three options. One is to install the steel strap with stamped checkering available from Wilson. Held in place by the grip panels, it's not the real thing but is far better than a smooth frontstrap. Another alternative is to have a pistolsmith attach one of the straps with cut checkering offered by Cylinder & Slide. The frontstrap has to be slightly modified and the strap attached with solder or industrial grade epoxy. When properly installed, you have to look hard to determine that the frontstrap of the gun was not checkered. A final alternative to stippling is the installation of a wraparound rubber grip.

GROOVING AND SERRATING

Extra grasping serrations or grooves milled into the side flats of the slide out near its muzzle are a good idea on open-sighted competition guns used by experienced shooters. They make it a bit easier to slightly retract the slide to make sure a round is in the chamber during a match, and can prevent sight bite when one is attempting to clear a jam. The extra serrations are quite handy on a competition gun wearing a safety thumbguard on one side, and a necessity if it has an ambidextrous safety with guards on both

164

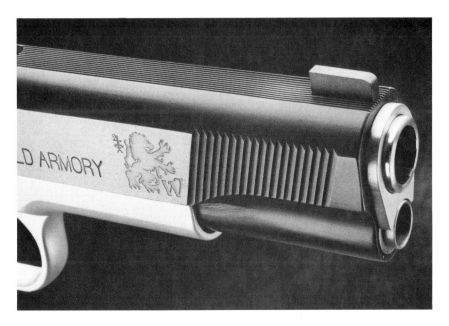

Forward-angled grasping grooves at the front of the slide and serrations on its top surface by Steve Woods. *(Stephen Longley photo)*

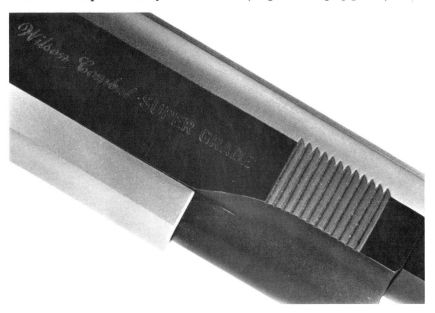

Grasping grooves at the front of the Colt slide of a Wilson Super grade.

Built by the Springfield Armory Custom shop, the slide on this gun has extra grasping serrations at the front.

sides that shield the rear serrations from the thumb. Conversely, the grooves are useless on a gun with an optical sight as most mounts interfere with retracting the slide by grasping it toward its front.

Earlier I mentioned custom treatment of the rear of the slide. Having horizontal grooves cut into the heel of the slide looks nice and usually is less expensive than checkering. The extractor's rear also is grooved. Visualize checkering without the vertical grooves and you have it. Some say it looks as good, others claim it doesn't. If both are successfully executed, I like one about as well as the other, but since it's your money, only you should decide which goes on your gun. If the horizontal grooving is on your list, you might want to specify the same line count as on the rear sight's leaf. Many pistolsmiths do anyhow, even when the customer forgets to mention it.

Before leaving the subject, I must mention that most pistolsmiths are aware of the fact that a custom gun should be fired a few rounds before the rear of its slide and extractor are grooved or checkered. Quite often, a new extractor shifts in a clockwise or counterclockwise direction after the gun is fired and then settles in that position. If it happens after the checkering is cut, the checkering on the slide and extractor will be out of alignment. Some would relegate such a detail to the nitpicker basket, but I consider it one of those subtle signs of master class workmanship.

A feature seen on an increasing number of custom guns are grooves cut into the top surface of the slide from front to rear. Some pistolsmiths also machine a flat along the top, often making additional cuts on each side to form an integral rib, similar to that on Colt's Gold Cup. Parallel grooves are then machined along the top of the flat. Although not seen as often, the flat is sometimes checkered. A grooved slide has become especially common on Government Models built for USPSA/IPSC competitive shooting, with the grooves often extending out to the compensator's muzzle. The coverage varies, but usually is about half an inch wide and cut with 25 to 40 grooves per inch. Checkering on this area usually is 30-inch or finer. Anything less looks a bit coarse, but is just as functional.

As theory has it, the grooves prevent light from deflecting off the top of the slide and interfering with the sight picture. That's probably true if the slide is coated with bumper-shiny chrome plating, but since few are these days, this custom detail should probably be colored aesthetics only. It does look good when done properly. Pistolsmiths have been doing it for decades and the wide integral rib sitting atop the slide on Colt's Gold Cup would look somewhat naked without it. Some competitive shooters prefer to leave the top of the compensator smooth, as grooves on that area have a tendency to collect difficult to remove powder fouling residue and lead spray from cast bullets. Incidentally, in 1992, Colt made the flat-top slide standard with its enhanced upgrades of the Government Model, Delta Elite, Combat Elite, Commander, and Officer's ACP.

There are those who consider grooving, serrating, and checkering on the slide of a fullhouse custom gun well worth the cost while others prefer to spend their money elsewhere. From a practical point of view, these custom modifications are not absolute necessities, but then, the same could be said of custom Government Model pistols in general, and of bass boats and golf clubs, and season football tickets.

8

Metal Preparation and Finishes

T O describe in technical detail all the various metal finishes presently available could take several chapters, so I'll simply hit the high spots and leave the details to pistolsmiths.

Several universally accepted methods are used in testing the corrosion resistance of metals, as well as the various finishes and coatings applied to them. One is to subject them to a condition of close to 100 percent humidity at a temperature of 120 degrees Fahrenheit. Another way is to place them in a test chamber where they are continuously sprayed with salt water. In a salt spray test, rust will start forming on the surface of bare carbon steel in less than 30 minutes. A blued steel finish will usually start rusting in about an hour, while steel with a Parkerized finish will resist corrosion for approximately two hours.

Bare stainless steel usually will start discoloring at around 80 hours while carbon steel protected by a good hard chrome finish will shed rust for about 60 hours. The rust resistance rating of electroless nickel is about 10 times higher than that of hard chrome, but it has to be several times thicker to earn that rating. Its hardness rating usually is around 50 on the Rockwell C scale, making it considerably softer than chrome, but since it is thicker, the wear quality of the two is close to the same. Nickel is more easily scratched than chrome.

Before getting all excited and choosing a finish based on what you have just read about spraying guns with salt water, keep in mind that those tests are accelerated. One hour in the torture chamber is probably equivalent to

169

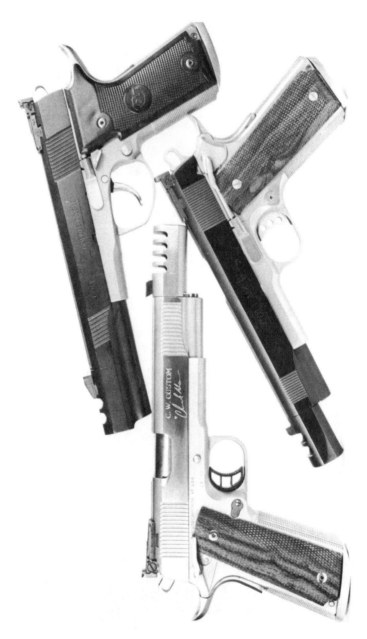

Three different metal finish treatments. From top to bottom:
(1) Chuck Warner Colt Double Eagle compensated gun with Black-T on
slide and bead-blasted stainless steel frame. (2) Chuck Warner
Signature-Grade Caspian with DuraChrome on slide and frame. (3) Bill
Wilson Super Grade with blued slide and Metaloy on frame.

leaving a gun outdoors on a rainy day for at least 12 hours or possibly even longer. Shortly before writing this, I hunted brown bear in southeastern Alaska where it rains more often than it doesn't. During that hunt, the sky poured buckets for at least six days and my rifle stayed soaking wet. Its barreled action was coated with hard chrome and I intentionally neglected to wipe it dry or oil it during the entire hunt just to see how the finish would hold up. Not a single spot of rust appeared anywhere on the metal.

Based on my good and bad experiences with various metal finishes, I would say the quality of application is probably as important as the material used. When properly applied, a good hard chrome finish will probably withstand the salt spray test considerably longer than 60 hours. On the other hand, if the process is rushed, the chrome will have a tendency to build up quicker on small, rounded edges and thinner on large, flat surfaces. A poor quality chrome finish can allow the metal to start rusting as quickly as a blued finish.

In contrast to my experience with a hard chrome finish on the Alaskan hunt, I once had the barreled action of a big game rifle coated with electroless nickel and on some areas the finish was so thin, the rifle had rust spots all over it from hunting about half a day in the rain. At about the same time, I had another rifle hard chromed and the finish chipped off the head of its action bolts the first time I touched them with a screwdriver. Neither finish was to blame, but the companies that applied them surely were. Like everything else in life, you get what you pay for in metal finishes.

A good hard chrome or electroless nickel finish from a reputable company is extremely durable. Unlike the chrome plating on the bumper of your 1955 Buick, or on the two hunting rifles mentioned earlier, a properly applied coat of chrome or nickel won't chip, flake, or peel off. Both are a form of plating, but rather than merely sticking to the surface of metal like a coat of paint, they form a molecular bond with it.

With a hardness rating that usually exceeds 70 on the Rockwell C scale, chrome is extremely scratch and wear resistant. Government Model frames and slides from one major manufacturer have average hardness ratings of RC-27 and RC-38, respectively. Those made by another large company are rated at RC-33 and RC-45. It doesn't take a rocket scientist to figure out that a skin of industrial grade chrome on a custom gun will extend the life of its accuracy job by drastically reducing wear on the rails of its frame and slide.

Hard chrome also has a lower coefficient of friction than carbon steel and comparing its self-lubricating properties to that of stainless steel is like comparing grease on glass with sandpaper against sandpaper. When two pieces of stainless rub together, they have a tendency to gall, whereas chrome against chrome has no such bad habit. This is why it is not unusual to see custom stainless steel guns wearing a coat of hard chrome. When it comes down

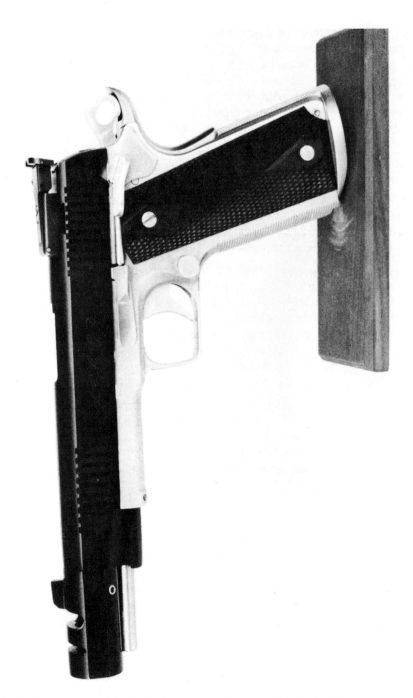

Bob Cogan gun with hard chrome on frame and blued slide.

Bob Cogan compensated gun with hard chrome finish on its Caspian slide and frame.

to the nitty gritty of choosing a low-maintenance, trouble-free, and affordable finish for a custom gun, it is tough to beat those with names like Durachrome, Metaloy, Enduraguard, SSK Khrome, NP3, and Checkmate Chrome.

The exact coloration of chrome and nickel will vary from company to company, although less variation usually is seen in the former than the latter. As a rule, hard chrome is a bit brighter and gives a custom gun a bit more character. There was a time when I didn't like electroless nickel because the guns I had seen wearing it were a drab gray. One in particular was about the same color, but had a rather odd pinkish hue. The gray finish wasn't bad for a hunting gun, but didn't do a lot for its appearance. More recently, I examined guns with the electroless nickel finish from other companies and could not see any difference between their appearance and that of those covered with hard chrome. I also have seen battleship gray chrome finishes. I'm mentioning all of this not to imply that one color is better than the other, but to point out that they do differ and you should make sure the finish your pistolsmith recommends will give your custom gun the look you are after.

For those who don't care for the color of chrome and nickel, there are various Teflon® finishes with Black-T being the best with which I have any experience. In this process, the metal is first vapor degreased and then sandblasted so the phosphate and chromate undercoatings will adhere to its surface. The final Black-T coating is applied and then heat cured. As its developer describes it, Black-T is a codispersion of fluoropolymer resin, Teflon® , and graphite in a thermosetting binder that produces a low friction coating free of stick-slip characteristics. Since this type of finish totally seals the surface of the metal, its resistance to rusting in the salt spray test exceeds 500 hours. It also will adhere to all types of metal, including stainless steel and aluminum.

Available in coal black or NATO olive green, this is an extremely handsome finish. Unlike most finishes, it is applied to all the component parts of a gun, including the firing pin, trigger, and sear. Due to its Teflon® and graphite content, Black-T has a lower coefficient of friction than chrome or nickel and moving parts coated with it require little to no lubrication. On the negative side, it is not as durable as the metallic coatings and will eventually disappear from high friction, metal against metal areas, such as the rails of the frame and slide.

Several hybrid finishes that combine two or more materials to form a tough and rust-resistant finish are available. One is Bob Cogan's Black Chrome. It consists of a black surface material applied on top of either hard chrome or electroless nickel. Its surface wear quality is lower than the underlayer of chrome or nickel, but is said to be 10 times higher than blueing and six times higher than Parkerizing.

Steve Woods Colt Commander with Black-T on all interior and exterior metal surfaces.

175

Another interesting hybrid finish is NP3 available from Robar. This process consists of a mixture of electroless nickel and Teflon®. If you were to examine this finish with an electron microscope, you'd see sub-micron particles of Teflon® intermixed with the nickel molecules. Its coefficient of friction is extremely low and yet its resistance to wear and corrosion are extremely high. If you like a gray coloration on a custom gun, NP3 is worthy of consideration, but it is the most expensive finish presently available.

Blueing is the traditional metal finish for firearms and the majority consider it the most handsome. I totally agree. On the negative side, it scores quite low in durability and resistance to rusting when compared with other types of finishes. For these reasons, I like a blued finish on a gun made for looking or casual shooting, but prefer other finishes on working guns.

Dropping a bunch of gun parts into a tank full of blueing solution is easy, but the polishing job is what separates the superb from the mediocre. A professional polish job is easy to spot at a glance and a poor job will scream at you from 50 yards away. If the metal preparation is performed correctly, the original contours of each part remain unchanged during the buffing operation. Flats stay flat, lettering stays clean, sharp corners stay sharp, and transition points separating flat from rounded surfaces remain distinct.

As blueing the slide of a Government Model goes, I like a high-gloss polish job on its side flats and an extremely fine, velvet, bead-blasted finish up top. An especially nice custom touch consists of a thin transition groove machined along both sides of the slide separating its flats from the rounded contour of its roof. This obviously doesn't make the gun shoot any better, but it looks great and is a relatively inexpensive modification.

There are those who like the rust-resistant quality of stainless steel, but don't care for its appearance. One of the more common solutions is a finish called black chrome sulphide. It reportedly reduces galling between moving parts and (when new) the finish is quite attractive. I have tried this one and found its wear quality to be lower than that of a good blue job. I could almost rub it off with a finger. Whether or not my experience is typical for the same type of finish applied by other companies, I can't say, but the one job I tried was less than satisfactory.

Most companies that specialize in applying various finishes to custom guns do an excellent job, but I've also heard some horror stories. One gunsmith was spending about $25,000 per year with a plating company and had to look somewhere else because a high percentage of gun parts arrived at his shop covered with nicks and scratches due to improper packaging for shipment. He switched to another company and was quite satisfied until a batch of expensive barrels arrived with their bores coated with splotches of plating.

At that point I introduced my friend to a chap who had flawlessly hard-chromed a gun for me and the last I heard they were getting along just fine.

This is not to badmouth plating companies, but to emphasize why it is best to have the job done by or through a pistolsmith. Since you are paying him for the job, he and not the plating company should be responsible for its outcome. If the job happens to be unsatisfactory, a pistolsmith who sends dozens of guns to a plater each year has a lot more clout in getting the job corrected than you. Equally important is the fact that when the finish is applied, clearances between moving parts of a gun may be reduced enough to cause malfunctions, something the gunsmith can take care of before shipping it back to you. Believe me, strange and mysterious things can happen to a gun after it receives its new skin. An example follows.

In order to avoid the possibility of nicks and scratches on the final product, some pistolsmiths perform the major fine-tuning and test firing of a completed gun before its finish is applied. After the gun returns from the finisher or plater, it is carefully final tuned and test fired before being shipped to the customer. I once had a carry gun built by a pistolsmith who lived just down the road from my home. He and I tested the gun together while it was in the rough. It gobbled up everything I fed it, including handloads with Speer's often difficult to digest 200-grain jacketed hollowpoint. Off went the gun for its beautiful coat of hard chrome. When it came back the gun wouldn't feed anything except hardball ammunition! After working with the gun for about half an hour, the pistolsmith had it running on every type of fuel poured into its magazine. Had the gun been returned directly to me, I might have spent endless hours getting it back up to the speed of which I knew it was capable.

Metal Preparation

Regardless of the type of finish applied to steel, its appearance is almost totally dependant on how the metal was prepared prior to its application. This applies to blueing, hard chrome, electroless nickel, Teflon® and other types of finishes. None will conceal or cover up surface blemishes. Most actually will highlight them. Some pistolsmiths offer only top-grade metal prep, while others let the customer's budget decide. For sake of clarity, I'll refer to the three levels of workmanship as grades A, B, and C.

Government Model frames and slides vary considerably in surface appearance from manufacturer to manufacturer and often from gun to gun from the same company. This especially holds true for frames. Some are relatively smooth with only minor roughness and tool marks. Others are quite rough all over with the worst having small surface pits and voids as a result of the forging or investment casting process. Even those frames with a relatively smooth overall finish sometimes have small machine marks or other surface imperfections in hard-to-reach areas. Two common trouble spots on the frame are the surfaces of the finger relief cuts adjacent to the trigger and at the front terminus of the trigger guard and frame. Slides often are rough on the radiused surface of the recoil spring tunnel.

Grade C preparation consists of a bit of smoothing up here and there, but usually represents little improvement in metal surface appearance. This is never seen on the higher grade packages, but is perfectly acceptable for a no-nonsense gun built for the hard knocks of hunting or personal defense. If I were to have a rough-duty 10mm or .45 built for sloshing through muddy swamps in pursuit of wild hogs and such, I would be perfectly content in knowing that a Grade C metal prep job lurks beneath its hard chrome skin. No small number of those who have custom guns built for competitive shooting are quite happy with this type of metal preparation. They are more concerned about accuracy and the gun going bang with each squeeze on its trigger than with appearance.

Grade B metal prep is a big step beyond Grade C, but it is still shy of perfection. The really obvious blemishes have been removed, but the small and often extremely hard to reach ones remain. I would say more custom guns go out with this type of job than with the next step up which is as it should be because the Grade A stuff can take a terrible toll on the family budget.

A gun described as the highest grade is not actually a high-grade gun unless it has undergone Grade A metal prep. No nick, scratch, dent, bump, tool mark, or excuse can be found even when a critical eye is aided by a jeweler's loupe. All flats remain perfectly flat through the polishing job. Look down the sideflats on the slide and you won't see a single ripple. Transition lines separating flat from rounded surfaces are arrow-straight, lettuce-crisp, quite sharp, and not rounded off by a runaway buffing wheel. Curved transition lines snake gracefully over the gun with no bobbles, waves or dips. Some pistolsmiths describe this operation as complete dehorning and sculpting.

Regardless of what it is called, this is definitely not power tool country, although there are those who seem unaware of it. This is an uncommon amount of patience, a steady and skillful hand, and an eye for the proper flow of lines, all thrown into the pot with a big helping of elbow grease. This is perfection a bit beyond perfect. This is pride in workmanship and ownership at its highest level. This, along with metal checkering quality, is what separates the artists from the rest. This is what can make a grown man go glassy-eyed and speak in an unknown tougue—just before he fumbles for his checkbook.

This Steve Woods carry gun has the Grade A metal preparation beneath a hard-chromed frame and blued slide.

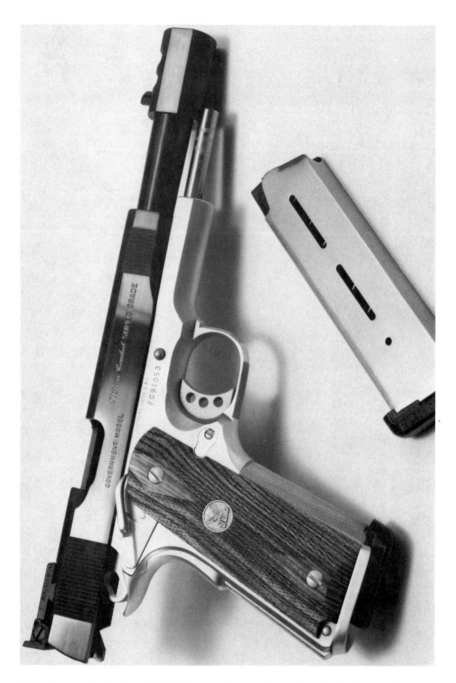

This Super Grade by Bill Wilson and crew has the Grade A metal
preparation beneath its Metaloy-coated frame and blued steel slide.

180

9

The Barrel

Factory Barrels

A top-quality, properly fitted barrel accounts for a lion's share of the credit in transforming an inaccurate Government Model into an accurate one. Opinions vary on what percentage of accuracy should be credited to barrel quality and fit, but most pistolsmiths seem convinced that it's in the 80 to 90 percent range with most guns. All other factors, including slide to frame fit, probably account for no more than 20 percent of the gun's accuracy, possibly less.

Before aftermarket Government Model barrels became available from so many sources, it was common among pistolsmiths to include modifications to factory barrels in the accuracy packages they offered. The underlug and hood of the barrel were first made oversize by welding and then cut back down for a tighter lockup. Most of today's craftsmen prefer to start with a new barrel and many insist on it, but a few still offer those modifications to factory barrels.

The bore quality of quite a few factory barrels I have slugged and examined with a 6x bore scope ranged from poor to acceptable to as good as the best seen inside custom barrels. In the better barrels, land and groove diameters were quite uniform from chamber to muzzle and bore surface finish was extremely good. Typically, I found the bores of chrome-moly barrels to be a bit smoother than those of stainless steel. This is due to the fact that when being bored and rifled, chrome-moly has a higher self-lubricating level than stainless. For this reason, stainless has more of a tendency to surface gall. At the very worst, some barrels of chrome-moly and stainless steel looked

This Wilson Tactical Special conversion of the Colt Officer's ACP has a sleeved barrel with muzzle flange.

like they had been bored and rifled with a dull rattail file. Even with extreme variations in bore quality among factory barrels, poor accuracy with them is more often the result of an extremely rough muzzle crown and/or a loose fit between the barrel and slide during lockup.

The Government Model barrel originally was designed to feed the .45 caliber hard ball load with its full-metal-jacketed bullet of roundnose form. Consequently, its chamber entry throat was purposely left extremely narrow. When shooters decided to use bullets of other styles and forms in the gun, it became necessary to widen the throat and polish the break-over point of the chamber for smooth feeding, or "polish and throat the barrel" as it is commonly described. The modification works fine when performed by professional craftsmen who know what they're doing, but many barrels have been ruined or made unsafe by shadetree pistolsmiths who removed so much metal an excessive amount of the cartridge is left unsupported when it rests in the chamber. The result often is a blown case, a damaged gun, and possibly an injured shooter.

Factory barrels on most of today's guns have a wider chamber entry throat and for this reason usually require no more than a slight polishing for smooth feeding. Some will feed ammunition with most types and styles of bullets with no modification. I have a factory-original Colt Government Model which was built sometime in 1991. It gobbles up handloads with any bullet except the Speer 200-grain jacketed hollowpoint without missing a lick. Another gun I owned, which was made during the same year, choked on practically everything I tried in it except hardball loads. You win a few and lose a few.

If the bore quality of a factory barrel is good, the end result can be quite satisfactory when it is used in a custom gun. I've shot some Government Models that averaged two inches at 25 yards with a variety of loads. On the opposite side of the tracks, some barrels were not capable of such a high level of accuracy; something often difficult to detect until the gun is completed and test fired. If that happens, it becomes painfully obvious that money wasted on having a factory barrel modified would have been better spent on a custom barrel. What it boils down to is this: top quality custom barrels available from the top barrelmakers are consistently good while mass-produced factory barrels, even those from the same company, vary in quality from awful to excellent. When having a custom gun built I would rather cut a corner or two somewhere else if necessary and start from scratch with the best barrel money can buy.

In many factory guns, the barrel is forced upward to its locked position by the barrel link alone rather than the barrel underlug riding over the slide lock crosspin. The width of the underlug often is considerably smaller than the width of its mortice in the frame and the fit between the hood of the barrel and the slide are extremely sloppy. In addition, the bottom hole in the barrel link often is an extremely loose fit with the slide stop crosspin, and its top hole fits loosely with its retaining pin in the underlug. Up front, the fit between the barrel and its bushing is loose and the bushing fits loosely in the slide. In combination, those sloppy fits between component parts add up to extremely inconsistent lockup from shot to shot, resulting in a variable barrel-to-sight relationship from lockup to lockup. The barrel will point in one direction for this shot and then over toward Aunt Hattie's hen house for another shot.

Custom Barrels

When a custom match-grade barrel is manufactured, its underlug is intentionally left oversize in length, width, and thickness. This enables the pistolsmith to fit the barrel for an extremely tight and consistently uniform lockup from shot to shot by reducing underlug width for a close fit with its mortice in the frame and by cutting the bottom of the underlug so it bears uniformly against the slide stop pin as the barrel travels forward. As the bottom surface of the underlug rides over the pin, it cams the barrel upward to its locked position. This is a far more uniform and durable method of pushing the barrel upward to lockup than relying on the barrel link alone to do the job. Additionally, the upper and lower holes in the barrel link are a tight fit with the link retaining pin and the slide lock crosspin.

The hood of a custom barrel also is oversized and must be reduced slightly in width and length for a close and uniform fit with the breechface and sidewalls of the slide. How important is hood to slide fit? Opinions differ, but I'm convinced it can definitely influence accuracy. One of my Gold Cups consistently scattered its shots horizontally until a pistolsmith discovered that the left rear corner of its hood was making hard contact with the slide breechface. Three or four strokes on the hood with a file solved the horizontal stringing.

Barrel to bushing and barrel bushing to slide fit are important, but less so than what goes on at the rear. If everything consistently locks up tightly and uniformly out back, the barrel likely will be pointed in the same direction from shot to shot with a reasonably snug fit up front. Barrel bushing to slide fit can be so tight as to require a wrench for removal and some pistolsmiths highly recommend it. That's OK for some shooters, but with the possible exception of a bullseye gun, it is not acceptable to me. The gain (if any) in accuracy by opting for an extremely tight bushing fit over a snug fit that allows removal with the fingers alone is not worth the hassle on competition guns because it makes taking down for cleaning too aggravating. I have shot custom guns with barrel bushings so tight it almost took a pipe

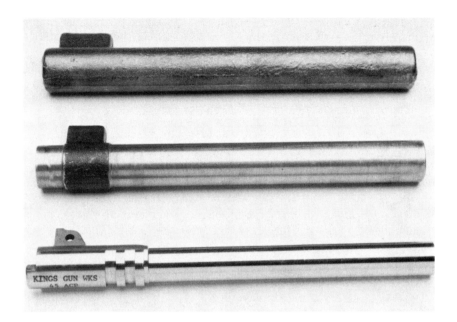

King's Gun Works barrels in three stages of completion. From top to bottom: (1) forging, (2) forging rough-machined, (3) completed barrel.

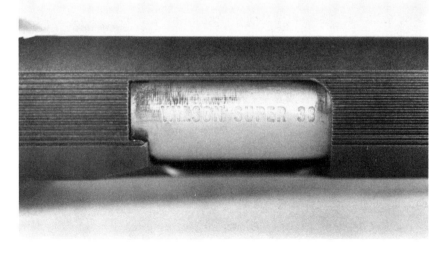

A custom fit between the slide and barrel greatly contributes to a gun's accuracy.

wrench to budge them against guns that had finger-tight bushings and found absolutely no difference in accuracy.

Three grades of aftermarket barrels are available. One is made to simply drop into the gun as a replacement for a worn-out factory barrel. Like a factory barrel, its exterior and interior dimensions are machined to rather generous dimensional tolerances. I'll call this type Grade C.

Next, we have what I like to describe as the Grade B barrel. During manufacture, its dimensions were held to a more narrow tolerance range, thus it is likely to produce better accuracy than a Grade C barrel. Grade B barrels usually are included in the better-quality barrel/compensator kits which often are described as "drop-in" units. Semi-drop-in is probably a better description since they will drop in some guns and won't in others. Bore and groove diameter and bore finish in this grade barrel is usually (but not always) a notch or two above the Grade C.

Grade A barrels are the same as Grade B except they are intentionally manufactured with oversized exterior dimensions for a precise fit by a qualified pistolsmith. The chamber is sometimes reamed a bit closer to the minimum side of the dimensional tolerance range than the chamber in a Grade B barrel, and much closer than for a Grade C. All else being equal, the tighter chamber in A and B grade barrels has a positive effect on accuracy because it better aligns a cartridge with the bore than a factory-spec chamber. On the negative side, it must be kept cleaner than a standard chamber.

Chamber throat or leade length varies considerably among the various barrel makers. It also will sometimes vary a bit from barrel to barrel made by the same company. This seldom affects accuracy, but as a rule, a maximum load developed in a barrel with a long chamber throat will be too hot for a short-throated barrel. By the same token, a maximum load developed in a barrel with a short chamber throat will generate lower pressures and therefore velocities in a long-throated barrel. Some barrels are intentionally throated long in order to reduce chamber pressure. Barrels in 9x23mm Super available from CP Bullets are good examples.

Earlier I mentioned that of the factory barrels I had examined with a bore scope, those made of stainless steel had rougher bores than their chrome-moly cousins. I do not find this to be true of the better quality custom barrels. For this reason I prefer a stainless custom barrel but would rather have a chrome-moly factory barrel.

Standard lengths for custom barrels are 3½, 4¼, five, and six inches. The latter is used in comp guns with full-length Government Model slides and usually ends up at about 5½ inches after the compensator is installed. The barrel will end up a bit shorter on short-slide guns. Some of the longer compensators allow the use of barrels closer to six inches in length when a standard-length slide is used, but there are those who consider the overall length of such a gun to be a bit unwieldy for competitive shooting. Opinions differ on how a comp gun should balance and feel, but for USPSA/IPSC competition, I like an overall length of nine to 9½ inches from muzzle to heel of slide. I also prefer a slightly muzzle heavy gun with its balance point about halfway between the front of the trigger and the inner surface of the trigger guard. Others prefer the balance point to be at the front of the trigger.

Barrels shorter than 5½ inches are fine on comp guns chambered for most cartridges, but it is a good minimum when loading the .38 Super and CP 9x23mm Super for USPSA/IPSC competition. Major power velocity can be squeezed from a five-inch barrel, but if it is much shorter, chamber pressure with those two cartridges has to be increased more than I prefer in order to gain back the required velocity.

Some custom barrels are made entirely from scratch in a shop belonging to the pistolsmith or in a shop with which a pistolsmith is affiliated. For example, if Irv Stone, Al Capone, or Bill Jarvis installs a barrel on your gun, it was manufactured in their shop. Other pistolsmiths buy bored and rifled blanks and do all the machine work in their shop. They start out with a blank of extremely large diameter and end up with a barrel complete with chamber,

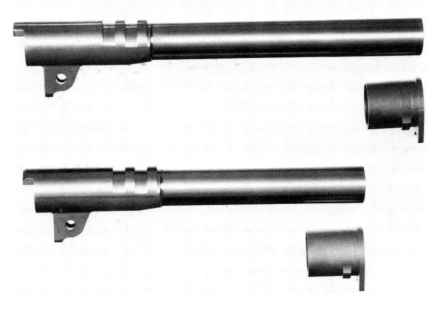

Two Wilson bushing-type barrels: Top, six-inch barrel for use with a compensator. Bottom, standard five-inch barrel.

locking lugs, underlug, hood, and correct outside contour. Jim Stroh is one pistolsmith who does this.

Some pistolsmiths have barrels completely bored, rifled, and final machined by an outside manufacturer and then have their name or the name of their shop etched or rollmarked on the hood of the barrels. C. W. Custom barrels, for example, are manufactured by Storm Lake Machine of Monroe, Washington, a manufacturer of top-grade proprietary barrels for a number of other pistolsmiths and aftermarket parts companies as well. When Storm Lake ships a barrel to C. W. Custom, it has a short chamber. After fitting the barrel to a gun, Chuck Warner then cuts its chamber to final depth with a Clymer finish reamer, ending up a bit shorter than standard. Most custom barrels in .38 Super, for example, measure in the neighborhood of .905 inch from the rear surface of the hood to the headspacing shoulder of the chamber. The SAAMI maximum length of the .38 Super case is .900 inch which should mean that when a cartridge is chambered, the mouth of its case is only .005 inch from its headspacing shoulder. Since average length for the .38 case is closer to .895 inch, however, Warner cuts the chamber at .900 inch, or .005 inch shorter than standard. The shorter chamber makes for more positive headspacing. It also increases the life of the extractor since energy delivered by the firing pin is absorbed by the headspacing shoulder of the barrel rather than the extractor's claw.

Some pistolsmiths prefer to make the final cut on a chamber as Warner does, while others prefer to use barrels completely chambered by the manufacturer. If properly executed, either method works fine.

Regardless of whether a pistolsmith manufactures a barrel entirely in house, partially in house, or buys it from an outside vendor and has his name stamped on it, the end result can be exactly the same. Where a barrel is made is not important as long as its quality and material are the best available. Good steel, a straight and uniform bore and groove diameter from one end of the barrel to the other, a relatively smooth bore finish, a round and concentric chamber, and a smooth muzzle crown, combined with a high-quality installation is what separates the excellent from the not so good. If you choose a barrel with the name of a reputable company or individual stamped on it, you won't go wrong. I am using barrels with "Wilson," "Caspian," "C. W. Custom," "Heinie," "Bar-Sto," "CP," "B.A.T.," "Centaur Systems," and "Brown" rollmarked on their hoods and all are excellent.

Bushing-Type Barrels

Several styles of barrels are used in custom Government Model pistols. Most common is the original type which utilizes an alignment bushing at the

Bill Jarvis compensated gun with a barrel of his manufacture.

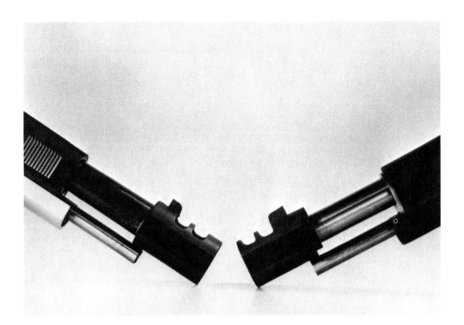

Left, Wilson sleeved barrel with compensator. Right, Wilson bushing-type barrel with compensator.

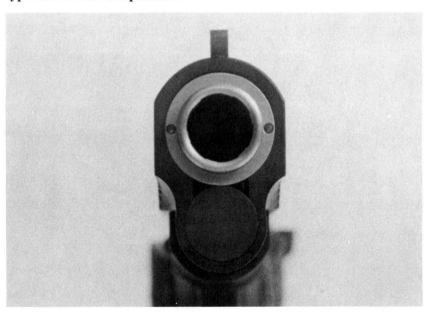

Muzzle view of Jack Weigand's barrel bushing which eliminates the old finish-scratching bushing wrench.

190

muzzle. The best bushing of this type is available from Jack Weigand. Its design eliminates the need for the old bushing wrench that can slip and ruin the finish on a gun.

Many years ago, Irv Stone, the maker of Bar-Sto barrels, introduced the collet-type bushing but eventually abandoned it because of its tendency to break, split, and shed fingers at the wrong time. Colt picked up the idea with its Series 80 guns and the change was praised as a move in the right direction by all except those of us who shot the guns enough to know differently. Not one of the better ideas in Government Model evolution, Colt dropped the collet-type bushing from production during the late 1980s. I believe the Delta Elite was the first standard size Series 80 gun to wear a solid bushing.

Pachmayr introduced the spherical-type barrel bushing on its custom guns and it later became available as an aftermarket part from Briley. Visualize a huge ball bearing with a hole drilled through its center swiveling inside a barrel bushing and you've got the idea. As theory has it, this swivel or socket design enables the muzzle of the barrel to return closer to the same relationship with the slide from shot to shot than is possible with the standard bushing. It is a novel idea, but since a custom gun with a properly fitted standard bushing will keep its bullets inside two inches at 50 yards, the jury is still out on whether or not this particular custom part represents progress or is simply the most expensive barrel bushing available.

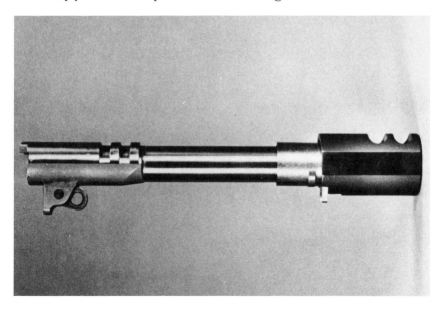

Richard Heinie's match-grade barrel with a dual-chamber compensator of his design.

The truth of the matter is, all types of bushings are rapidly becoming somewhat obsolete for compensated guns as other styles of barrels that eliminate them entirely gain in popularity. They will, however, continue to be the thing to use on most security blanket guns as well as guns built for Limited Class practical pistol competition.

Sleeved Barrel

The sleeved barrel eliminates the need for a barrel bushing and has been used on thousands of compensated guns. The barrel is first threaded and then a reverse-taper sleeve is installed and secured with industrial-grade epoxy. The outside diameter of a straight, nontapered section at its muzzle end is a close fit with the inside of the slide. Some sleeve designs extend from the rear of the compensator to just forward of the front locking lug of the barrel, while others are shorter. Some are integral with the compensator while others are separate. The one-piece design is reportedly more durable, but if it has to be replaced due to eventual wear, its compensator must be replaced or its integral barrel sleeve chopped off. With the two-piece design, the barrel sleeve can be replaced and the same compensator reinstalled without modification.

The full-length sleeve on the barrel of this Wilson Super Grade extends from the rear surface of the compensator to just forward of the front locking lug.

The sleeved barrel most often is used on compensated guns, but is becoming quite popular on carry guns. For that installation, the muzzle end of the sleeve usually has a flange which is contoured to match the slide's profile, for appearance sake. Simply described, it looks like a compensated barrel with all except the rear of the compensator sawed off.

I believe Detonics originated the concept of a sleeved barrel in a carry gun, but the first one I saw that really looked good was on the #W116 Tactical Special, a custom conversion of the standard Government Model introduced by Bill Wilson in 1991. I liked the idea and when Wilson introduced the same type of barrel in shorter lengths I had one installed on a custom Officer's ACP. The fat, stubby barrel comes with a full-length recoil spring guide rod and a single 22-pound spring. It is far superior to the factory dual-spring setup, eliminates the short and easily broken barrel bushing of the Officer's ACP, is remarkably accurate, and looks trick to boot.

Heavy Barrel

The heavy barrel might best be described as a sleeved barrel with an integral sleeve as the exterior shape of the two is about the same. As far as I know, this concept, along with the full-length recoil spring guide rod, also was introduced to the Government Model pistol by Detonics. In lieu of a standard-weight barrel threaded for a sleeve, the heavy barrel is turned to a reverse-taper or coned contour. Out near its muzzle the diameter is large enough to fit closely with the inside of the slide.

Fluting a heavy barrel has become mildly popular. The flutes reduce weight a tad, increase the exterior surface area of the barrel for more rapid heat dissipation during rapidfire shooting, and really makes a racegun look, well, racy.

Whether or not a heavy barrel is superior to a sleeved barrel of the same diameter depends on who you ask. The heavy barrel has no sleeve to come loose, but then I have never seen one installed by a competent pistolsmith do so anyhow. Its thicker wall makes the heavy barrel a bit more rigid since the wall of a standard diameter barrel is thinned considerably when it is threaded for a sleeve. This may be more important on a .45 ACP barrel than on a .38 Super barrel or on a barrel with the extra weight of a compensator hanging from its muzzle, but probably is not super important on any type of barrel. As odd as it might seem, of the numerous modifications the USPSA allows on a Limited Class competition gun, the installation of a heavy or sleeved barrel is not one of them.

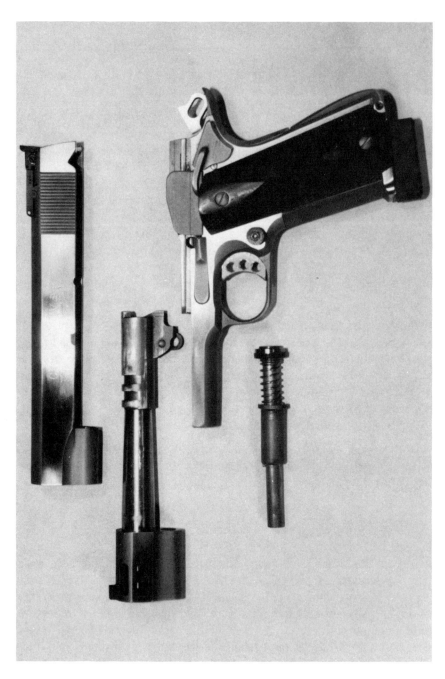

Jim Garthwaite compensated Commander with heavy barrel taken down for cleaning.

194

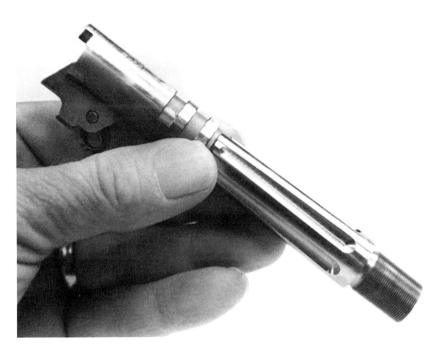

With its muzzle already threaded for the installation of a compensator, this C. W. Custom heavy barrel has been fluted to reduce weight.

Jim Stroh's Design

One of the more unusual heavy barrels I have seen is made by Jim Stroh. He inserts a 6½ inch long, two-inch diameter section of rifled barrel blank into his milling machine and whittles away everything that doesn't look like a barrel, a compensator, and a front sight. In case you missed the significance of what you've just read, Stroh's barrel, compensator, and front sight are one solid chunk of steel rather than three separate parts joined together by mechanical means. It is best described as a Government Model barrel wearing an integral compensator which wears an integral front sight.

Heavy barrels are installed mainly on compensated guns used for competitive shooting. If this type is installed on a noncompensated gun, the muzzle of the barrel would, for aesthetics sake, need to be threaded and a flange installed to cover the end of the slide, thus defeating part of the purpose of the heavy barrel. For this reason, the sleeved barrel will probably remain popular on both carry and competition guns, while the heavy barrel will be used mainly on the latter. According to my crystal ball, there will come a time when nothing but heavy barrels are used on compensated guns.

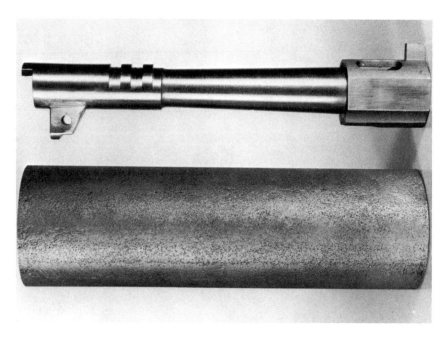

Jim Stroh's barrel with its integral compensator and front sight is carved from a huge barrel blank.

Centaur Systems Quadra-Lok

Another unusual design in heavy barrels is the Centaur Systems Quadra-Lok, which is similar in shape to the old Detonics barrel. Originally intended as a drop-in barrel requiring no pistolsmithing for installation, its tight lockup is made possible by a rather unique design. Small steel shims ranging in thickness from .001 to .010 inch are stacked, by trial and error, in a slot on the top side of a special slide stop crosspin. A .078-inch hardened steel roller is then placed atop the stack of shims. Once the correct combination of shims is installed, the roller bears against the barrel's underlug as it returns to battery, camming the barrel upward for a tight lockup with the slide. This elevating of the rear of the barrel forces a fulcrum band machined into the top of the barrel against the inside surface of the slide roof which in turn levers its muzzle downward against the bottom of the slide. The snug and consistent lockup at front and rear keeps the barrel to slide relationship consistent from shot to shot. This barrel is best installed on a gun with adjustable sights as it will drop bullet point of impact considerably as compared to the factory barrel.

When using the Centaur barrel as a drop-in, most shooters stick with the shim-type camming system, but some pistolsmiths eliminate the slotted slide

196

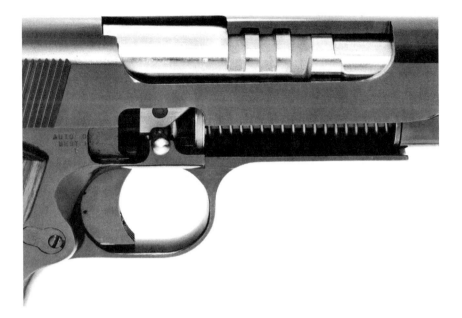

Cutaway gun with Centaur Systems heavy barrel. Note shim-type transverse shaft of the slide lock and pivot band just forward of the front locking lug.

The Centaur Systems heavy barrel.

stop and cut the underlug for a standard slide stop. I am told that another method of fitting this type of barrel also utilizes a standard slide stop, but a bit of metal is removed from the top of the fulcrum band in lieu of modifying the underlug. Some pistolsmiths also modify the rear entrance of the recoil spring tunnel of the slide for a rear-entry recoil spring plug so the small diameter Centaur recoil spring guide rod can be replaced by one of larger and more standard design. The larger diameter rod allows the use of a standard size shock buffer and recoil spring.

Advantages and Disadvantages

The various styles of barrels have their advantages and disadvantages. The sleeved and heavy types add an ounce or so of weight out front and don't heat up quite as quickly during rapidfire. They also delay unlocking of the barrel a tiny bit during firing. On the negative side, their initial cost usually is greater and they cost more to replace. Although this would be of significance only to those who shoot a custom gun many thousands of rounds annually, the barrel wears against the interior of the slide rather than against a replaceable bushing.

Charles Burdette shooting the A Head for Trouble stage at the 1992 USPSA Area VI championship match with his Aimpoint-sighted C. W. Custom .38 Super built around the Caspian high-capacity frame.

When everything, including barrel quality and quality of installation, is equal, I have yet to detect any difference in accuracy between the standard bushing-type, the sleeved, and the heavy barrels. Of the custom compensated guns I have worked with, only four would consistently average two inches for 10 shots at 50 yards. All were chambered for the .38 Super. One had a Wilson sleeved barrel, one had a C. W. Custom heavy barrel, and the other two had Caspian bushing-type barrels. As might be expected, I would just as soon have one type as the other.

The Fully Supported Chamber

The Government Model pistol has a two-piece feed ramp with a lower section on the frame and an upper section on the barrel. When a cartridge is chambered, part of its case just forward of the extraction groove hangs unsupported in midair above the heavily beveled ramp of the barrel. When a cartridge fires, the only thing separating the shooter from chamber pressure is a thin wall of brass. Assuming that headspace is not excessive and the nonsupporting area of the barrel has not been excessively increased by a polish and throating job performed by the less talented, this is a satisfactory design as long as factory ammunition is used in the gun. The same applies to factory-equivalent handloads put up in cases that are in good shape.

Cartridge in a standard factory barrel without the integral feed ramp and full-support chamber.

199

On the negative side, if the chamber pressure generated by a load greatly exceeds what the case was designed to retain, the case will rupture at its unsupported area and dump rampaging propellant gas into the wrong part of the gun. Some of the gas will travel into the magazine, some will scream back along the bottom of the slide and exit on both sides of the ejector and what is left will head in other directions. This also will happen at relatively low chamber pressure levels if a case is loaded so many times it loses its elasticity and becomes brittle. Whatever the cause, the result can be quite spectacular. If the shooter is wearing safety glasses (as he should be) and luck is on his side, the damage usually is limited to a ruined magazine, wood grip panels reduced to splinters, a bleeding hand and/or face, and quite a bit of embarrassment. If the shooter is unlucky, any rounds remaining in the magazine can explode when the case in the chamber blows.

As the term commonly used in describing it implies, a custom barrel with a fully supported chamber supports the case back to the front edge of its extraction groove. The barrel also has an extremely long integral feed ramp which eliminates the original two-piece design. Since Browning later incorporated this design into the barrel of his Hi-Power pistol, one wonders how many times he might have wished he had done the same with the Government Model. In addition to the Browning 9mm, dozens of other autoloaders being built by various manufacturers have this type of chamber.

When a barrel with full-support chamber is installed in the Government Model, a mortice has to be machined into the feed ramp area of the frame for the integral feed ramp of the barrel. In addition to offering a chambered cartridge more support than the original barrel design, it also improves cartridge feeding. When guns with both types of barrels are built by the top pistolsmiths, there is very little difference in reliability, but I'm convinced that a gun built by the average pistolsmith will feed a variety of bullet types and styles more reliably when the full-support barrel with its integral feed ramp is used.

When factory loads only are used in a custom Government Model, the standard barrel is satisfactory. The same goes for handloaders who do not exceed factory load chamber pressures and discard cases after they have been pounded by two or three heavy firings. However, too many competitors in the action shooting games try to put too many miles on cases with extremely heavy loads. For them, the full-support barrel is the only way to go. I believe this type of barrel is one of the wisest investments any practical pistol competitor can make, not because it might give some handloaders a false sense of security when using excessive loads, but because it extends the safety margin of heavy but safe loads by a considerable degree. I'll go even further by stating that I would rather not build a competition gun in any caliber without this type of barrel.

This custom barrel with its full-support chamber and integral feed ramp supports the case of a .38 Super cartridge back to its extractor groove.

When a full-support barrel is installed, a mortice has to be cut into the frame for its integral feed ramp.

Custom barrels with full-support chambers are available from Caspian in 9x21mm, 9x23mm Super, .38 Super, .40 S&W, 10mm Auto, and .45 ACP. CP Bullets, the company who introduced the 9x21mm and 9x23mm Super, offers the same type of barrel in those calibers. King's Gun Works has them in .38 Super, 9x23mm, .45 ACP, and 10mm Auto. Bar-Sto and Gun Craft offer them in .38 Super, 9mm Luger, 9x21mm, 9x23mm, 10mm Auto, and .45 ACP. I'm sure other makers of custom barrels eventually will follow suit. A full-support barrel is slightly more expensive and costs a bit more to have installed, but after witnessing several shooters blow .45 ACP cases with standard barrels, I am convinced it is some of the cheapest insurance available. As this is written, Springfield Armory's .38 Super is the only Government Model pistol that comes from the factory with this type of barrel.

It is extremely important to remember that all barrels of this type are not created equal. Some barrels support the case all the way back to the front edge of its extraction groove. Others are described by their makers as full-support, but really aren't. When having a new barrel installed on your gun, or when having a custom gun built from scratch, it is best to spell it out clearly in your specifications. In other words, you want a barrel with a full-support chamber that actually does fully support the case.

202

Locking Lug Engagement

The Government Model is designed to function with less than 100 percent engagement of its locking lugs as assurance that it will lock up and fire even when the locking recesses in the slide contain small quantities of dirt, crud, or other debris. The lugs on some of the older barrels measure as much as .070 inch high with locking recesses in the slide measuring .075 inch deep. Those of current production usually average somewhere between .055 and .065 inch.

Out of curiosity, I checked the locking lug height and locking recess depth of three new Colts and came up with the following; Delta Elite barrel (.060 inch front and rear lug); Delta Elite slide (.061 inch rear recess, 0.058 inch front recess); Commander barrel (.055 inch front, .057 inch rear); Commander slide (.061 inch front and rear); Gold Cup barrel (.054 inch front and rear); Gold Cup slide (.059 inch front, .058 inch rear). Locking lug to recess engagement of those slides and barrels measured 57, 54, and 49 percent, respectively.

It is common to see around 50 percent lug engagement in some of today's guns, although much less is considered insufficient. Around 50 percent or a bit more is adequate for average shooters who feed their pistols no more than a few hundred rounds each year, but it's not something of which even they should be proud.

Today's practical pistol competitors put more rounds through a gun in a week than some shooters burn up in a lifetime. The result has been battering or flanging of the locking lugs and slide locking recesses in guns with minimum engagement. This has probably caused more pistolsmiths to take a serious look at this detail of the Government Model than all other factors combined. Opinions differ on the ideal degree of locking lug engagement, but based on the opinions I've heard expressed by pistolsmiths and barrel makers, around 70 percent is about optimum for the rear lug of guns that are shot a lot with heavy loads.

Manufacturing tolerances of Government Model factory parts being as generous as they are, a considerable increase in locking lug engagement can cause a problem with some guns. When the rear of the barrel is elevated to full engagement, the firing pin may strike the primer too far off center for reliable ignition. This problem can be solved by the installation of an offset bushing in the breech face of the slide to slightly elevate the tip of the firing pin, an item available from Brownells. I'm not sure how common a problem an off-center firing pin is with fitted barrels, but of the many custom guns I have examined, only one had the bushing in its breechface.

Jim Stroh skins the same cat in a different manner. He starts with an extremely large, oversized blank and machines the exterior surface of the barrel slightly eccentric with the axis of its bore. Stroh also uses this type of barrel when full locking lug engagement would tilt the muzzle of a standard barrel downward so far the front sight must be lower than the .180 inch minimum most shooters prefer, or the rear sight has to be adjusted too high. If the Bo-Mar and other adjustable sights of its type are adjusted much higher than .090 inch, they may eventually rocket to parts unknown when subjected to long strings of heavy loads.

Determining Locking Lug Engagement

Before leaving this particular department, I should mention that determining the degree of locking lug engagement is a rather simple procedure. It is especially good to do so when a gun is purchased with the intention of feeding it a steady diet of full-power handloads. Here is how it is done. Field strip the gun, measure the height of the locking lugs on the barrel with a dial caliper, and then place a small ball of children's Play Dough™ into the slots behind them. Assemble the gun and push the slide forward to full lockup. Now field strip and measure the distance from the top of each locking lug to the top of the Play Dough™. Subtract what you get from the length of the lugs and you have measured lug engagement. If, for example, one of the lugs is .060 inch high and the second measurement is .030 inch, engagement with its recess in the slide is 50 percent or close to that figure. The front lug will show a bit less engagement due to the fact that the muzzle of the barrel is tilted down about one degree during lockup. Needless to say, don't forget to clean out the Play Dough™ before reassembling the gun.

Barrel Life

How long a Government Model barrel will maintain acceptable accuracy is influenced by many factors. I've heard of barrels in .38 Super comp guns giving up the ghost after digesting as few as 2,000 rapidfire rounds. Moving to the opposite extreme, I have shot one barrel of the same caliber that was still producing respectable accuracy after 60,000 Major power rounds, but it had been used almost exclusively with cast bullets. The late, great pistol shot, Ed McGivern, once fed over 75,000 cast bullets to a Smith & Wesson .38 Special revolver and claimed it was still plenty accurate. Most of his shooting was rapidfire. On the other hand, he washed out the barrel of a Model 1917 S&W in .45 ACP with less than 4,000 rounds of hardball.

Various barrel makers use different steel alloys and some are a bit softer than others. Soft steel erodes quicker than hard steel. When the best alloys are used in both, stainless probably will outlive chrome-moly by about

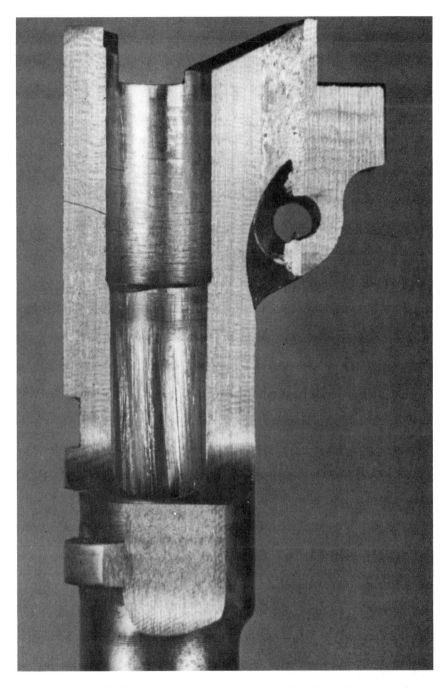

This cutaway .38 Super barrel reveals severe chamber throat erosion.

10 percent. In other words, if a good chrome-moly barrel will digest 40,000 rounds before needing replacement, a stainless steel barrel of equal quality might last another 4,000 to 5,000 rounds. The difference in accuracy life between the two types of steel is obviously more important to those who shoot a lot than to those who don't. I would say the greatest advantage stainless has is its higher resistance to rusting, whereas rust can virtually destroy the accuracy of a dirty chrome-moly barrel in a matter of days.

Extremely high temperature is the number one cause of barrel erosion and as chamber pressure is increased so is the burning temperature of the propellant gas. The burning temperature of powders is higher than the melting point of steel, but the barrel doesn't melt like a candle because the heat is applied for only a tiny fraction of a second. The increase in temperature caused by an increase in chamber pressure is why 10mm Auto handloads loaded to 35,000 CUP will burn out the chamber throat of a barrel quicker than those loaded to 25,000 CUP. A Major power load with a 135-grain bullet in the .38 Super will wash out a barrel quicker than a Major power load with a 150- or 160-grain bullet because the lighter bullet must be loaded to higher chamber pressures in order to reach the same level of performance. The same goes for light and heavy bullets in all other cartridges for which the Government Model is chambered. Everything, including barrel quality, being equal,

Cast bullets are easier on a barrel than jacketed bullets because they do a better job of sealing off the bore and preventing propellant gas from blowing by like a torch.

a barrel in .45 ACP will last longer than a barrel in .38 Super, 9x21mm, 9x23mm, 10mm Auto or .40 S&W because it operates at lower chamber pressure.

For obvious reasons, rapidfire shooting washes out a barrel much quicker than slowfire. This is why some practical pistol competitors who travel the professional circuit use up several barrels each season.

When cast and jacketed bullets are loaded to the same velocity, the accuracy life of a barrel is longer with the former, but for a reason many shooters don't understand. When a cartridge is fired, a small portion of the propellant gas rushes past the bullet and down the barrel before it can escape the grip of the case and move forward to seal off the bore. A cast bullet is relatively soft; for this reason the gas pushing on its base causes it to obturate rather quickly to seal off the bore.

A jacketed bullet is much harder and therefore takes longer to seal off the gas. If its diameter is a bit smaller than the barrel's groove diameter, gas may continue to escape between it and the surfaces of the grooves until it exits the muzzle. The high-speed gas escaping around the bullet has about the same erosive effect on the steel as an acetylene torch. This along with a cost savings is why it's not a bad idea to use cast bullets for practice and switch to jacketed bullets for competition. I prefer to use jacketed bullets for practical pistol competition, not because they are necessarily more accurate, but because the lubricant on cast bullets and minute particles of molten lead exiting the bore produce enough smoke to interfere with one's vision during a match.

Before swearing off jacketed bullets forever, keep in mind that what you just read was written by someone who shoots Government Model pistols rapidfire in competition. It is something to be concerned about if shooting thousands of rounds each year is on the agenda. Moving to the opposite extreme, I doubt if the average custom pistol owner will wear out a barrel in a lifetime regardless of what type of bullet is used.

Accuracy Comparison
(Factory vs. Custom Barrels)

Gun	Colt Officer's ACP
Caliber	.45 ACP
Custom barrel	Wilson
Slide to frame fit tightened	Yes
Number of different loads tried	10
Range	20 yards
Best accuracy with factory barrel	5.1 inches
Best accuracy with custom barrel	1.7 inches
Average accuracy with factory barrel	6.6 inches
Average accuracy with custom barrel	2.4 inches

Most individual load accuracy improvement 67%
Least individual load accuracy improvement 55%
Overall average accuracy improvement 64%
Pistolsmith . . . . .Warner

Gun . . . . .Colt Government Model
Caliber . . . . .45 ACP
Custom barrel . . . . .Wilson
Slide to frame fit tightened . . . . .No
Number of different loads tried 12
Range. . . . . .25 yards
Best accuracy with factory barrel. .4.4 inches
Best accuracy with custom barrel .1.3 inches
Average accuracy with factory barrel. . . . . .3.9 inches
Average accuracy with custom barrel . . . . .2.4 inches
Most individual load accuracy improvement. 62%
Least individual load accuracy improvement 48%
Overall average accuracy improvement 38%
Pistolsmith. . . . . .Wilson

Gun . . . . .Colt Gold Cup
Caliber . . . . .45 ACP
Custom barrel . . . . .Heinie
Slide to frame fit tightened . . . . .No
Number of different loads tried 10
Range. . . . . .25 yards
Best accuracy with factory barrel. .4.1 inches
Best accuracy with custom barrel .1.6 inches
Average accuracy with factory barrel. . . . . .4.5 inches
Average accuracy with custom barrel . . . . .2.9 inches
Most individual load accuracy improvement 61%
Least individual load accuracy improvement 8%
Overall average accuracy improvement 36%
Pistolsmith . . . . .Warner

Gun . . . . .Colt Delta Elite
Caliber . . . . .10mm Auto
Custom barrel . . . . .Bar-Sto
Slide to frame fit tightened . . . . .Yes
Number of different loads tried 10
Range. . . . . .25 yards
Average accuracy with factory barrel. . . . . .5.0 inches
Average accuracy with custom barrel . . . . .2.6 inches
Most individual load accuracy improvement 61%
Least individual load accuracy improvement 23%
Overall average accuracy improvement 47%
Pistolsmith . . . . .Dichiara

10

The Fire Control System

Standard Trigger Designs

The triggers of factory guns range from terrible on some models to quite good, but not outstanding on Colt's Gold Cup. Most pistolsmiths offer two types of trigger jobs: One involves making various modifications to factory component parts; the other utilizes new state-of-the-art custom parts. If the family budget will allow only the former, by all means go for it as a good trigger and decent sights on an autoloader are second only in importance to reliability.

On the negative side, nothing that can be done to factory trigger components will ever make them equal to fine-tuned custom parts available from sources like Wilson's, McCormick, Kings, and others. Several of my custom guns have extremely lightweight components and you have to compare such a gun against one with a factory trigger to believe how much difference there can be. My old Warner-built, switch-top comp gun in .22 Long Rifle and .38 Super was the first custom gun I tried with a titanium hammer, hammer strut, trigger, and firing pin and I was amazed at how it felt. It had zero weight variation from pull to pull, and broke like an icicle. You can really feel the difference when dry-firing two guns side by side. When the hammer drops on a gun with standard-weight fire control components, it vibrates in the hand like a tuning fork. In contrast, vibration is all but nonexistent in the gun with lightweight components. You pull the trigger and it simply goes "thud" when the hammer drops. It really feels good, but I'll have to admit, the near total absence of vibration is probably more important to bullseye shooters than anyone else.

Bob Cogan compensated Delta Elite with his pivoting trigger.

A variety of lightweight triggers are available from Kings Gun Works. The two in the bottom row with extra-wide fingerpieces are for the Colt Gold cup.

When an extremely light pull is desired, a lightweight trigger is the only way to go as it helps to prevent the hammer from following the slide during the firing cycle. Custom aftermarket triggers range from light to super light, but once weight drops below 100 grains or so, any practical difference between the various brands exists mostly in the minds and imaginations of shooters and manufacturers.

How light trigger pull weight should be depends on the shooter and the gun's intended use. I really don't believe the trigger on a self-defense gun should be lighter than 3½ pounds and four pounds is probably about ideal.

On a gun used for practical pistol competition, I like a trigger to break crisply at about 2½ pounds with zero backlash. Some competitors like it even lighter, but I believe 2½ pounds represents the practical limit unless a pivoting trigger is installed. Don't buy a used car from someone who says a 2½ pounder won't hold up when subjected to the pounding of heavy loads. One of my comp guns in .38 Super has digested many thousand of rounds of Major power loads and its trigger has not been touched by a pistolsmith since the day the gun was built. Its trigger breaks precisely at 39 ounces and the hammer has never followed the slide down a single time.

The super-light trigger pull is not for everyone. Someone new to practical pistol competition should start with a clean, crisp pull of 3½ to four pounds

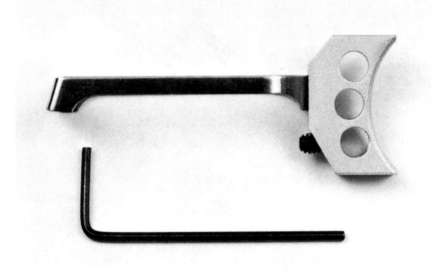

This lightweight Wilson trigger weighs less than 80 grains.

and then have it made lighter if desired when more experience lies beneath the belt. Within reason, consistency in a trigger is more important than how much pressure must be applied to it before the gun goes bang. I would rather have a trigger consistently break at four pounds from pull to pull than to break at two pounds with one pull and three pounds on the next.

The pull weight of a trigger can be reduced considerably by properly lubricating the various component parts. Applying an extremely light coat of lube to the bottom and top surfaces of the trigger's fingerpiece, and to the outer surfaces of its stirrup, will decrease friction between it and the frame. A special grease applied to the engaging surfaces of the sear and hammer, as well as on the crosspin that holds the sear and disconnector in position further reduces friction. For more on this subject see Chapter 19.

Custom aftermarket triggers are available with a short or long fingerpiece. They also are available with a wide fingerpiece for the Gold Cup frame. As a rule, shooters with large hands prefer the long trigger while those with small hands go for the short version. Those of us with hands of average size can live happily ever after with either. I have both types on various guns, and would just as soon have one as the other. Contrary to popular opinion, however, I believe more shooters would be better off with the short trigger than with the long. If in doubt about which trigger is best for you, choose the short one. The short trigger definitely is a better idea for a self-defense gun, especially if it is carried during cold weather as it leaves more room inside the trigger guard for a glove-clad finger.

One thing I have never read or heard mentioned is the fact that the wider the fingerpiece is on a trigger, the lighter pull weight appears to be. This is why a 3½ pound trigger on a Gold Cup feels about the same as a three pound trigger on the Government Model with its narrow fingerpiece. This probably is never discussed because most pistolsmiths don't like to mill out a Government Model frame for the wider trigger. It is, however, the reason some shooters prefer to have a custom gun built around the Gold Cup frame.

The Series 80 Trigger

All else being equal, the trigger pull weight of a Colt Series 80 gun is a bit heavier than those on earlier guns because the spring-loaded firing pin block must be depressed by the trigger in order for the gun to fire. How much difference is there? Not as much as popular opinion seems to claim. I checked the weights of trigger pulls on two custom guns, then removed the firing pin block mechanism from both guns and reweighed them. The difference in weight with and without was 3.8 ounces for one gun and 4.1 ounces for the other. In other words, the Series 80 firing pin block adds about one quarter pound of weight to the trigger. So, assuming that 2½ to 2¾ pounds

This Chuck Warner Officer's ACP has a Heinie lightweight Commander-style hammer and short trigger.

Steve Woods' compensated Colt with long lightweight aluminum trigger. *(Stephen Longley photo)*

Jim Stroh gun with a short trigger.

is about the lower limit in weight for a Series 70 or earlier gun without going to a pivoting trigger, I believe we also can assume that somewhere in the neighborhood of 2¾ to 3 pounds represents the lower limit for a Series 80 gun. I want to emphasize that this experiment was included only to illustrate that from a practical point of view, the difference between triggers on the Series 80 and earlier guns is not as great as some folks seem to believe. Neither I nor any pistolsmith I know recommends the removal or deactivation of any safety device on the Government Model pistol. Besides, not many shooters actually can tell the difference between a 2½- and a 3-pound trigger.

The Pivoting Trigger

For many years pistolsmiths have attempted to improve the trigger of the Government Model pistol by coming up with several variations of the pivoting design. The best I have seen is available from Gun Craft. Machined entirely from steel, it consists of a thin fingerpiece which pivots on a trigger shoe. Rather than the stirrup being attached to the fingerpiece as on a trigger of conventional design, a stud on its front surface extends through the shoe where it is exposed to the backside of the pivoting fingerpiece. After the trigger shoe has been hand-fitted to the frame, a hole is drilled and tapped through the bottom of the trigger guard and into the shoe. A 6-32 screw is then installed to retain it in a fixed position.

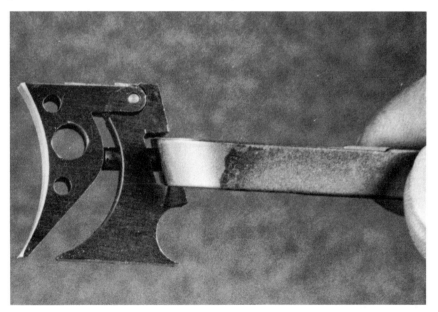

Gun Craft pivoting trigger.

Due to the mechanical advantage of its lever-type design, the pivoting trigger reduces the amount of finger pressure required to fire the gun as compared to a conventional trigger. In other words, it reduces the perceived weight of the trigger. For example, if the hammer to sear relationship is such that, say, 4 to 4½ pounds of pressure on the fingerpiece of a conventional trigger is required to fire the gun, only 1½ to 2 pounds will be required with the pivoting trigger. This is important because it allows a competitor to have a Government Model pistol with an extremely light trigger pull without resorting to an extreme and possibly dangerous reduction in the hammer and sear engagement surfaces.

The Gun Craft pivoting trigger system is available with a curved or straight fingerpiece for all Government Model variations including the Gold Cup, as well as for the high-capacity frames made by Caspian and Para-Ordnance. According to my RCBS electronic scale, total weight of the Para-Ordnance version is 283.7 grains, or 0.65 ounce. This is only 22 grains heavier than the factory trigger on Colt's Gold Cup.

Hammers

I vividly recall the first time I practiced drawing and dry-firing my Gold Cup for an upcoming Tactical class (now called Limited class) match. On about the third speed draw, I impaled the web of my hand between thumb and trigger finger with the spur of the gun's hammer. The gun wore a Commander-type hammer during my next practice session. This type of hammer is available from several sources in steel or titanium. For a weight comparison of this and other Government Model component parts, see Chapter 20.

One of the lightweights also enables you to add a bit of weight somewhere else, for example, in the new custom barrel. The weight difference between a standard and Commander-style hammer is slight, but each fraction of an ounce adds up when you're trying to keep the gun as light as possible for carry use. It also can be important when trying to keep weight within the USPSA rule for a Limited class gun which restricts total heft to a maximum of three ounces more than its factory-original weight.

A lighter hammer also reduces lock time, or the time elapsed between hammer fall and primer ignition. When a titanium hammer is combined with a hammer strut and firing pin made of the same material, lock time is reduced 50 percent and sometimes more. This is why bullseye shooters are being attracted to super lightweight fire control components like ants to a Sunday picnic.

The titanium hammer also comes with two disadvantages that are worth noting. First, it is considerably more expensive than a steel hammer of equal

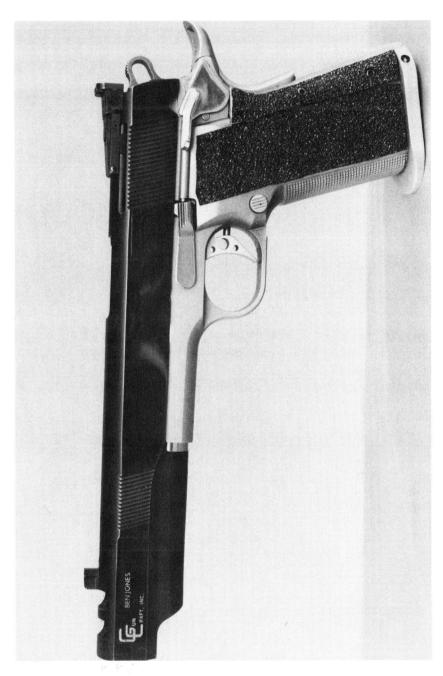

Built by Ben Jones and Kim Stroud, this high-capacity compensated gun on a Para-Ordnance frame has a Gun Craft pivoting trigger.

Wilson lightweight Commander-style hammer.

Brown lightweight Commander-style hammer.

220

Jack Weigand eliminates the spur on his Quick-Lock hammer to reduce weight.

quality. Secondly, the thin walls on both sides of the disconnector timing slot in the bottom of the slide will quickly wear grooves in the top of the hammer. Once the grooves become deep enough, the slide will bump against and may even hang up on the hammer as it returns forward toward battery during the firing cycle. I had to replace the titanium hammer on a .38 Super comp gun which has the old-style Caspian slide at about the 20,000 round mark.

The Titanium Firing Pin

When first hearing about its availability, I figured the titanium firing pin was nothing more than a ridiculously expensive gimmick. Then I tried one and now consider it one of the better ideas for a competition gun. When first introduced, it was promoted by its developer as a way of reducing lock time, but I quickly discovered a few more benefits.

You may have noticed elongated firing pin skid marks on the primers of cases fired in your Government Model pistol. This most often happens when heavy loads are used. It can be caused by two things during the firing cycle. One is an underpowered or worn-out recoil spring. The other is the heavy steel firing pin failing to fully rebound back into the slide before the breech end of the barrel starts moving downward toward its unlocked position. When that happens the tip of the firing pin is subjected to a tremendous amount

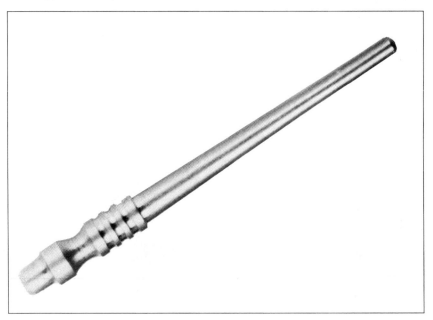

Kings' titanium firing pin.

Merle Edington shooting part two of the three-part Twist and Shout stage of the 1992 USPSA Area VI Championships.

of shear stress as it plows a furrow across the primer's surface. Eventually, this can cause the firing pin to snap like a twig. Installing an extra-power firing pin spring often will solve the problem with a steel firing pin, but since the titanium pin rebounds so much quicker than its steel cousin, it (along with the heavier spring) is a far better way to go. The benefits of titanium don't stop here.

Rather than bore you with a lot of technical jargon, I'll simply say that when the weight of a firing pin is reduced, its velocity is increased. For this reason, the amount of energy it delivers to the primer is the same as for a heavier and slower firing pin. However, there's a bit more to it than that. Studies conducted many years ago by SAAMI and the United States Army proved conclusively that a lightweight firing pin with its snappy, low-impulse energy delivery is more effective in detonating a primer than a heavier pin with its slower, high-impulse delivery of energy.

Is any of what you've just read worth a hill of beans to the average shooter? It may or may not be, but the results of a couple of experiments I conducted with the .38 Super may be of interest.

Anyone who uses Small Rifle primers in .38 Super Major power loads probably has already discovered that the Remington No. 7½ with its extremely thick and tough cup has no peer for that application. The problem is that some guns won't deliver enough firing pin energy to consistently light its fire. I had tried the Remington primer in handloads for one of my competition guns and misfires approached 2 percent. Out of curiosity, I replaced its factory firing pin with titanium. Four thousand rounds later the gun had not missed a single beat. Since then I have used thousands more of Remington's No. 7½ primer in two .38 Supers without a single misfire. So, if you use rifle primers in the Super, the 10mm Auto, the 9x21mm, or the .40 S&W as many competitors do, a titanium firing pin is one of the cheapest pieces of misfire insurance available.

I also have received reports from other shooters of improvements in the accuracy of custom Government Models when a titanium firing pin is installed. I have not taken the time to substantiate those claims beyond reasonable doubt, but do know the lighter firing pin does appear to have a tendency to decrease the velocity spread of handloads with some combinations of powders, bullets, and primers. During one of my experiments I chronographed several loads consisting of the Remington 7½ and CCI BR-4 primers, HS7 and AA-7 powders, and bullets weighing from 125 to 147 grains in a gun with its factory steel firing pin. I then installed a titanium firing pin and chronographed the same loads again. With the titanium pin, the average velocity of all loads increased by an average of almost 2 percent, but possibly of greater significance, velocity spread decreased by as much as 40 percent. It could be that more uniform velocity from round to round is why some shooters have experienced better accuracy with the titanium firing pin. I do have my doubts about any gun with less than match-grade accuracy potential showing any significant difference in accuracy by switching its firing pin.

If you decide to install a titanium firing pin in your gun, make sure it is the correct length. Standard length for most guns is in the neighborhood of 2.295 inches, but for reasons I have yet to uncover, Colt changed to an average of 2.260 to 2.265 inches in the Series 80 guns. The longer firing pin is better in a custom gun simply because it doesn't have to travel as far before impacting the primer. This becomes especially important when an extra power firing pin spring is used and when shooting .38 Super handloads with Small Rifle primers.

Back when I had my first Super built around a Caspian frame and slide, the pistolsmith installed a Smith & Alexander titanium firing pin. After shooting thousands of rounds without a single misfire, I decided to try a titanium pin from another source. When using handloads with the Remington 7½ primer, I immediately began to experience a couple of misfires every 200 rounds or so. Switching back to the S&A pin eliminated the problem. I then compared the dimensions of the two firing pins. The S&A was 2.293 inches long compared to 2.262 inches for the other. Of all of the titanium firing pins I have tried, only the S&A (now called SA Shooting Accessories) and the Wilson measure a full 2.293 to 2.295 inches. They can be used in Series 70 or 80 guns.

Firing pin diameter also is important. The tip or nose of the firing pin should be a close fit with its orifice in the breechface of the slide and yet not so snug as to bind. Colt firing pins made for guns in .45 ACP usually measure around .090 inch while those for the 9mm Luger and .38 Super run around .070 inch. Those dimensions are fine for many slides, but those with an oversize orifice need a larger diameter firing pin. One solution for such a slide in 9mm or .38 Super is to have the pistolsmith turn down a .45 ACP firing pin to the correct diameter. Perhaps the simplest way to whip the problem is to install a titanium pin. The tips of those made for the .45 ACP and .38 Super I've measured were .003- to .005-inch larger in diameter than Colt firing pins.

The only negative comments I've heard about the titanium firing pin is its possible tendency to cause pierced primers when some brands of standard pistol primers are used with heavy loads for the 10mm, .40 S&W, and .38 Super. I have not experienced this problem, but have heard it can happen. Two shooters also have told me that they experienced misfires with titanium firing pins when loading Small Rifle primers in .38 Super handloads, but as it turned out, they were using extremely light mainsprings in their guns. A mainspring lighter than 18 pounds should not be used with a titanium pin.

Beavertail Grip Safeties

The beavertail grip safety is one of the more popular options on custom guns for a number of reasons. It eliminates the possibility of a minor, yet painful, injury lovingly described as hammer-bite by preventing the web of the hand from being pinched between the hammer and the top of the grip safety. I have fired thousands of rounds in various Government Model pistols with the factory safety and have yet to experience my first case of hammer-bite, but it is not an uncommon event among those with fleshy hands, especially if the gun is gripped with a high hold.

A beavertail safety distributes recoil over a larger area of the hand. This is especially important to those who fire thousands of rounds each year. Its larger surface area also makes the gun a bit easier to control when heavy loads are fired. Last but extremely important to those who compete in practical pistol matches, a beavertail makes the Government Model much easier to draw quickly from a holster.

Various styles of beavertail grip safeties are available. One is a drop-in unit that requires no modification to the gun, It is an improvement over the original

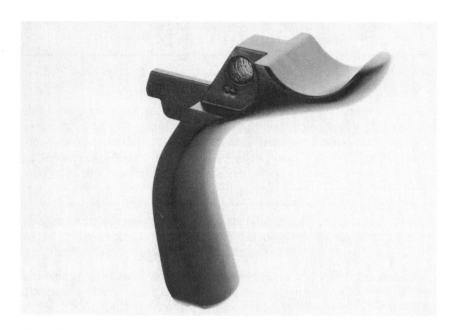

Kings Gun Works high-sweep grip safety.

The installation of this Wilson high-sweep grip safety distributes recoil over a broader area of the hand, and enables the hand to grip the gun higher and closer to the axis of its bore.

226

version and quite similar to the enhanced style introduced on Colt guns in 1992. It does not improve handling and control as well as a safety that requires modification of the gun, nor does it increase metal-to-hand surface area contact as much. It is better than the old style safety.

The two types of beavertails most often installed on custom guns are the standard and high-hold (or high-sweep as it is commonly called). When installed on a gun with an extended frontstrap, the latter style allows the hand to be positioned a bit higher on the grip of the gun and therefore closer to the axis of its barrel. For some shooters, this slightly reduces muzzle jump during firing and makes the gun somewhat easier to control with heavy loads, especially during rapidfire shooting. This style often is positioned so high up on the gripframe that a clearance mortice has to be machined into its top surface to give a Commander-style hammer enough room to travel to its cocked position. An exception is Kings' No. 206 high-sweep, the shape of which eliminates the need for the hammer clearance notch.

I think the high-sweep safety is a neat idea and prefer it on my custom guns, but it is not everybody's cup of tea. Some shooters rest the thumb of their strong hand atop the thumb safety tab and when using this type of beavertail the palm of their hand often fails to depress it enough for disengagement. Of course, this is a problem for some, even with the standard style of beavertail. On the other hand, many who use the high-thumb, high-grip hold never experience this problem. I'm one of them. For obvious reasons, it is best to try guns with both styles of safeties to determine which works best for you before deciding on this particular detail of a custom gun.

Perhaps this is a good place to mention the Wilson "humptail" style of beavertail safety as it is an excellent cure for the problem I have just described. Even when a gun is gripped as high as possible, the heel of the hand contacting the hump on the tail of the safety will still push it far enough forward for disengagement. Great idea.

Extended Thumb Safeties

I have no idea who came up with the idea of an extended thumb safety for the Government Model, but wouldn't exactly faint from shock if someone told me it was Armand Swenson. During the late 1960s the California pistolsmith took the idea a step farther by introducing his patented ambidextrous safety. It went on to enjoy great popularity and regardless of what company makes the same type today, most shooters with a bit of gray in their hair describe it as a Swenson-type. The Swenson design is simple, yet ingenious. The transverse shafts of the left- and righthand thumb tabs are linked together with a tongue and groove arrangement. The baseplate of the righthand tab extends forward where it is held in place by the gun's grip panel.

Steve Woods' gun with ambidextrous thumb safety and Brown high-sweep grip safety. *(Stephen Longley photo)*

228

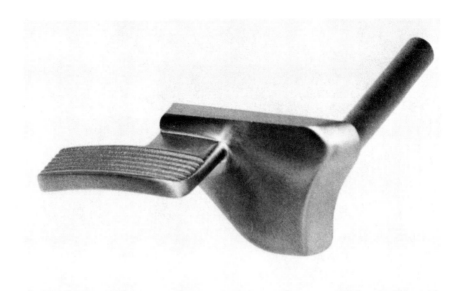

Wilson extended thumb safety.

As its name implies, the greater length and width of the tab on an extended safety presents more surface area to the thumb than the shorter factory version. This makes it easier to operate when the hand is wet, clad in a glove, or when in a hurry. The tabs on the various brands and styles range from relatively narrow to extremely wide, the latter often preferred by those who rest the thumb of their strong hand atop the tab while shooting the gun.

When I first started competing in practical pistol matches, an extended safety was near the bottom of my modification priority list. I had already become quite accustomed to shooting the Government Model and my thumb never failed to sweep its safety down. Then while shooting a custom gun owned by a friend, I discovered that I could better control it by resting my thumb atop its wide safety tab. In addition, that thumb-high hold feels more natural and comfortable to my hand, especially if the gun has an extended frontstrap and high-sweep grip safety.

I do have one criticism of extended safeties made by some companies. Rather than the baseplate having a beveled rear end, it terminates with a sharp, square edge that digs uncomfortably into the web of the hand with a high-thumb hold. It can be modified by the pistolsmith who installs it, but considering what those babies cost to begin with, it really should be done at the factory. Perhaps all who make this aftermarket part eventually will closely examine the one available from Wilson and see the light.

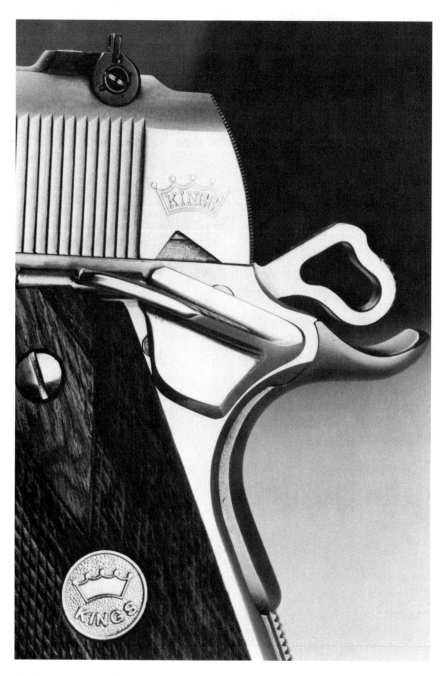

Al Capone's installation of a Kings lightweight hammer and extended thumb safety.

Ambidextrous Thumb Safeties

An ambidextrous safety looks nice on a custom gun and is a great idea for lefthanded shooters, but is seldom used by those of us who shoot the Government Model from its righthand side. As theory has it, the ambi safety enables a righthander to operate it with the thumb of the weak hand when it is gripped by that hand. In truth, most practical pistol competitors disengage the safety with their strong hand thumb before transferring the gun to their weak hand. They are likely to continue doing so unless the USPSA rules are changed to require the safety to be disengaged after it is shifted to the weak hand.

What I have just said does not apply to those righthanded competitors who draw a pistol with their strong hand in a rather unorthodox manner for weak hand shooting. First there's the Plaxco draw, I call it this because I believe J. Michael Plaxco was the first to use it in competition. Rather than grasping the entire grip of the gun during the draw, it is lifted from the holster with the hand wrapped around the lower half of the grip and then transferred to the weak hand. In this case, an ambidextrous safety is a necessity. The same applies to what I call the Bianchi Cup draw with an optical-sighted gun. The competitor grasps the scope with his strong hand, lifts the gun from its holster, and then transfers it to his weak hand.

In a real-life situation rather than while at play, an ambi safety could possibly save the day if the strong hand of a right-handed shooter were to suddenly

Kings ambidextrous thumb safety.

231

Like most practical pistol competitors, J. Michael Plaxco considers a good trigger extremely important. *(Zediker Publishing photo)*

become disabled. Even then I'm not sure it offers any great advantage over the standard extended safety when the gun rests in the hand of someone who really knows how to use it. Given enough practice, a righthander can learn to grasp the gun with his weak hand in an emergency situation and sweep down the tab of the standard safety with the first joint of the index finger of that hand. It also is possible to arch the weak hand thumb over the top of the gun and down on the safety, and then quickly return it to the right side of the grip before pulling the trigger.

Ambidextrous safeties are available with narrow and wide finger tabs. The latter style is great for the thumb-high hold on a competition gun. It is not a good idea for those who grip the gun with the more conventional thumb-low position as the top of the thumb can push the safety to its engaged or "on" position while the gun is being fired. On a self-defense gun carried concealed, the wide tab is likely to snag on clothing and disengage the safety before the draw is complete and the gun's muzzle is pointed safely away from the shooter's body. In addition, a gun so equipped won't fit into some holsters.

I believe the ideal extended safety for a carry gun has a tab no wider than .150 to .200 inch. The tab on most aftermarket safeties is considerably wider than my maximum, but any good pistolsmith who owns a sharp file can remedy that. Except for southpaws, I have a rather low opinion of any type of ambidextrous safety on a carry gun, but I'm definitely among the minority with such an opinion. When an ambi is installed on a carry gun built for a lefthanded shooter, its left-side tab can be ground off if desired, leaving only the baseplate on that side of the gun.

A righthanded shooter, I like the left-side tab on a competition gun to be in the neighborhood of .300-inch wide if the gun wears a thumb guard, and about .350 inch if it doesn't. I really don't care for an ambi safety, but if a gun has one anyhow, I want the righthand tab narrowed to .150 inch. A wider tab on the right side tends to dig uncomfortably into the knuckle of my hand when it is gripping the gun as high as possible. On the other side of the trail, others have no problem using an ambi with an extremely wide thumb tab on both sides. The only way you will know what works best for you is to try several styles.

The Thumbguard

When using a thumb-high hold, the inside edge of the thumb can rub against the side of the slide, retard its cycle momentum, and cause the gun to malfunction. This is more likely to happen when relatively light loads are fired in the gun with a recoil spring bordering on too heavy, but I've had it happen with full-power loads in a perfectly tuned gun. The guard prevents that by shielding the slide from the thumb. Several styles are available for installation on the left and right sides of the gun. Some pistolsmiths weld an extension plate onto the thumb safety, but the more common variety attach to the frame and are held in position by the grip panel. The Wilson No. 143 is this type. Simple to install, it fits over the slide latch/thumb safety plunger housing and is held in place by the grip panel. The Pachmayr and Lauck versions for the left side of the gun have an integral plunger housing and actually replace the factory housing. They also are held in position by the grip panel, although some pistolsmiths go an extra step by drilling and tapping the frame and securing them with a couple of small screws. Guns built by Jim Garthwaite and Dave Lauck usually come with this extra bit of insurance.

Some thumbguards extend far enough up the side of the slide to completely cover its grasping serrations. On an iron-sighted gun, extra serrations machined at the front of the slide is a popular solution. For an optical-sighted gun, the installation of a slide handle is the only way to go. Those two items are covered in the chapters on slide modifications, and checkering and serrating.

For obvious reasons, becoming accustomed to riding the safety of a competition gun wearing a thumbguard could prove to be a fatal habit if the same is done with a self-defense gun that does not have a guard.

The narrow righthand lever of the ambidextrous thumb safety on this Wilson Tactical Special is an excellent choice for a carry gun.

234

When it comes to thumbguards, nobody makes them bigger than Dave Lauck. *(Mike McCoy photo)*

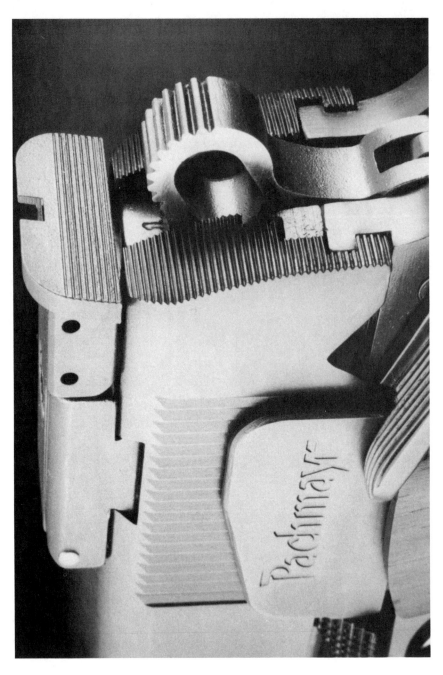

Steve Woods gun with Pachmayr thumbguard installed. *(Stephen Longley photo)*

236

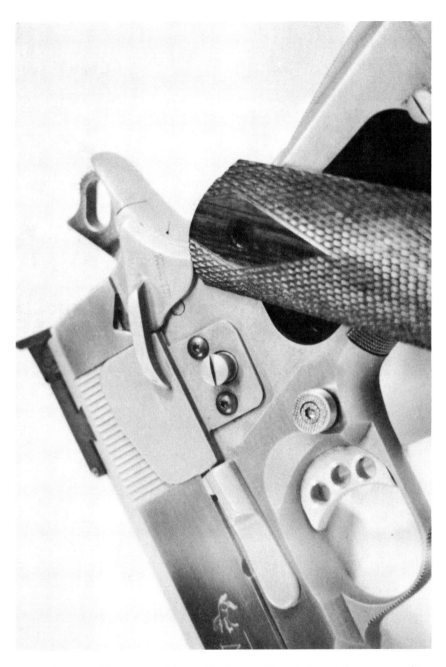

When Jim Garthwaite installs a Pachmayr thumbguard, he secures it with two small screws located on either side of the grip panel screw bushing.

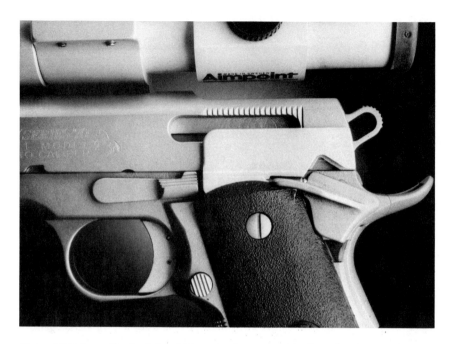

Steve Woods optical-sighted Para-Ordnance with Gun Craft thumb-guard. *(Stephen Longley photo)*

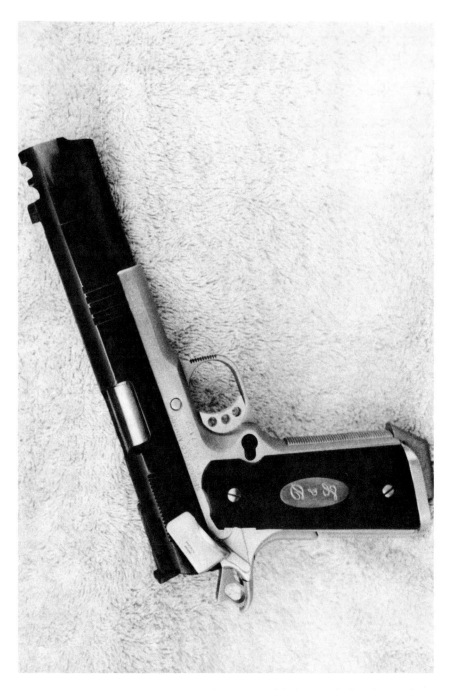

Dave Lauck's ambidextrous thumb safety with integral thumbguard.

11

Open Sights

THE sights on the Model 1911 were designed to be as rugged and unobtrusive as possible, yet adequate for battlefield use. Sitting extremely low on the slide, the half moon front blade and dovetailed rear leaf weren't likely to snag on a soldier's jumper, overcoat, or poncho as he drew the gun from its hip or shoulder holster. Low-profile, low-visibility sights also are extremely rugged and will shed blows without serious damage that would put some of the higher sights out of commission. Even in law enforcement circles within the private sector, many have considered Browning's original design quite adequate for the job. FBI man Melvin Purvis, whose name is synonymous with that of hoodlum John Dillinger, carried a Government Model and would have nothing else but its factory-original sights. Of course, he may not have been aware of better sights available in those days and he certainly couldn't have predicted what was ahead.

A large majority of today's shooters consider factory sights inadequate, although the higher visibility versions on late model Colts really aren't too bad. This is why companies such as Wilson's, Heinie, Millet, MMC, Bo-Mar, Novak, Trijicon, Meprolight, and Wichita have become so successful in aftermarket sights. Factory sights on some variations of standard Government Model pistols manufactured by various companies today are a bit better than those made back in the 1920s. Those on Colt's enhanced series of guns are better than those on the older Government Model, Commander, and Officer's ACP, but even they aren't something one finds many shooters bragging about. Probably the best that can be said of most factory sights is that they increase the price of the gun wearing them by very little.

Frank Garcia shooting one of his last matches with open sights before switching to an optical-sighted gun.

This classic Colt Commander carry gun by Kim Ahrends has night
sights with tritium inserts.

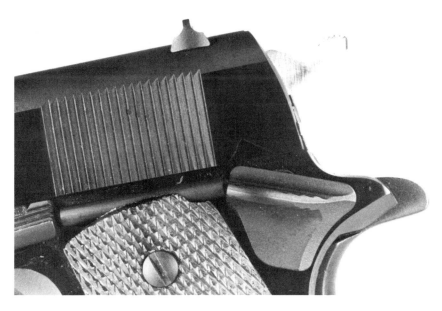

Rear sight on Colt Government Model is low-profile, low-visibility style.

Most factory sights are adequate for a limited amount of shooting, but the pounding of hundreds of rounds of heavy loads often will cause the rear sight to catapult from the slide. Front sights also have been known to bounce off and hide in the grass, although I'm told this is less common with the sights on post-1964 Colt guns with the .125-inch tenon as opposed to the old .055-inch tenon. Of greatest importance is the fact that most factory sights are a bit crude for precision shooting. Less important is the fact that the rear sight has no elevation adjustment and can be windage-adjusted only by hammering it east or west in its dovetail slot. The problem is, the rear sight and slide are relatively soft. A whack or three left, two back right, another in the opposite direction, and suddenly you've got a loose sight. Peening or lightly stippling the bottom surface of a loose sight is a quick fix, but why go to the trouble when far better options are available for little more cost than a chisel or center punch needed for the job.

Most aftermarket drop-in rear sights have an important feature seldom seen on factory sights. When the sight is resting snugly inside the dovetail cut in the slide, one or two retaining screws hold it securely in place. Keep the screw or screws tight and the sight will never break loose from its moorings. Years ago I installed a Wilson No. 61 on a .45 caliber Tactical class gun, zeroed

243

Front sight on Colt factory gun is rugged, but many shooters consider it too low.

it, and then staked its locking screw with a dab of Loctite™. Many thousands of Major power rounds later it still nestles in its dovetail as if welded.

Rear Sights

As a rule, bullseye shooters prefer relatively high sights on wadcutter guns and on the hardball variety built for leg matches. The rear sight is simply installed in the factory dovetail, or attached to a thick steel base or full-length rib which is permanently mounted to the top of the slide.

High-visibility sights on other types of custom guns are almost always mounted as low on the slide as possible, (commonly called the low-mount position). This is quite practical and usually by choice on guns used for various forms of action shooting competition. I consider low-mounted sights an absolute necessity on a carry gun, especially if it is carried concealed beneath clothing. Any sharp corners and edges also should be removed, or "melted," as most call it. So if someone tells you the rear sight on his custom pistol has been lowered and melted, you now know what he is talking about.

When the availability of aftermarket adjustable sights for the Government Model was limited, it became fashionable to mill out the slide and install a

244

Springfield Armory wadcutter gun with sight rib.

Springfield Armory hardball gun with high-profile sights.

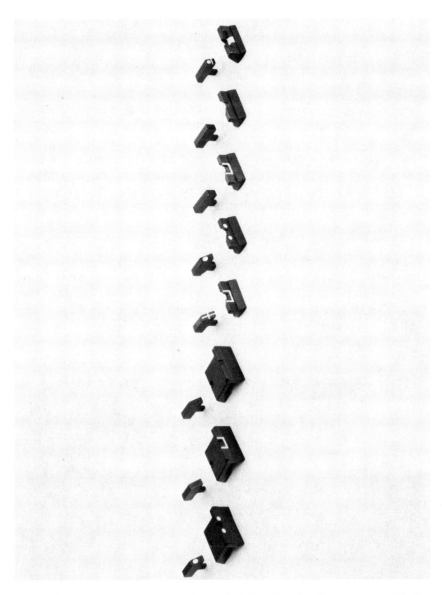

Kings Gun Works offers a variety of sights for the Government Model and its variations. From bottom to top, No. 109, Kings target sight, 3-dot system; No. 108, Kings target ramp front, white outline rear; No. 107, Kings target ramp front, plain rear; No. 105, Kings hardball cross bar front, white outline rear; No. 104, Kings hardball 3-dot system; No. 103, Kings hardball plain front, white outline rear; No. 102, Kings hardball plain front and rear; No. 101, King-Tappan combat-sight yellow dot front, white outline rear.

Smith & Wesson adjustable in the low-mount position. It looks nice, especially on a custom carry gun, and some pistolsmiths still offer it, but many of today's shooters consider the surface area of its leaf a bit small. For this reason, other sights of more modern design have made installation of the Smith & Wesson somewhat obsolete.

Ideally, a custom rear sight is designed so that when installed, its backside is positioned fairly close to flush with the slide's rear surface. Its leaf also is relatively tall and wide. The height slightly elevates the line of sight and the large surface area improves sight definition and acquisition. The latter feature is easily demonstrated by holding a Government Model in each hand in the shooting position, one with the factory rear sight, the other with a good custom sight. The eye is drawn more naturally to the custom sight because its notch is highlighted by the extremely large and uncluttered surface area of its leaf.

When most aftermarket sights with the large leaf are mounted in the factory dovetail slot in the slide, they greatly improve sight acquisition, but there is a negative side as well. The high mounting works fine on a bullseye gun, or one used for plinking tin cans and paper targets, but is likely to snag clothing when carried concealed or used in the various types of action competition. For those types of guns, the high-visibility sight with a low-mounted style of installation is impossible to beat.

Steve Woods installation of a Wichita rear sight. *(Stephen Longley photo)*

248

Steve Nastoff Officer's ACP with Heinie sights. *(ACRI Studio photo)*

A rear sight is lowered into cuts made in the slide by a milling machine. Almost any sight can be installed in this manner, but the most commonly seen are the Bo-Mar, Wichita, and Smith & Wesson adjustables; and the Wilson, Heinie, and Novak semi-adjustables (windage only). A single style of cut takes care of most sights, but three are available for the Bo-Mar. The fully protected style positions the rear surface of the sight leaf slightly beyond the slide's heel. In other words, the rear surface of the slide actually extends about one-fourth of the way up the surface of the sight leaf. This style of installation is for guns without the Series 80 firing pin block and is a specialty of Bill Laughridge.

Two other styles of installation commonly seen with the Bo-Mar are what I call standard and deluxe. On the standard cut, the rear flat is simply machined from one side of the slide to the other. It takes less time and therefore usually costs less than the deluxe cut, but isn't quite as attractive. On the deluxe cut, small fenders of metal are left on both sides of the frame adjacent to the windage adjustment screw of the sight. A half circle cut in the righthand fender allows access to the windage screw. The slide on one of my comp guns came from Caspian with the deluxe Bo-Mar cut and the workmanship is as good as I have seen from any pistolsmith. Incidentally, Caspian also offers slides with no sight cuts at all which is a neat option when building an optical-sighted competition gun.

Al Capone's installation of a Smith & Wesson rear sight on a Colt Officer's ACP.

Millett rear sight lowered into a Colt slide.

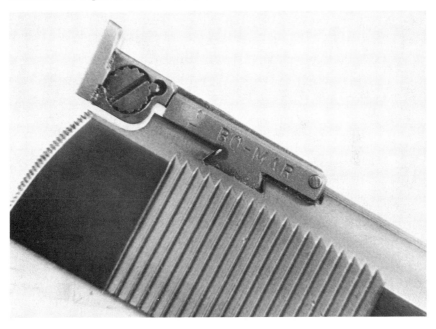

Bo-Mar rear sight installed with standard cut in a Colt slide.

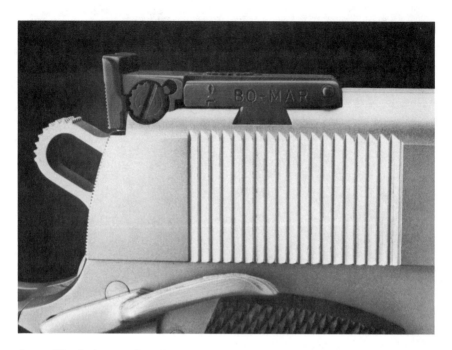

Steve Woods lowered and melted installation of a Bo-Mar rear sight with the deluxe cut in the slide. *(Stephen Longley photo)*

Top-notch workmanship on a lowered rear sight is easy to spot; there should be no daylight showing anywhere between the bottom surface of the sight and the top surface of the machine cut in the slide.

The rear end of a sight can overhang on a bullseye gun or plinking gun, should not overhang on a gun used for action shooting, and absolutely must not overhang on a carry gun. Combine an overhanging sight with a Commander-style hammer and you have partially concealed the hammer from access by the thumb. This can make the hammer difficult to reach with the thumb for cocking and lowering. Such a sight also is more easily damaged if the gun is dropped on a hard surface. This type of sight can be used on a carry gun with a standard hammer spur, but even then it leaves a great deal to be desired.

Pistolsmiths offer a dehorning modification of the rear sight which involves removal of all sharp corners or edges. There is no need for this modification on a target pistol, but it is an absolute necessity on a carry or competition gun. If not removed, the sharp corners can snag on clothing when the gun is drawn from a concealed position and they are likely to slice the hand when in competition.

252

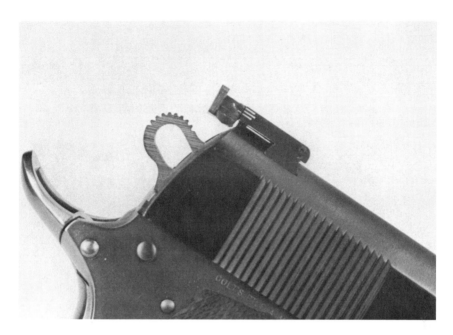

For reasons obvious to the eye, a Commander-style hammer is not a good choice to use on a gun with an overhanging rear sight.

The Front Sight

Front sights come in many styles and shapes. On competition guns, most shooters prefer a plain black front sight with its flat rear surface cut on a 90-degree angle to the slide. Most also prefer the blade's face to be serrated to cut down glare. When the sight is mounted out on a compensator, I prefer the undercut style, but am definitely in the minority.

Sights with colored inserts are fine for those whose eyesight requires them, but they tend to fade away when held against a light-colored target on a bright, sunny day. The blacker the better for contrast on a competition gun and most competitors even spray the front sight with sight black before stepping to the line. Of course, if the sights have inserts, sight black can make them temporarily disappear.

Contrasting Inserts

I can take or leave colored inserts on a carry gun, but I am probably a member of the minority here, too, as most shooters seem to prefer them. The way I see it, if it's too dark to see plain black sights, it's usually too

253

Brown dovetailed front sight.

This Wilson three-dot front and rear sight set is quite popular on carry guns.

dark to see the colored inserts unless you are backlit from behind, something you probably want to avoid when using a carry gun for its intended purpose. The truth is, colored inserts in sights probably serve the same purpose as those ugly massive trigger guards with flattened or curved front surface and cast checkering on some factory autoloaders—they sell guns.

Although it is seldom seen on custom guns, some shooters prefer a front blade with a gold bead for indoor or night competition. I think this is a good idea for some applications. Nelson Ford says this is an especially popular option among his customers. All of which brings up an excellent reason for the specifications of a comp gun to include the front sight dovetailed to the compensator. That type of installation makes it easy to switch front sights for different shooting conditions.

Night Sights

What I mentioned about sights with colored inserts does not apply to the so-called night sights. With their light-producing tritium inserts, Trijicon, Meprolight, and Wilson sights have to be the all-time best idea in open sights for carry guns. They have become extremely successful in law enforcement circles, a good example being their adoption by the FBI. If I were a cop or

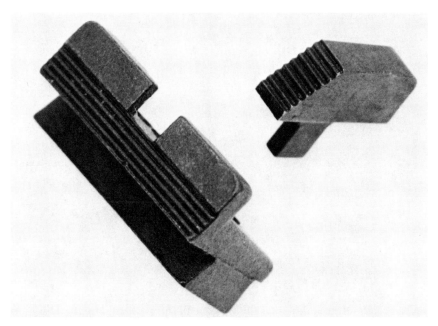

For those who don't care for colored inserts, the Wilson standard Combat sight is good choice.

The brass bead front sight on this Nelson Ford carry gun makes it an excellent choice for shooting during poor light conditions.

Charles Burdette applies sight black to his C. W. Custom compensated gun in preparation for a match. *(C. W. Custom photo)*

This Wilson Tactical Special wears Trijicon night sights with tritium inserts.

security officer who walked the night beat, you can bet my sidearm would wear sights that glow in the dark. Meprolight also offers them for rifles and shotguns; lawmen who are issued either gun should take note of their availability. A Miami friend of mine is not in law enforcement, but does live in a neighborhood that went from good to bad over the years. She likes the glowworm sights because when her Commander is lying on a small table beside her bed with its muzzle pointed away, she can quickly and silently locate it without switching on any lights in the room.

I predict that night sights will become extremely popular on various firearms other than those used for self defense when shooters discover their suitability for other applications. As open sights go, they are the best thing going for competing in practical pistol matches held indoors or at night. The same goes for hunting big game with a handgun. Additionally, I have Meprolight sights on my .416 caliber Remington Model 700 dangerous game rifle and a bead from the same company is mounted on the ventilated rib of my 12 gauge turkey gun.

Some brands of standard sights are available in several width options for the front blade and rear notch. If those you decide on come in one size only, a pistolsmith can modify them with a few strokes of the file. The combination to go with depends on the type of sight picture you prefer. I like to see a great deal of daylight on both sides of a relatively wide front blade. On a 5½ inch competition gun with the sight mounted out on the compensator (about 7½ inches of sight radius), this means .130-inch wide for the front blade, and rear notch. Move the front blade considerably closer, like the 5½ inch radius of the Heinie sights on my Officer's ACP, and its width remains the same, but the notch out back is increased to .140-inch wide. I'm saying all of this not to imply that those dimensions are correct for everyone, but to illustrate an option worthy of consideration when planning a custom pistol.

The Gold Cup Slide

The Bo-Mar rear sight is not commonly installed on the Gold Cup for one simple reason. If its slide is milled out for the popular low style of mounting, the new cut doesn't clean up the mortice machined into it at the factory for the Elliason sight. It can be welded up and recut as Jim Stroh and others do, but most pistolsmiths prefer not to do this. The larger Wichita sight will clean out the factory cut and this is why most pistolsmiths recommend it.

Some shooters say the Wichita sight looks fine on the Gold Cup. Other people think it's too wide and spoils the otherwise clean lines of the relatively narrow integral rib atop the slide. On a plain, no-frills working gun, I'll cast my vote with the former school of thought. On a fullhouse custom gun with

258

Trijicon night sights with tritium inserts are available for a variety of guns.

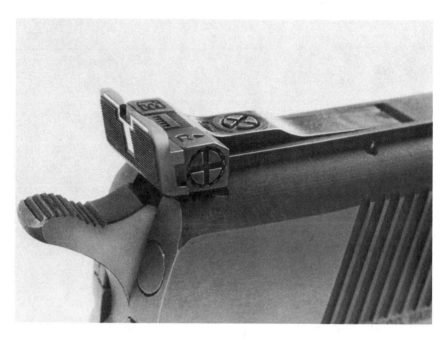

Millett rear sight installed on a Colt Gold Cup.

all the fancy trimmings, the latter choice gets the nod. Except for the Millett drop-in which closely copies the profile and shape of the Elliason, no after-market sight looks as good on a custom Gold Cup as the one Colt puts on it at the factory. On a carry or competition gun, either of those three sights should be dehorned, defanged, melted, or whatever you choose to use in describing the removal of sharp corners and edges.

The truth of the matter is, the Elliason sight is much more rugged than some who advocate replacing it would have us believe. I have known lawmen who carried Gold Cups for years with no complaint. I also know several casual IPSC competitors who use accurized Gold Cups in Tactical (now called Limited) class matches and never have a problem with its sight. Counting practice and match shooting, they probably average about 5,000 rounds per year, not much shooting by IPSC competition standards, but probably more than the average shooter uses in several years.

Even with all those kind words, I'll have to admit the factory sight won't hold up as well as some aftermarket sights, especially when worn by a competition gun that eats up 500 rounds or so of heavy Major-power loads each week. For resisting the pounding from no more than a few hundred rounds per month, the Elliason is plenty rugged. Replace the transverse factory roll pin with solid steel, wedge a chunk of shock buffer or rubber band between it and the slide to eliminate sight bounce, and it will last longer than the average shooter. On the other hand, if a gun is to be fed thousands of heavy loads each year, other options in sights are not a bad idea.

Adjustable vs. Semifixed Sights

As rear sights on custom Government Model pistols go, I still prefer what I always have on some guns, but have come full circle with others. I use to prefer a fully adjustable rear sight on all guns and still do if a gun is to be used with a lot of different loads of various power levels and bullet weights. On a carry gun, however, I have come to prefer the ruggedness, simplicity, and subtle beauty of a sight of fixed or more correctly described, semifixed, windage-adjustable only design. In fact, an adjustable sight with its many component parts makes me a bit nervous on a carry gun. I settle on one load, stick with it through high or low water, and never have a need for adjusting the sight. Many good sights are available and everybody has at least one opinion about everything, but I prefer that a install-it-myself carry gun wear the Wilson No. 61. On a custom carry gun, I would rather send my money to Richard Heinie for a set of his sights or to Wilson, Meprolight, or Trijicon for those illuminated with tritium.

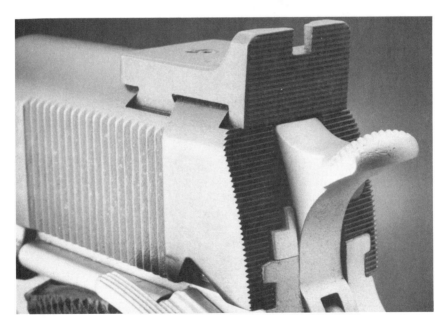

Steve Woods installation of a Heinie rear sight. *(Stephen Longley photo)*

261

If you decide on a windage-only adjustable rear sight and the pistolsmith who does the work is relatively close, you might consider the following. I had a custom Officer's ACP carry gun replete with Heinie sights built by Chuck Warner who lives up the road apiece from my home. When placing my order, I specified that I be allowed to zero the gun before it received any metal finishing. When it was ready to go, I arranged to meet Chuck and his trusty file at the range on a day when he would be there fine-tuning other customers' guns. As it turned out, the two factory loads I wanted to use in the gun were about four inches low at 25 yards. So, Chuck kept filing down the front sight and I kept feeding the little snub-nosed .45 the Remington and Cor-Bon 185-grain JHP +P loads until it began chewing out the center of the target. Only then did my Officer's ACP head out to Pat Connors for blueing and DuraChrome.

Some pistolsmiths will ship a custom gun to the customer before its final finish is applied and let him shoot it with the load to be used. The customer ships the gun along with targets shot back to the pistolsmith who compares bullet point of impact with line of sight and regulates the sights accordingly. The final finish is then applied and the gun shipped to the customer.

Steve Woods installation of a Novaks rear sight. *(Stephen Longley photo)*

What I have just described is a nice luxury to have, but is not an absolute necessity. If you have already decided what load will be used in the gun, most pistolsmiths will regulate its fixed sights accordingly. When having my first Wilson comp gun in .45 ACP built, I specified that its windage-adjustable rear and post front sights be regulated to print dead-on at 50 yards with a cast 185-grain semiwadcutter loaded to a power factor of 185. Precisely dead center at 50 yards is where the gun shot when I first got it and that is exactly where it shoots today. In fact, it will keep any bullet weighing from 180 to 230 grains in the A-zone of the USPSA/IPSC target out to 50 yards. I don't recall ever being able to honestly say that the lack of a fully adjustable sight on the gun has caused me to lose a match. Nor do I recall ever experiencing a single problem with the sight. To me, this is extremely important.

Bob Bailey double-tapping his Limited class gun.

12

Optical Sights and Mounts

OPTICAL sights have been used on Government Model pistols by bullseye shooters for many years, but practical pistol competitors stuck with open sights for decades for a couple of reasons. For one, the typical long eye-relief pistol scope used by the bullseye bunch is too heavy, its exit pupil is too small, and it doesn't have a large enough field of view for the thoroughbred race guns used in most action shooting games.

Then came relatively lightweight battery-powered red-dot sights with their large field of view and noncritical eye alignment, but action shooters didn't immediately go for them because most believed nothing was as fast as open sights for their sport. Jerry Barnhart turned a lot of heads, changed a lot of minds, and proved the majority wrong by winning the 1990 USPSA championship with a Tasco ProPoint riding atop his .38 Super. Doug Koenig fanned the blaze even higher by beating all comers in the world championship match as he watched the red dot bounce from target to target. Almost overnight everyone who loves equipment races either had an electronic sight on their comp gun, or wished the competition didn't. Then came more scope mount designs than fleas on a stray coon dog.

I'm sure we haven't seen the end of the electronic sight evolution for the shooting sports, but as I pen these lines, the Swedish-made Aimpoint 5000 Mag Dot and the Japanese-made Tasco PDP3BD ProPoint, both with 30mm tubes, are absolutely dominating the action shooting sports. The lighter and smaller Ultra Dot sight from Action Arms is popular among the bullseye bunch because they prefer to mount an electric sight directly to the slide. It is seldom used by action shooters because of its extremely narrow field of view. Other

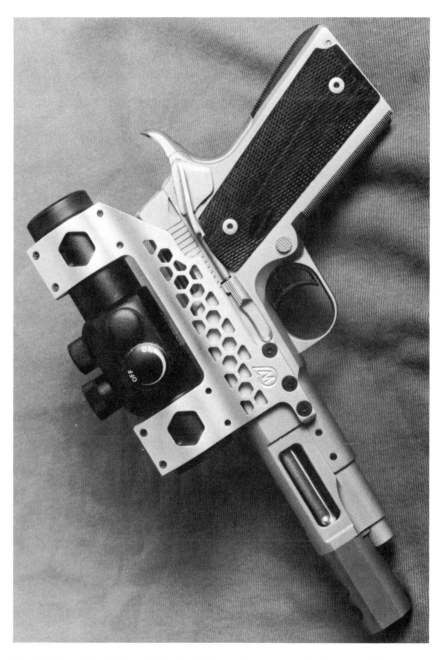

Jack Weigand's lightweight Stabalizer frame-attached mount has integral rings and extends far enough to the rear to eliminate the necessity of a thumbguard.

Electronic sights have improved considerably since Colt introduced this one.

Jerry Barnhart started the optical sight ball rolling among USPSA practical pistol competitors when he won the 1990 National Championship match. *(Front Sight photo)*

red-dot sights are available, but those three are preferred by the majority of shooters. Most Unlimited class practical pistol competitors prefer the optional big-dot on the Aimpoint and ProPoint as it subtends five to six inches at 50 yards and is fast to pick up by the eye.

Nominal weight of the three sights is 6.0 ounces for the Aimpoint and ProPoint, and four ounces for the Ultra Dot. The pairs of rings that come with them weigh 2 to 2.5 ounces. Depending on the design, mounts weigh anywhere from just under 2 to over 5 ounces.

The Bushnell Trophy illuminated sight is a good one for hunting and some competitive shooting, but as this is written most practical pistol shooters are waiting for it to become available with a fat-dot option. Its red dot subtends one-half inch at 50 yards, which is considerably smaller than those in the action shooting sports prefer. The Trophy has a 30mm tube, weighs around 6 ounces and is slightly over 5½ inches long. A fat-dot option would make it as popular in the action shooting games as the Aimpoint and ProPoint.

As Unlimited class practical pistol competition goes, the electronic sight offers far more advantages than disadvantages. The added weight makes a

Doug Koenig gave the optical sight ball another swift kick by becoming the 1990 International IPSC champ. *(Front Sight photo)*

Steve Woods gun with his Competitor scope mounts and Aimpoint optical sight. *(Stephen Longley photo)*

Built by Neil Wiggans, this compensated gun has a Wilson frame-attached scope mount.

Once the Bushnell Trophy becomes available with a fat-dot option, it should become popular among practical pistol competitors.

gun a bit more sluggish, meaning it doesn't spring from the holster in a flash nor does it handle as quickly as an iron-sighted gun, but once you get it rolling along, it is much faster when engaging multiple targets. Rather than dividing your concentration between front to rear sight alignment and front sight to target alignment, you simply plaster the red dot where you want the bullet to go and squeeze the trigger. The electronic sight has proven to be a godsend for older eyes that have lost their ability to focus on close objects—for example, the front sight on a pistol. I know older shooters who hung up their competition guns due to arms becoming a bit short and are now back in the heat of battle thanks to the electronic sight.

Back in the 1920s and 1930s when telescopic sights on rifles were still a relatively new idea, many hunters didn't trust them. Dozens of quick-detachable scope mounts were introduced so the glass sight could be removed and backup iron sights used in case something inside the gizmo suddenly went haywire. Today, many hunting rifles wear only a scope and some don't even come from the factory with open sights.

The electronic sight story has been about the same. A lot of shooters simply didn't trust them. Some of the distrust was justified. During the first couple of years the Aimpoint and ProPoint sights were used in competition, quite

Frank Garcia shooting a stage with his optical-sighted .38 super.

a few failed. There were two problems. For one, it took pistolsmiths a while to figure out how to make the Government Model eject spent cases to the right rather than up into the body of the scope. A steady beating by ejected cases caused some scopes to bite the dust. Secondly, scope makers had to relearn something they had previously learned when scopes that withstood the punishment dished out by the most powerful centerfire elephant rifles bit the dust when installed on a mild-mannered air rifle that generated about as much recoil as a chipmunk's sneeze. Like the spring-powered air rifle, an autoloading pistol subjects a scope to a double-whammy type of recoil shock. Once the scope manufacturers put two and two together, the failure rate of electronic sights greatly improved. Aimpoint beefed up its scope's tube and made improvements inside to electrical components to prevent them from breaking loose from their moorings.

Something else that had to be figured out was how to keep a compensator from spraying the objective lens of an optical sight with powder fouling and cast bullet spray. It is not as bad with a mount that positions the scope as far to the rear as possible, especially on a gun with a standard-length slide. Combine a short-slide gun with a forward-positioning mount and it will drive you crazy. I believe it is best for the scope's objective lens to be no closer than two inches from the rear port of the compensator and the farther away the better. On my gun with a Pegram ICBM mount, the objective lens of its ProPoint PDP3BD (with front extension tube) is four inches back of the rear gas port. If I attached an Aimpoint 5000 to the gun with the same mount, its front lens would still be just over 2 inches back of the port.

Pistolsmiths went a long way toward solving the problem by designing new compensators with the rear gas port located farther forward. Richard Heinie's Double-A comp was one of the first designed specifically for optical-sighted guns. Other excellent designs for glass guns include Steve Woods' Third Generation, and Chuck Warner's TCP (Triple Chamber Progressive). Some say a compensator that diverts the gas a bit forward at about 45 degrees is the solution, but I have not found this to be true. The critical question here is not how the expansion chambers, deflector plates, and ports are shaped, but how close the rear port is to the scope's objective end.

How important is the electronic sight on a competition gun? I can't speak for everyone, but I do know the two things that quickly moved me up a notch in USPSA classification. One was switching from the .45 ACP to the .38 Super. The other was having a red-dot sight installed on the .38 Super. The Super made me faster and the bouncing dot made me more accurate.

There always will be those who say the electronic sight takes the practical from practical pistol competition, but they tend to overlook the fact that what was practical yesterday may not be today and what is practical today may not be tomorrow. From a practical point of view, the electronic sight may be a good idea for police work. Think about the hundreds of rookies who have never held a gun in their hand before joining the force. One of the more difficult things for them to learn is the importance of a correct sight picture. An electronic sight would enable them to learn more quickly because all they have to do is plaster that red dot on the target and squeeze the trigger. They probably would be able to shoot more accurately, too. Which is worse, a cop who can't hit the target with a "practical" gun, or a cop who can with an "impractical" gun? If this sounds far-fetched, consider the following.

During days of yesteryear, the revolver was the lawman's sidearm of choice, and many practical-minded folks predicted that the autoloader would never replace the wheelgun as it has done today. Some say the compensated barrel is less than practical, but at least one major law enforcement agency is toying with the idea for certain tactical applications and others are taking a serious look at it. The twenty-first century lawman may be toting a compensated autoloader with a sight that contains a computer chip-size battery pack with a tiny solar panel. The sight might even be controlled by some type of magnetic switch that turns it on when the gun is drawn from its holster. The sight might be about the size of a pencil, but twenty-first century optical wizardry would give it a wider field of view than the scopes with their big 30mm tubes used by old-timers like Barnhart and Koenig back in the twentieth century. The gun might even come from the factory with an electronic sight as an integral part of its slide. Who can say for certain what will or will not be practical? All we know for certain is what was practical yesterday.

Quick-Detach Mounts

Three different designs of mounts are available for attaching an optical sight to the Government Model pistol. One is the quick-install, quick-detach type that requires no modification to the pistol. This style is quite popular but it has three shortcomings. It lacks the rigidity of other mounts, has more tendency to vibrate loose, and, if not carefully installed, can scratch a gun's finish.

Grip-Attached Mounts

Then we have the grip-replacement type. A few bullseye shooters still use this type and it does have its advantages. It is relatively inexpensive, easily installed, easily removed, and requires no permanent modification of the gun. This one also has a couple of disadvantages. It replaces one of the grip panels

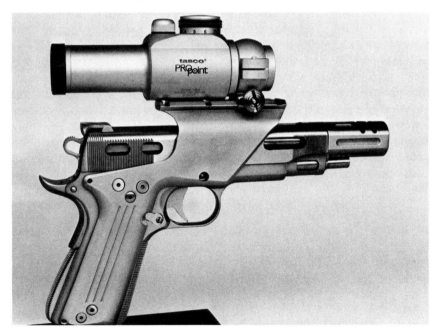

This lightened Bob Cogan gun has an Aimtech mount that replaces the righthand grip panel. Note the pivoting trigger.

(some shooters don't like the feel of a gun with checkered wood on one side and aluminum on the other). Checkering the metal panel helps some. This type of mount positions the sight much higher above the centerline of the bore than most frame-attached mounts. That's OK for hunting, but bullseye shooters don't like a high-mount scope because the increase in surface area makes the gun more difficult to hold steady in a strong sidewind. Most practical pistol competitors also want the optical sight as low as possible.

The grip-replacement type of mount definitely fills an important niche in the scheme of things. Take my switch-top gun, for example. If I decide to head into the swamp for a bit of wild boar hunting, I can easily attach a 1x or 2x pistol scope, install either the 5-inch Bar-Sto or the 5½-inch compensated barrel in 10mm Auto and be all set for that application. By replacing the scope with an Aimpoint red-dot sight, I'm equipped for casual practical pistol competition. If I decide to press the 10mm into service as a carry gun, the 5-inch barrel is installed and the mount removed entirely.

Frame-Attached Mounts

This type of mount is by far the most popular for Unlimited class practical pistol competition and bullseye shooters are beginning to adopt it. As a rule, it is lighter and more rigid than the grip-attached type. Some designs also position the optical sight extremely low and as close as possible to the bore. This is important on a competition gun for several reasons. For one, it makes the gun handle and feel better than when the sight is mounted extremely high. Most shooters who make the transition from open sights also will find a low-mounted scope easier to learn to use. Some courses of fire require a competitor to shoot through a narrow horizontal slot in a barricade or other obstacle. When the line of sight is considerably higher than bullet path, as is the case with a high-mounted scope, the possibility of the bullet striking the bottom edge of the shooting port is good.

The frame-attached mount requires drilling and tapping holes in the frame and has become so popular that Caspian and Springfield Armory's Custom Shop offer it as a factory-performed, extra-cost option. The mere thought of those extra holes in the frame absolutely horrifies some pistol owners. I agree if the topic of conversation is a custom gun used for several purposes, but on one used for nothing but Unlimited class practical pistol competition, it is the only way to go. On that type of gun the optical sight is never removed unless it breaks, so the extra holes beneath the base of the mount don't matter. In fact, most custom optical-sighted competition guns being built today don't even have open sights. The same could be said of a gun used strictly for hunting.

Built by Chuck Warner, this high-capacity Caspian in .38 Super has Jack Weigand's frame-attached mount holding a fat-dot Aimpoint.

Steve Wood's Competitor frame-attached mount holds an Aimpoint optical sight on this C. W. Custom Para-Ordnance in .38 Super.

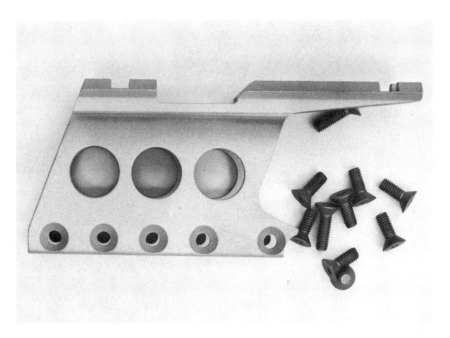

The Wilson mount attaches to both sides of the frame with 10 screws.

Most of the better mounts I have seen are milled from aircraft-grade aluminum stock. A few are made of other materials such as steel, magnesium, titanium, and carbon fiber. Designs vary considerably. As examples, the Pegram ICBM and Woods Competitor mounts attach to one side of the frame, while the Wilson, Weigand, and Caspian attach to both sides. Some mounts have an integral ring (or rings) for holding the optical sight, while others utilize separate rings. The Weigand integral ring-type Stabilizer and Wilson No. 320 with its separate rings support the front and rear tubes of the scope while some of the others grasp the front tube only.

Which design is best? I'm really not sure, but I do like to see a mount attach back at the thick area of the frame rather than out on the thin wall of the recoil spring shroud. The shroud or dust-cover-attached mounts are OK if a narrow steel plate is soldered to the frame to add more beef in that area, but it is a costly operation. I have the most experience with the mounts available from Dave Pegram and Steve Woods. They attach to the thick part of the frame on the righthand side. I have yet to have an Aimpoint sight fail in either. One manufacturer of red dot sights is convinced that when both the front and rear tubes of a scope are supported by the mount, it is subjected to considerably less stress than when held by the front tube only. This sounds logical and may be true, but I believe being hammered by cases ejected from

Competition guns built by Springfield Armory's Custom Shop are available with the frame already drilled and tapped for scope mounting.

This frame came from Caspian with the optional holes drilled and tapped for Jack Weigand's Stabilizer scope mounts. Two holes not used at front are filled with headless screws.

an improperly tuned gun has caused more scopes to bite the dust than mount design.

When all factors, including cost, are considered, the Weigand Stabilizer, the Woods Competitor, and the Pegram ICBM are among the very best designs in frame-attached mounts for competition guns. They are extremely rigid, have integral rings, position the scope low and to the rear, attach to the side (or sides) of the frame just forward of the slide catch, and they are relatively light. If the scope will be detached and reattached often, the Wilson No. 320 with its separate rings is tough to beat.

Choosing between the designs with separate or integral rings boils down to how often the sight will be removed and how close you want it to the top of the slide. If the installation is more or less permanent (as on a competition gun), I believe integral rings are the better idea. As a rule, the integral ring-type is lighter and positions the sight lower on the gun. The bottom surface of the scope on my Warner .38 Super with the ICBM mount is .035 inch from the top of the slide, about the diameter of wire used in making standard-size paper clips. Probably the safest bet is to throw the ball into your pistolsmith's court and let him decide which mount is best for you, your gun, and its intended application.

Richard Heinie's .38 Super compensated gun wears a Tasco Pro-Point attached with a CPMI mount. Note the grasping handle at the rear of the slide.

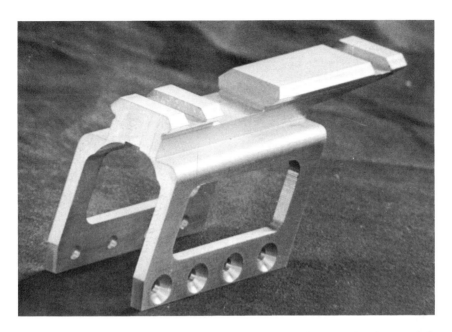

This Caspian aluminum mount attaches to both sides of the frame and has separate rings for holding the scope.

Installing a frame-attached mount requires a lot more skill than simply drilling and tapping holes in the frame. If it is not mounted at about a one degree angle, you may run out of elevation adjustment on your red-dot sight before reaching zero. In addition, the Government Model pistol was not designed for wearing a scope and a considerable amount of skill is required on the part of the pistolsmith to tune the gun for the reliable ejection of spent cases. The lower the scope, the tougher is the tuning job. The ejection port on most guns also will have to be lowered. Opinions vary on the correct dimension from the outer edge of the port to the bottom of the slide, but one pistolsmith says .400 inch for his mount.

Keep It Legal

Most pistolsmiths know it is illegal to alter or obliterate the serial number of a gun and any gun so modified is subject to seizure by BATF agents. Since Government Model pistols made by most companies have the serial number on their frames, it would be awfully easy for someone who is not aware of this particular law to innocently drill and tap holes where they should not go. The possibility of doing so is not as great with a Caspian frame as its serial number is located high up on the side. The number is located quite

Built by Don Fraley, this .38 Super comp gun wears a Red Buff mount with integral scope rings.

Dave Pegram's ICBM scope mount on a .38 Super Warner Signature Grade Caspian in an Ernie Hill Fas-Trac holster.

low on a Colt frame. As I said before, most pistolsmiths know this is a no-no, but to be on the safe side it doesn't hurt to mention it when having the job done.

Now for the Criticisms

The very worst thing I can think of to say about mounting an electronic sight low on the Government Model pistol is it usually makes the gun more load sensitive. While wearing open sights, my old .38 Super would gobble up and spit out any Major load I decided to feed it. After the glass sight was installed it became a bit more choosy. Before, it worked great with any bullet from 125 to 180 grains in Major power loads. Now, it doesn't care for extremes in bullet weight and sings a happier tune with those ranging from 145 to 160 grains. It's probably best to have the pistolsmith ejection-tune an optical-sighted gun for one particular load and then stick with it through thick and thin.

Keeping the extractor tuned also is extremely popular. The extractor of an open-sighted gun has to lose a lot of its original tension before the clean ejection of spent cases is affected. Not so with an optical-sighted gun. If its extractor loses four or five pounds of tension, ejected cases may start colliding with the bottom of the scope and bouncing back inside to tie up the gun. I have devoted a few more words to this subject in Chapter 19.

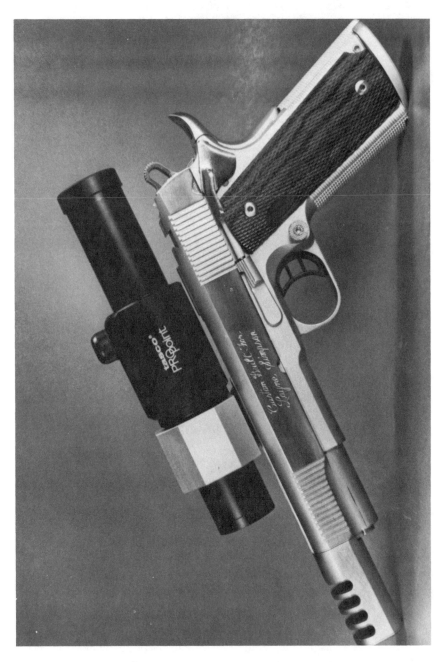

Attached to the righthand side of the frame, this Pegram ICBM frame-attached mount on a C. W. Custom .38 Super positions the scope extremely low and close to the top of the slide.

You can stack this one over in the nitpicking basket if you like, but I would like to see the ProPoint and Ultra Dot sights come up with a more uniformly round red dot. Their irregular-shaped dot seems to disrupt my concentration more than the nice round dot in the Aimpoint sight.

Except for those minor complaints, I consider battery-powered sights the best thing to happen to practical pistol competition since the .38 Super.

13

Magazines

POOR gun maintenance, junk handloads, and cheap or damaged magazines cause more malfunctions in Government Model pistols than all other factors combined. In theory, the bargain magazine exists, but in real life it does not. Since firearm reliability is the number one priority, the best magazines money can buy are dirt cheap at any price. This especially holds true if the gun is to be used for self defense. Not having tried them all I won't say which brands are good or bad, but I will say this, nobody subjects magazines to anywhere near as many miles of torture as practical pistol competitors and you'll seldom see them use any except the Wilson and Shooting Star.

The Custom-Tuned Magazine

Some guns are more magazine sensitive than others. One of my .38 Super comp guns will feed cartridges reliably from any magazine of that caliber I own. Another comp gun of the same caliber is reliable only with the magazines that were tuned especially for it by the pistolsmith who built the gun. One of my switch-top guns never complains about the magazine it gobbles up cartridges from when wearing its 10mm top assembly. When I switch to the .45 ACP, the same gun will feed reliably only from the magazines that belong to it and it alone. Some of the best money you can spend on a custom gun is to have the pistolsmith include several fine-tuned magazines in the package. Incidentally, some gunsmiths include a set of tuned magazines with their higher custom packages. If, for example, you order a Wilson Super Grade, or a C. W. Custom Signature Grade, six magazines accompany the gun.

Wilson No. 116 Tactical Special.

To illustrate how a properly tuned gun and its magazines are supposed to function, I'll tell you about a little exercise I once subjected a Wilson Super Grade in .38 Super to. The gun came with six tuned Wilson 10-round magazines. I picked a magazine at random and filled it with five loaded rounds and five fired cases in a staggered fashion, starting with a fired case at the bottom of the stack and ending with a loaded round on top. Then I inserted the loaded magazine in the Super Grade, manually chambered the top round, and squeezed the trigger. The gun went bang and chambered the fired case next in line as smoothly as grease on glass. I then manually ejected the fired case and repeated the sequence until the magazine was empty. Not once did the gun refuse to feed a fired case.

Blued vs. Stainless Steel

A stainless steel magazine costs a bit more than blued steel, but it is worth ever penny. When magazines are used in summertime competition they often are handled by sweaty hands that can cause the blued steel version to rust before you return home from a match. The same thing can happen while they are worn concealed against the human body. The next best thing to a stainless magazine is the standard version with its blued finish replaced

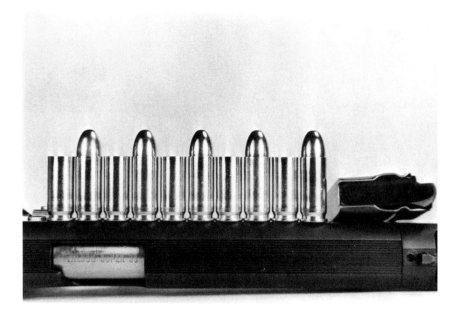

When the tuned magazines of this Wilson Super Grade in .38 Super are loaded alternately with fired cases and loaded rounds, it feeds them all without missing a lick.

with hard chrome. The chrome is applied inside and out and usually makes the magazine slide in and out of the gun more smoothly because of the slicker finish.

Increased-Capacity Magazines

Wilson and Shooting Star magazines are available with standard or Plus 1 capacities, the latter holding eight .45 ACP, nine 10mm Auto or .40 S&W, or 10 .38 Super or 9x23mm cartridges. Spring and follower kits are also available for installation in other magazines. The kit made for the Colt Officer's ACP magazine increases its capacity to seven rounds.

Extra-capacity magazines are nice to have, but whether or not they are worth the extra cost depends on their proposed use. For the action shooting games they do have advantages. I once kept computerized records of every match I shot during a 12-month period with various guns in .38 Super, 10mm Auto, and .45 ACP. Extra capacity magazines saved time-consuming reloads in close to 20 percent of the stages I fired. When shooting all other stages, standard-capacity magazines would have held all the firepower needed.

Some shooters buy extra-capacity magazines and load them to the gills only when shooting stages in which the extra round offers an advantage. On other stages, they load the magazines to one cartridge less than full capacity or use the standard-capacity variety. It sounds like a good plan, but it causes me to miss reloads. Due to the higher tension placed on its follower spring when the additional round is squeezed into an extra-capacity magazine, considerably more force is required to seat it deeply enough into the pistol for its notch to engage the latch. If you become accustomed to pushing home standard-capacity magazines and then switch to a Plus 1 type during a quick reload, chances are you won't slam it home hard enough to lock it into place. The result is one round on the target and the rest lying at your feet.

The increased spring tension in extra-capacity magazines can also give some pistols a touch of indigestion. Guns that smoothly feed ammunition with jacketed hollowpoint or semiwadcutter bullets from standard-capacity magazines often won't feed the top round from a fully loaded, extra-capacity magazine. This most often happens when the first round is chambered manually, but also can plague the shooter when the gun attempts to feed the top round during its firing cycle. If a gun won't feed the top cartridge, a quick fix is to switch entirely to roundnose bullets or top off each magazine with a cartridge loaded with a roundnose bullet.

I say this not to condemn extra-capacity magazines, but to point out that they can be more temperamental than the standard type. I like them and use them exclusively in my carry and competition guns. Even though I don't always need the extra round in competition, it is handy to have when I do need it.

When buying magazines, make sure they can be returned unused if they aren't compatible with your gun. Due to the tolerance ranges within which manufacturers work, some magazines aren't suitable for use in various guns. This applies to those from different manufacturers as well as those of different lots from the same manufacturer. Combine a maximum-dimension magazine with a minimum-dimension well in a gun and you have got a magazine that won't eject freely. When receiving a batch of new magazines, it is best to insert each into the gun to make sure they drop freely when you hit the release button.

Before heading to the range and transforming unused magazines that can be returned for exchange into used ones that can't be, you should make sure each of them will lock back the slide of the gun when empty. To perform this test, insert each magazine into the gun and fully retract its slide. If the slide stays back, the magazine has passed test Number 2. If it doesn't, what you do next depends on the follower's material. If the follower is metal, a pistolsmith can adjust it so it will push the slide release into its locked position. If the follower is composed of a synthetic material, the manufacturer should replace it.

How Many Magazines?

For a carry gun, I like to have three tuned magazines, one for the gun and two in a belt pouch. On the majority of stages in most club-level practical pistol matches I have shot with a standard Government Model in .38 Super, five magazines were plenty, but occasionally I have needed as many as seven. When using high-capacity guns like the Caspian, McCormick, and Para-Ordnance, two magazines will get you through most stages even if a mandatory reload is required, but four is better.

If a magazine acts up during a match, a spare awaiting duty and already tuned for the gun can save the day. If the weather has been or still is bad during a match, you won't believe how much mud magazines will gather when dropped onto the ground during fast reloads. I have shot matches over sandy soil, and every magazine dropped to earth was filled with abrasive. If your squad is large, you usually will have time to disassemble and clean each magazine before firing the next stage. If not, your only alternatives are to feed your custom gun ammunition from filthy magazines, drop out of the match, or have plenty of spares in your range bag. Truth is, the practical pistol competitor really can't have too many magazines, which isn't good news as quality doesn't come cheap.

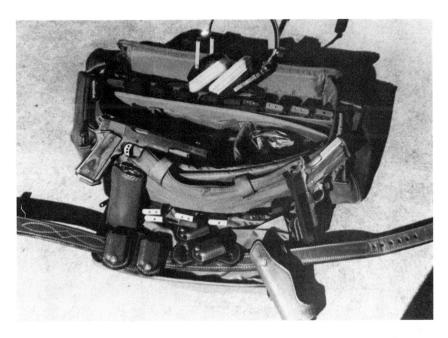

A practical pistol competitor simply can't have too many magazines.

Magazines for competition guns should be consecutively numbered and have your name or initials on them. If one malfunctions during a match, it is easier to remember which one it was if they all have different numbers. An indelible pen used to write on slick surfaces such as photographs works fine and is available at camera supply shops. The identification marks will have to be freshened occasionaly as they tend to wear away as the magazines are used. This is why an electric pencil is an even better way to do it.

If you shoot in practical pistol matches, it also is a good idea to eventually accumulate two sets of magazines for your gun. One set is subjected to steady use during practice and the other is reserved for matches only.

Magazine Bumpers

You have only to experience an interruption of concentration by the pain that comes from pinching the skin on the palm of your hand during a fast reload to fully appreciate why all magazines should have extensions or bumpers attached to the floorplate. They are available in two thicknesses, thin for guns without a magazine well funnel, and thick for those with it. In competition, magazine bumpers can cut fractions of a second from speed reloads. A fraction gained here, another gained there, and before you know it, you have

Practical pistol competitors are rough on magazines.

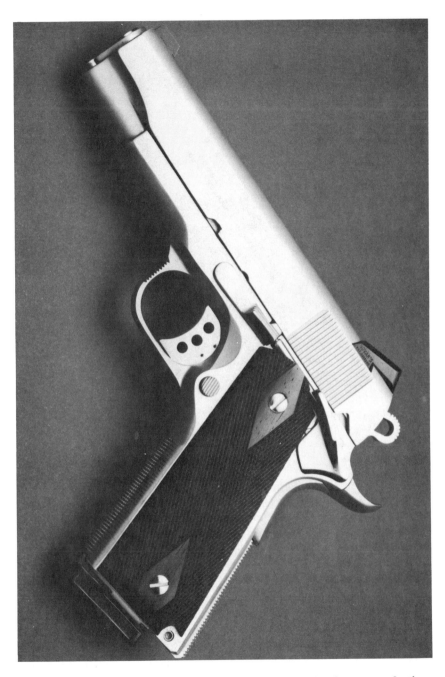

The magazine in this Dave Lauck custom Commander has a synthetic bumper. *(Mike McCoy photo)*

293

This view of a C. W. Custom gun illustrates why a magazine used in a gun wearing a magazine well funnel must have a bumper attached to its floorplate.

won a match. Some magazines come with a bumper already attached, while others will need an aftermarket bumper installed. Forget about the glue-on type; nothing less than metal screws can be depended on to hold a magazine bumper in place.

Many of the better magazine bumpers are made of tough, impact-resistant synthetic materials and will last about as long as the gun or shooter. Some also are made of aluminum. Bumpers machined from solid brass or aluminum for Government Model, Para-Ordnance, Glock, Springfield Armory P-9 (and other CZ clones), SIG, Berretta, Browning Hi-Power, and Taurus magazines are available from B.A.T., Glades Gunworks, and C. W. Custom. The brass bumpers are relatively heavy and come with advantages as well as disadvantages. On the positive side, with the extra weight at the bottom end of an empty magazine, it has more of a tendency to land base down in the dirt or mud when it is ejected from the gun during competition. On the negative side, if the magazine lands mouth first anyhow, the extra weight of the bumper tends to drive more dirt and debris into its innards. Brass bumpers add more weight to a gun than some shooters want. Attach a brass bumper to a fully loaded Para-Ordnance magazine and you're holding a lot of weight in your hand.

For those shooters who want to add an extra touch of class to a custom gun, C. W. Custom takes the brass bumper idea one step farther. They are available with a finger groove milled into each side or hand checkered 20 lines per inch. Personalized versions come with the owner's name, initials, consecutively numbered, or a combination thereof. You might say these are for those who have everything.

The Officer's ACP Magazine

Earlier I mentioned the availability of spring and follower kits that increase the capacity of the Officer's ACP magazine by one round. I know one lawman who carried this little gun with its standard magazine and two nine-round Government Model magazines in his belt pouch. Or at least he did until I pointed out what could possibly happen. The long magazine will work in the short gun, but depending on the combination it could prove to be a fatal mistake. When the extra long magazine is shoved home in some guns, its catch notch will slip over the magazine catch and end up with its feed lips blocking the path of the slide. This won't happen when the slide is forward, but if the gun is shot to slide lock and the long magazine shoved home, it can tie up the gun. The best and safest bet for the Officer's ACP is three Plus 1 magazines, one in the gun, and two in a belt pouch. That adds up to 21 rounds which represents a lot of firepower from such a small gun.

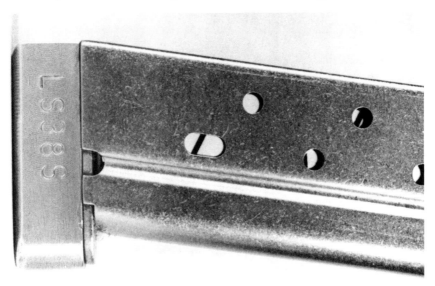

The C. W. Custom brass bumper on this magazine has the owner's initials and the caliber.

With its Plus 1 kit, the magazine of this Colt Officer's ACP Tactical special built by Wilson's holds seven rounds.

Magazine Springs

The standard weight for the factory Government Model magazine spring is 9½ pounds. This is a good compromise, but when fed extremely light loads, some bullseye guns feed more smoothly and more dependably with a lighter spring. Wolff reduced-power springs are available with six-, seven-, and eight-pound ratings. At the extreme opposite end of the power range, some bowling pin shooters feed their guns loads that are so heavy a bullseye shooter is inclined to dig a foxhole when within 100 yards of them. Some of those guns feed more reliably with an extra-power spring with a rating of 10 or 11 pounds. Those weights also are available from Wolff.

Magazines and Turtle Wax

A blued steel magazine will rust both inside and outside, but if it is protected by a film of oil, dust and grit from miles around will flock to it. The best way to protect blued steel from rusting (yet not attract dirt) is to apply several coats of paste wax, the type made for putting a shine on automobiles. Turtle Wax is a good choice. Rub on a thin coat, let it dry, and buff it just as you do your Jaguar. Three or four coats will last a long time and the magazine won't rust. It also makes the magazine glide into the gun like grease on glass. The protective coating won't last as long on magazines used in competition, but one wax job will last for many months on a carry gun's magazines.

If the feed lips on a magazine become dinged or bent, a gun may refuse to feed cartridges from it. Unless the magazine is completely worn out, a good pistolsmith can restore it to working order for considerably less than the cost of a replacement.

14

About Those Coil Springs

I NEVER cease to be amazed at the number of Government Model owners who are unaware of the fact that certain springs are not meant to last the gun's lifetime. As a result, literally hundreds of frames and slides have been battered, cracked, and otherwise rendered worthless long before their time was up. The truth of the matter is, the manufacturers are more to blame than shooters since not a single one mentions replacement of springs in their owner's manuals. This was fine a few decades ago when most pistols were fed a box or two of factory ammo each year, but a lot of Government Models are now digesting as many rounds in a month as was common during the lifetime of the typical shooter of yesteryear. Hopefully, this chapter will help to educate pistol owners and manufacturers of the importance of spring replacement.

Two basic types of springs are available. First we have the constant-rate spring. Its coils are spaced the same distance apart and for this reason its storage of energy increases constantly along its full length of compression. For example, if a constant-rate spring stores one pound of energy during its first ¼ inch of compression, it will store the same amount of additional energy for each additional ¼ inch of compression. At close to full compression, the spring will have stored its rated amount of energy.

Then we have the variable-power spring, also called variable- or progressive-rate. Introduced by the Wolff company of Newtown, Pennsylvania, this type begins with a wide spacing between its coils on one end and the spacing becomes closer along its length. Consequently, the amount of energy stored varies along its line of compression. For example, if a variable-power spring

C. W. Custom Combat Gold Cup.

The coils on the righthand end of this Wolff variable-power recoil spring are closer together than those on the lefthand end.

stores, say, ¾ pound of energy during its first ¼ inch of compression, it might store an additional pound during the next ¼ inch, two pounds during the next, three pounds during the next, and so forth. During its final ¼ inch of compression it might store an additional four pounds of energy. The ratio of coil spacing determines how the storage rate of energy progresses as the spring is compressed.

The variable-power spring is a bit more expensive, but well worth it. Continuing with hypothetical examples, let's say we have two identical Government Model pistols with 18½-pound recoil springs. The slide on the gun with the variable-rate spring will be easier to retract because less muscle is required to set it in motion. Yet, when the slides of both guns are fully retracted, the same amount of energy required to propel them forward is stored in the two types of springs. Install a variable-power mainspring in the gun and the slide becomes even easier to retract when the hammer is down because the amount of force required to cock the hammer is less than with a constant-rate spring. All of this can be especially important to those who find the slide of an autoloader difficult to retract. My wife is a good example when she attempts to quickly rack back the slide on a Officer's ACP with a 24-pound recoil spring.

A variable-rate recoil spring also makes an autoloader more tolerant of variations in ammunition because it will function with lighter loads than if a constant-rate spring of the same energy rating is used. In other words, the variable-rate spring resists recoil the same as the constant-rate spring with heavy loads, but it will allow the gun to function as well with loads that are too light for the gun to function with a constant-rate spring.

The variable-rate spring probably is a bit easier on a gun. During the Government Model's firing cycle, the recoil spring must exert a great deal of energy or push on the slide in order for it to gain enough momentum to allow it to strip a cartridge from the magazine and ram it into the chamber. Once the nose of a cartridge bounces off the feedramp and the cartridge becomes aligned with the chamber, very little energy is required to shove it on home and to push the barrel into battery. A constant-rate spring applies the same amount of force to the slide from start to stop. This is why it slams all the way home with considerable force. In contrast, the variable-rate spring initially pushes on the slide with the same amount of force during cartridge feeding, but as it begins to regain its relaxed position, less force is exerted. Consequently, the slide returns home a bit more gently.

It might be of interest to note that manufacturers rate springs at the degree they will be compressed in a particular application rather than at full compression. When the slide of the Government Model is fully retracted, the recoil spring is compressed by about 1⅝ inches and it is at that degree of compression that the spring is rated. Considering it from another perspective, when a 10-pound spring is compressed 1⅝ inches, it has stored 10 pounds of energy, but is capable of storing a few more pounds when fully compressed.

The amount of energy actually stored by a cheap, bargain-basement spring can vary considerably from its factory rating. If the label on the package reads "18½ pounds," the amount of stored energy may vary by 10 percent or more. Top-quality springs (e.g., those made by Wolff and available from Wilson, Kings, and others) are held to a tolerance of 4 ounces with the error usually on the heavier side. If Wolff rates a particular spring at 10 pounds, it may store anywhere from 9¾ to 10 pounds of energy, but is more likely to be in the 10- to 10¼-pound range. This is well within a comfortable tolerance range for the Government Model pistol as a mere 4 ounces of variation in recoil spring weight will have no effect on its functioning, unless the spring initially is bordering on being too heavy for a particular job.

The Recoil Spring

All springs in the Government Model are required for proper functioning, but the recoil spring is the life of the gun. If its weight is too light for the

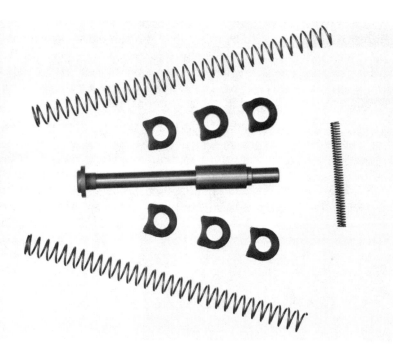

This Wilson kit comes with two recoil springs and a full-length guide, recoil shock buffers, and a firing pin spring.

load used, the slide may pound the frame until eventually it cracks. At the very least, the rear of the recoil spring tunnel of the slide will become battered. This peening of its rear entry can eventually turn its mouth inward thereby causing it to grab a coil of the recoil spring during the firing cycle. When that happens, malfunctions are likely to be the rule rather than the exception. A shock buffer (described in another chapter) will offer some protection from damage caused by an underpowered spring, but it won't last very long.

Some shooters are under the false impression that even if a recoil spring is lighter than it should be for a particular load, everything is fine and dandy. This simply isn't true. When the recoil spring is too light, its energy may be insufficient to shove the slide forward with enough force to strip a cartridge from the magazine and push it into the chamber. An underpowered spring can allow the gun to unlock a bit too early and drag the tip of the firing pin across the face of the primer of a spent case. Eventually, this can lead to a broken firing pin. Under a worst-case condition (e.g., when an excessive load is used in a barrel with an excessively throated chamber), a weak spring can result in a blown case.

If the recoil spring is too heavy for a particular load, it exerts an excessive amount of tension on the slide, causing a short-stroke malfunction during the firing cycle. In other words, the spring won't allow the slide to travel rearward far enough to pick up a cartridge from the magazine on its return trip.

Conversely, some shooters believe the absolute heaviest recoil spring that will allow the gun to function should be used. A friend of mine prefers to use a 24-pounder in .45 caliber Government Model pistols as opposed to the commonly recommended maximums of 16 to 18½ pounds for that gun and caliber. I see potential problems with such a practice. First, when a compressed spring unleashes that much energy on the slide, it travels forward at a higher velocity than is actually required for cartridge feeding and barrel lockup. The violent impact can destroy the extractor and an expensive custom trigger job in short order. It also can cause the firing pin in a pre-Series 80 gun to fly forward to fire the cartridge in the chamber. This especially holds true for those guns with firing pin springs weakened from age and/or lots of use.

Exceptions to the 18½-pound maximum for the standard Government Model are guns used in bowling pin competition. Since the pins have to be knocked completely off the table, many competitors use what are commonly called *killer loads* in their Government Model pistols. They are extremely powerful handloads, often with bullets heavier than 230 grains. Some of those loads require a recoil spring considerably heavier than 20 pounds. For obvious reasons, an extra-power firing pin spring is highly recommended for bowling pin guns.

Recommended recoil spring weight charts like the one in the Appendix have been floating around for many years, but they should be used only as a rough guide. The traditional spring rating for .45 ACP hardball loads in a 5-inch noncompensated barrel is 16 pounds, but a gun may leave the manufacturer with something considerably lighter installed. When factory personnel test-fire a gun prior to shipment, it is common for them to install whatever spring weight allows the gun to function properly. If a 16-pounder does the job, fine. If not, they try lighter springs until the gun works.

Every Government Model owner who shoots a variety of heavy and light loads in his gun should own a set of recoil springs with their ratings differing by about one pound. Wolff offers various Recoil Calibration Paks consisting of an entire set of springs at a savings of about 20 percent compared to buying them individually. A collection of weights ranging from eight to 25 pounds would cover every load you would ever want to use in a .45 caliber Government Model. If the calibration kit is for an Officer's ACP, a good range would be from 18½ to 24 pounds. A useful kit for the Commander would run from 12 to 20 pounds. Incidentally, one of the best modifications you can make

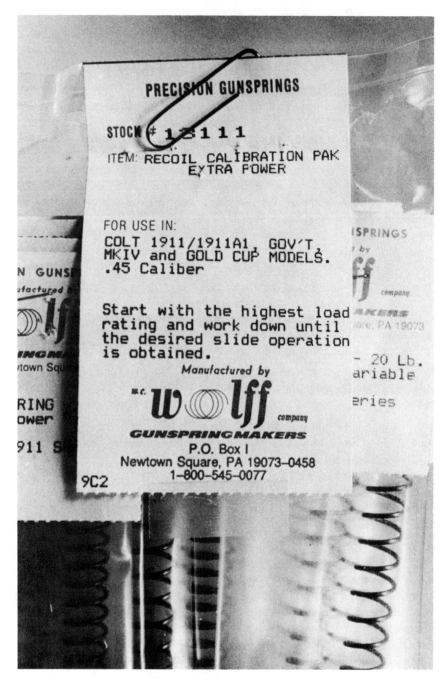

Wolff recoil spring calibration kit.

to the Officer's ACP and Delta Elite, whether it be a factory or custom gun, is the installation of a full length recoil spring guide and replacing the dual recoil spring setup with a single spring.

All springs in the calibration kit are reserved for no purpose other than to determine the correct weight for various loads. When one is installed in a gun, it immediately is replaced with a new one. If a spring is tried and found to be the wrong weight, it is returned to its factory packaging along with a label indicating its weight. It is not a bad idea to weigh each spring on a powder scale and list the weight in grains of each on an index card filed in the storage box with them. By doing so, you can easily identify each spring in case they do become mixed. Springs available from Kings Gun Works are color coded and come with a reference chart indicating the color assigned to each weight rating. It is a great idea.

Here is how the recoil spring kit works. Let's say you have just received your first new custom Government Model pistol in .45 ACP and intend to use it for three purposes. When the gun is serving security blanket duty at home (out of reach of children, of course), its magazine will stay full of Remington's powerful +P factory load with a 185-grain bullet at 1,140 fps. For those weekend USPSA/IPSC matches, you decide to handload a 185-grain cast bullet at an average of 975 fps. However, you also want to use the gun for close-range target practice with an even milder load. So you settle on the same cast bullet at about 750 fps.

What you have come up with are three loads with different requirements in recoil spring power. You have the entire spectrum covered because your recoil spring test kit consists of weights ranging from 10 to 20 pounds. The Remington factory load is the most powerful and for this reason it will require a stronger spring than the other two loads. Through a trial-and-error shooting and spring-switching session at the range, you determine that for your particular gun, an 18½ pound spring is perfect for that load. When fed the competition load, your gun won't function with such a heavy spring so by working downward in weight among your supply of springs you arrive at 15 pounds as ideal for it. Continuing on with the program, you end up at, say, a 12-pound spring for the target load.

If you arrived at the correct spring tension while shooting with a two-hand hold, run another 50 rounds or so through the gun while holding it with only the strong hand. Then do the same thing with only the weak hand. Firing with one hand does not place as much recoil resistance behind the gun and if the chosen spring weight borders on being too heavy, the gun may not function reliably unless held firmly with both hands. By the same token, if the gun functions reliably with a particular spring weight in your hands, it may not in the hands of your wife as most women don't offer as much resistance to recoil as the average man.

Kings' recoil springs are color coded.

306

A machine rest like the Ransom resists recoil more than when a gun is hand-held. Consequently, if a spring weight is chosen while shooting a gun in the rest, it may be too heavy to allow it to function reliably even with a solid two-hand hold. Looking at the same thing, but from the opposite direction, the correct spring weight for a hand-fired gun is too light for use in the Ransom Rest. I know of one gun that was pounded to death by about a thousand heavy loads because its owner was not aware of this. As a rule, a two-pound heavier spring should be installed in the gun if it is fired a great deal in the Ransom Rest.

It is important to remember that an autoloader often requires a lighter recoil spring when new than after it has been loosened up a bit with the firing of a thousand rounds or so. The second comp gun I had built in .38 Super would not function initially with a spring heavier than 9 pounds with 150-grain bullets loaded to Major velocity. After digesting about 2,000 rounds, it asked for a 10-pound spring. At the 5,000 round mark I had worked up to a 12-pounder and it remains the correct weight for that gun.

A change in bullet weight can require a change in recoil spring weight. My .38 Super optical-sighted gun uses a 12-pound spring with 147- and 150-grain bullets, but if I switch to Major power loads with 125-, 130-, or 135-grain bullets, the correct spring weight is either nine or 10 pounds, depending on the particular load. A change in slide weight also can require switching to a different recoil spring weight. If one of the red-dot electronic sights is installed on the slide of a wadcutter gun used in bullseye competition, the weight of its spring will have to be reduced by two to three pounds.

Different shooters have their favorite way of determining the correct spring weight for a particular load. Some replace the spring when it is pounded two coils shorter than its original length. The observation of case ejection during firing is another popular method. If ejected cases dribble out the ejection port and land at your feet, the spring is too heavy. If the cases land over six or eight feet away, the spring is too light. I prefer to take it one step farther by keeping an eye on the recoil buffer. If the gun is functioning perfectly and the slide has pounded the buffer to submission in less than 500 rounds, I gradually ease upward on spring weight in one-pound increments until the slide is only lightly kissing the buffer during each firing cycle. By closely examining the condition of the buffer each time the gun is field stripped for cleaning, I also can determine when the spring has lost enough of its original tension to require replacement.

It is a good idea to write down the correct spring weight for each load used in a particular gun. I have a shooter's log or diary with a section devoted to each of my autoloaders and it constantly reminds me what goes where.

Incidentally, when the correct recoil spring weight is combined with an extractor and ejector tuned by a pistolsmith who really knows his stuff, a gun will spit fired cases in a small pile rather than scattering them all over the landscape.

The Firing Pin Spring

If a Government Model or one of its variations or clones without the Series 80 firing pin block is accidentally dropped and lands muzzle down on a hard surface, inertia can possibly cause the firing pin to fly forward with enough force to fire a cartridge in the chamber. The possibility of this happening is even greater if the firing pin spring has weakened from age or use. An extra-power firing pin spring requires about 15 percent more energy to be driven forward and for this reason it is a far better choice for pre-Series 80 guns than the standard weight spring. Even better is an extra-power spring combined with a super lightweight titanium firing pin. This won't completely eliminate the possibility of a loaded gun firing when landing muzzle down, but does increase the odds in favor of the chap who drops it.

If the spring does not quickly retract the firing pin back into the slide before the breech end of the barrel begins to move downward for unlocking during the firing cycle, the tip of the firing pin can plow a groove across the face

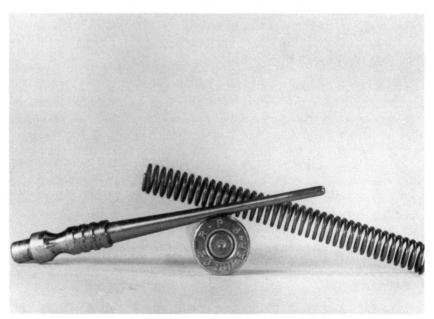

Titanium firing pin and its spring.

of the spent case's primer. This is called firing pin drag and it is a common cause of firing pin breakage in Government Model pistols with weak springs. An extra-power spring goes a long way toward preventing this from happening.

The slide of an autoloader should be eased forward rather than dropped on an empty chamber, but many shooters continue to ignore this very important rule. For those chaps, an extra-power firing pin spring offers another benefit. When the slide races forward and slams to a sudden halt, the inertia-type firing pin moves forward a bit. How far it travels depends on the weight of its spring. If the spring is weak enough to allow the heel of the firing pin to travel beyond the inner surface of a loose firing pin stop, the stop can drop down and cause the gun to malfunction. The stop should not be that loose, but it often is on factory guns and an extra-power spring is especially good malfunction insurance for them.

Even when combined with a reduced-power hammer spring, the heavy-duty firing pin spring won't affect the ignition of most primers. One possible exception is when those two are combined with a titanium firing pin and required to ignite Small Rifle primers used by most who load the .38 Super to Major power for practical pistol competition. I have two .38 Supers so equipped and have never experienced misfires even when using the Remington 7½ primer with its extremely thick cup, but have heard of it happening. Both of those guns also have a progressive-rate hammer spring.

The Mainspring (or Hammer Spring)

John Browning designed a great deal of overkill into several component parts of his big .45 so it would function under severe conditions. The extremely heavy 23-pound mainspring propels the hammer forward with far greater force than actually is required. It still isn't a bad idea if the gun is to be used out in a muddy battlefield, but quite unnecessary in a well-maintained custom gun used under more normal conditions. There are, however, those who still prefer the heavy-duty spring in their carry guns. A reduced-power spring in the 18- to 19-pound range reduces vibration, makes the hammer easier to cock, a bit safer to ease forward on a pre-Series 80 gun, and is plenty strong for lighting the fire of any type of pistol primer. Since less force is required to cock the hammer, the slide is easier to retract when the hammer is down. Even better is to use a variable-rate mainspring.

Incidentally, the variable-rate mainspring is a great idea for Colt's Double Eagle and if Wolff or some other company would start making it I'm sure they would sell a few. I know how well it works because I shot what was probably the first (and perhaps the only) fullhouse comp gun ever built around the big double-action gun. Chuck Warner, who built it, eliminated its synthetic mainspring housing and installed an SA Shooting Accessories magazine well funnel with integral mainspring housing. The Model 1911-type housing enabled him to use the Oglesby & Oglesby progressive rate mainspring and it worked miracles on the gun's double-action trigger.

Magazine Catch (or Release) Spring

There isn't a great deal to be said about the magazine catch spring except the reduced-power style is an excellent idea for a competition gun as only a light tap on the button ejects an empty magazine during a quick reload. Wolff makes them with one-, two-, three-, and four-pound ratings. Only the standard weight spring should be used in a carry gun for obvious reasons.

Recommendations on the frequency of spring replacement in the Government Model are included in the chapter on maintenance.

15

Odds and Ends

Full-Length Recoil Spring Guide

Replacing the short factory recoil spring guide with an extended version that reaches out near the muzzle of the slide on standard guns and even farther on those with compensators is not a necessity in all custom Government Models. However, many shooters don't consider a gun complete without it. Everybody seems to offer at least one recoil spring guide, including Wilson, Brown, Weigand, Heinie, Warner, Kings, and Alpha Precision. Most are made of stainless steel; rather unique among those is Jim Stroh's version with an integral head. The Heinie guide is tungsten and weighs 3.3 ounces, about 1¾ ounces more than a stainless steel rod. Moving to the opposite extreme, some pistolsmiths who specialize in building extremely lightweight guns for steel plate competition are now using full-length guides that reduce rather than add weight. Jack Weigand's polymer version weighs less than 0.3 ounce on my postal scale and the titanium guide made by Chuck Warner weighs around one ounce. Due to their extremely light weight, the Weigand and Warner guides are excellent choices for a carry gun as well as some competition guns.

I am convinced that a full-length guide rod improves the reliability of a gun simply because it supports and retains the recoil spring in a straight position over its entire length, rather than allowing it to snake around inside the gun as the short factory guide does. That characteristic keeps the amount of tension on the slide more constant from shot to shot. I also believe a recoil spring will last longer when supported over its full length, as it is not pounded

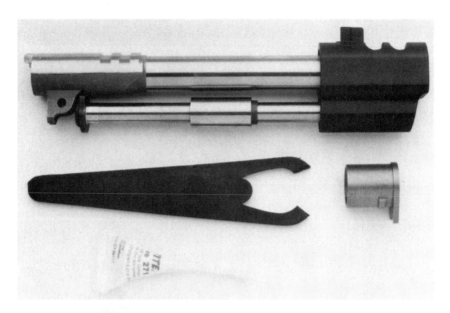

This B.A.T. Pro-Series V kit comes with a barrel, compensator, full-length recoil spring guide, spring plug, barrel bushing, bushing wrench, and Loc-Tite for securing the compensator to the barrel.

This Weigand full-length polymer recoil spring guide has a takedown hole (just forward of the fingers) and weighs less than $\frac{1}{3}$ ounce.

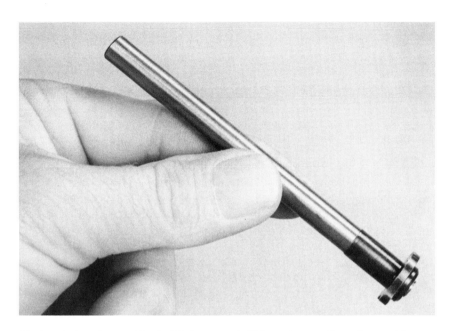

Made of titanium, this C. W. Custom full-length recoil spring guide weighs about 40 percent less than a steel version.

This Wilson full-length recoil spring guide and rear-entry plug is for the Colt Officer's ACP.

during firing while in a kinked position. The savings realized by replacing recoil springs less often eventually can add up to enough to cover the cost of the full-length guide. The long rod also holds the spring captive when the entire upper assembly is removed from the frame. Retract the slide, remove the slide stop, and everything will move forward and off the frame in one package. This is quite handy for taking a quick peek inside to inspect the shock buffer or for application of lube. Of course, you can do the same thing with the short guide, but the recoil spring can zoom off into the distance.

Here's an example of what this relatively inexpensive custom part can do. The first Delta Elite I worked with ate up its factory dual recoil springs at an alarming rate and chewed up the plastic head of the guide in short order, all causing a bit of battering between the slide and frame and sharp pains in the area of my wallet. After chucking Colt's better idea and switching to a full-length guide replete with shock buffer, and a Wolff 22-pound spring, the gun became more reliable, the battering stopped, and spring life increased dramatically. I had the same experience with an Officer's ACP except its stubby barrel bushing had a tendency to crack when digesting heavy loads. The exact same recipe cured its evil ways.

A full-length spring guide also supports the extra weight of the compensator when the slide is back during the firing cycle. One- and two-piece styles are available, the latter consisting of two sections threaded together. If at all possible, I try to avoid the two-piece type as it can loosen when subjected to the pounding of heavy loads. I've had it happen on a number of occasions and when using a gun so equipped in competition, I always keep an Allen wrench in my pocket just in case. Except on guns that absolutely require the two-piece version, I have converted mine to one-piecers by taking them apart, removing all oil from the threads with Outer's Crud Cutter, and staking them with industrial grade Loctite. Exceptions do exist, but as a rule if the guide does not extend beyond the muzzle of the slide, the one-piece style with a takedown hole will work. This applies to both standard and compensated guns. Some full-profile compensators require the use of a two-piece guide, one of several reasons why some shooters prefer the half-profile comp.

Far better than a two-piece rod with an Allenhead socket in its front end is a one-piece rod with a small takedown hole drilled through it (from side to side) about ⅜ inch beyond the muzzle of the slide when it is locked back. The Weigand and Warner rods come with the takedown hole already drilled, but some don't. Anyone with a drill press can handle the modification. The direction of the hole is not critical on guns with heavy or sleeved barrels, but it must run from three o'clock to nine o'clock on a rod used in a barrel bushing-type gun. The hole should be just large enough to accept the bent end of a straightened paper clip or other homemade takedown tool.

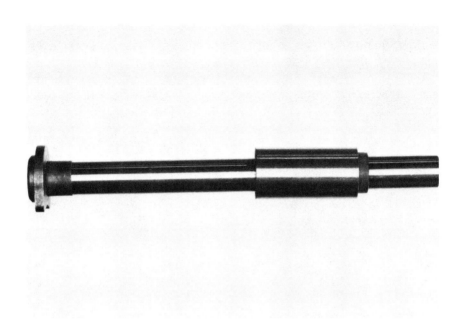

Wilson one-piece, full-length recoil spring guide rod with rear-entry spring plug.

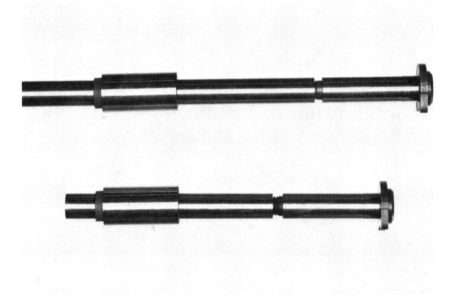

Wilson two-piece, full-length recoil spring guide rods with rear-entry spring plugs.

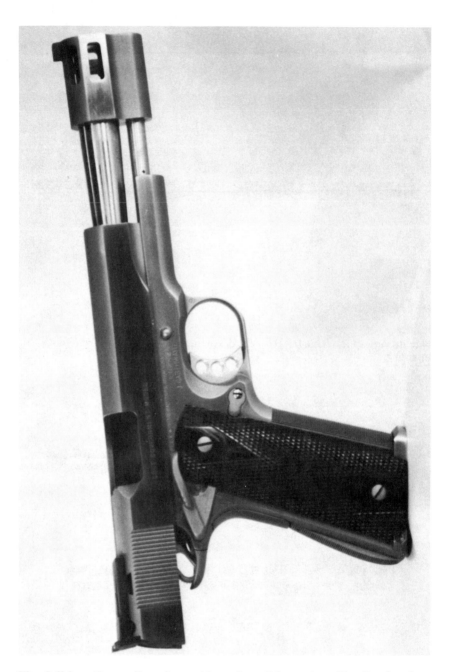

The full-length recoil spring guide rod on this custom Jim Garthwaite
gun supports the heavy barrel-mounted compensator when the slide is
back.

Recoil Spring Plugs

There are three basic types of recoil spring plugs. The factory version with its closed front and open rear ends retains the recoil spring by resting against the backside of the barrel bushing flange. In other words, it plugs the recoil spring tunnel in the slide so the spring can't escape out the front. When a full-length recoil spring guide is installed, the front of the plug must be open to allow passage of the rod as the slide travels rearward.

Two types of open-front plugs are available. The front-entry style enters the slide from the front and except for an opening large enough to allow passage of the rod, but too small to allow the spring to escape, it is virtually the same as the factory plug. It also is retained in the slide by the barrel bushing.

When the barrel bushing is eliminated by the installation of a heavy or sleeved barrel, a rear-entry plug is required. When this type is used, the mouth of the recoil spring tunnel in the slide has to be opened up slightly so the plug can be installed from the rear. Some pistolsmiths use a special reamer for this modification, others simply remove the tiny bit of metal with a rattail file or Dremel tool. Since there is no barrel bushing to retain this type of plug, an integral flange on its rear end rests against the rear surface of the recoil spring tunnel. I suppose this type of recoil spring plug could be called rear-retained while the other two could be described as front-retained.

The Humble Shock Buffer

A few decades ago, the terms recoil buffer and shock buffer were most often used in describing a rather complex modification made to the recoil spring guide. Pistolsmiths made them and they were offered commercially by several companies. A spring-loaded device, it was designed to cushion impact between the rear of the recoil spring tunnel of the slide and the head of the spring guide. Those shock buffers probably did protect the frame and slide from battering to some degree, but metal still impacted against metal with most designs.

Then some gunsmith probably punched a hole in a piece of leather or perhaps a section of old rubber innertube from his 1929 roadster, pushed it over the recoil spring guide, and carved it to the same contour as that of the guide's head. When the gun was fired, the soft material cushioned impact between the slide and frame and prevented battering even better than the mechanical variety. It also was inexpensive and easily replaced when worn out. Of course, our pistolsmith of yesteryear had no way of knowing it then, but he had discovered what today's Government Model owners buy by the thousands—the throwaway recoil buffer. Back in those days, a leather buffer

Brown front-entry recoil spring plug with open end for passage of a full-length spring guide during the firing cycle.

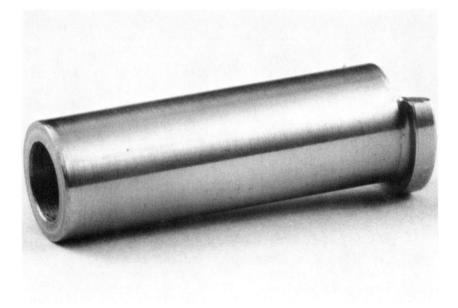

Brown rear-entry recoil spring plug for use with a full-length guide rod.

318

The front of the recoil spring plug on this gun is open to allow passage of the full-length guide rod during the firing cycle.

These Brown rear-entry recoil spring plugs are for, from left to right: 1. Government Model, 2. Commander, 3. Officer's ACP.

Arnt Myher shoots and scoots during a USPSA practical pistol match.
*(*Front Sight *photo)*

was better than no buffer, but it grew hard and less resilient with age, and rubber had a short life when kept soaked with gun oil. Then today's versions made of tough, oil-resistant materials came along.

Bill Wilson did not invent the shock buffer, and his company isn't the only firm that offers it, but he did more to popularize it than anyone else. More than one pistolsmith has told me that a far lower number of Government Model pistols come into their shops with cracked frames and slides since more shooters have become aware of two things. First, the recoil spring in the Government Model is not designed to last for the gun's lifetime. Secondly, for a cost of less than pocket change, the homely little shock buffer ranks up there with good gun oil as the cheapest firearm protection money can buy. Many companies offer them, including SA Shooting Accessories, Wilson, CP Bullets, and Tru-Flight.

One size shock buffer fits all Government Model variations and clones. How often it needs replacing depends on recoil spring tension. If the spring is the correct weight for the load being used, the little bugger can last 1,000 rounds or more. If the spring is too weak, it may not last 200 rounds. My .38 Super comp guns will go 1,500 rounds with Major power loads and their shock buffs will still have some life left, but I keep a very close watch on

Bill Wilson did not invent the throwaway shock buffer, but he did more to popularize it than any other pistolsmith.

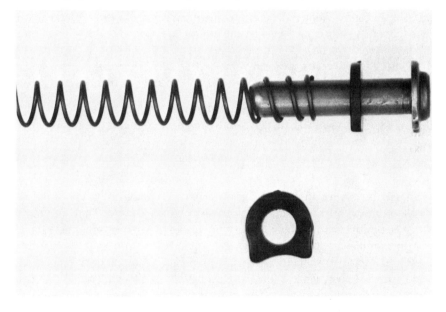

Made of a tough synthetic material, the inexpensive Wilson shock buffer slips over the recoil spring guide to prevent battering between the frame and slide.

their recoil springs and install new ones when they have lost enough tension to notice. Actually, so many variables are involved, the best rule of thumb is to simply keep an eye on the buffer and replace it when needed. The main thing to remember when discarding a worn-out buffer is that you are throwing away the pounding your gun would have taken without it. Whether the gun is a custom job or still factory original, its innards need the protection of a shock buffer.

It is not uncommon among competitors in the action shooting games to stack as many as three buffers on the recoil spring guide, not for the extra protection, but as a way of shortening the slide's cycle time. They are the ones who double-tap so fast you have to listen closely to hear two shots. This procedure usually works only if the gun has an extended ejector and is not for those who prefer to shoot the Government Model to slide lock in competition as the stack of buffers prevents it from traveling far enough to the rear to engage its catch. It is strictly a little trick used by those who ride on the edge of being quicker than quick when trying to gain any possible advantage over the competition. It most definitely is not something to do to a gun used anywhere except in a match.

While pounding several dozen shock buffers to submission over the years, I have yet to have one come apart inside a gun during practice or in a match, probably because I keep a close eye on their condition. However, I have heard of it happening. Since anything can and often does happen at the wrong time, it's probably not a bad idea to install a buffer in a carry or home defense gun during practice sessions but remove it at other times. If one did go to pieces, it could bind up the works and cause a malfunction.

Incidentally, some shock buffers are perfectly flat on one side only. The flat side goes toward the head of the recoil spring guide.

Grip Panels

Shortly before writing this, I surveyed quite a number of people from all walks of life who own custom Government Model pistols. Their interests ranged from the action shooting sports to weekend plinking, to nothing more than pure enjoyment in simply owning a good custom gun. The majority preferred factory or custom wood grip panels, the minority opted for wraparound rubber, while a few had never really put much thought into the matter. Among those who preferred mother nature's material, some were quite satisfied with those mass-produced by big factories, while others would accept nothing less than custom grip panels. Within the latter group, the majority preferred checkering while a smaller number wanted them smooth.

Ed Brown's Officer's ACP with all the trimmings.

323

How a gun feels is such a personal thing, it is best for the individual shooter to try grip panels of various thicknesses before taking the custom plunge. Some shops offer several options ranging from extremely thin to extremely thick (Kim Ahrends, Dave Wayland, and Craig Spegel are three such sources). I have average-size hands and prefer relatively thin panels, but a shooting pal with about the same size paws wants them just a little fatter than fat.

Most custom wood grip panels have a large bevel at the bottom, the same as on the factory versions. They are attractive on a gun with no mag well funnel. The same goes for a gun with a relatively narrow mag well that does not extend out from the sides of the grip frame by very much (the Wilson is a good example). As they say, beauty will always be in the eye of the beholder, but many custom gun owners think the nonbeveled or flush style looks better on a gun with a wide funnel such as the SA Shooting Accessories. Most custom makers offer both styles.

Custom wood smooth or checkered grip panels are available from Ahrends, Wayland, Spegal, Wilson's, Kings, Hogue, Herrett, and many others. Styles of checkering include full coverage, diamond, and skip-line. Checkering looks good and adds a touch of class, but does have a tendency to hide much of the natural beauty of the darker woods. I have examined many of Kim Ahrends' and Dave Wayland's gorgeous panels, all carved from a variety of highly figured trees. The dark streaks running through cocobolo, kingwood, tulipwood, bocote, and cordia seemed to be hidden less by the checkering than on some of the other varieties. If anything, checkering appears to highlight the figure in those woods. The dark, contrasting lines seemed to leap right through the checkering and catch the eye. I have Ahrends' tulipwood and cocobolo panels on a couple of very handsome comp guns in .38 Super. Two of my other equally handsome guns wear Wayland's bocote and cocobolo panels. Everyone who examines those guns for the first time drools over the beautiful wood before moving on to their other features.

Another Dave Wayland specialty is the inletting of German silver inlays into grip panels. Often the inlays are attractively engraved with various designs or the owner's initials. Wayland was the first to offer custom wood panels for the Para-Ordnance gun and his workmanship is flawless. Due to the design of that gun, the factory synthetic panels have to be used, but Wayland modifies them in a milling machine and then attaches a thin, hand-checkered cocobolo or bocote panel to their surface.

It would seem that sharp checkering on its grip panels would make a gun easier to control during firing and it does so on a factory gun. However, if a custom gun with checkered frontstrap and mainspring housing is held properly, those grooves in the wood contribute little to a firm one-hand hold. The checkering does serve a functional purpose with the two-hand hold as

The smooth wood grip panels on this Neil Wiggans custom gun have finger grooves cut specifically for the customer's hand.

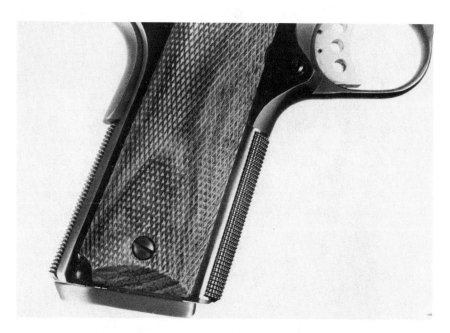

This grip panel with a bevel at its lower end looks fine on this gun with its narrow Wilson magazine well funnel.

it presents a no-slip gripping surface to the heel of the weak hand. (At least, that's what my hands have to say about the subject.) Truth is, choosing between smooth and checkered grip panels boils down to which feels and looks best to the individual. I prefer the looks of the checkered variety, but know people who want them as smooth as a baby's bottom.

On a gun with an aftermarket ambidextrous safety, the righthand grip panel holds the thumb tab in place on that side of the gun. When custom panels are ordered, this should be specified so the maker will know to inlet the inside surface of the panel. Depending on the brand, the left-side panel also may have to be relieved for clearance with the plunger housing on the frame and the safety tab on that side of the gun. This minor task is easily handled by a good pistolsmith.

Some shooters swear by the wraparound and two-piece grip covers made of black rubber or synthetics, while others swear against them with equal fervor. On the positive side, they are relatively inexpensive, improve gripping on a gun with a smooth frontstrap, and really don't look at all bad when matched up with a hard chrome metal finish. Some, like the Pachmayr, also have steel-lined panels (a comforting thing to have in your hand if a cartridge case blows). On the negative side, the rubber types increase the grip's

326

This compensated gun built by Dave Lauck has a metal nameplate inletted into its righthand grip panel.

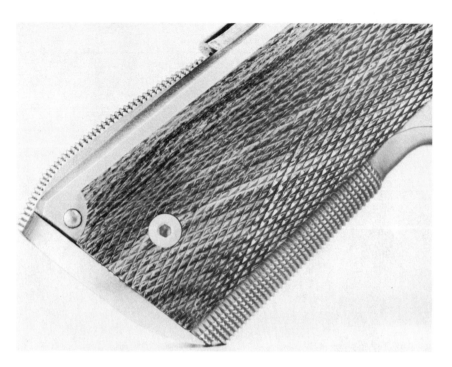

The nonbeveled end of this SA Shooting Accessories grip panel mates nicely with a magazine well funnel from the same company.

diameter, can get slippery in sweaty hands, and there are those who don't consider them as handsome as natural wood on some custom guns. The latter reason is why Dave Wayland receives more orders for his handsome custom replacement wood grip panels for the Para-Ordnance pistol than he can possibly fill.

Two of the best synthetic panels for a gun used in practical pistol competition are the Safariland R-53C Combat Grip and the Model 900 Speed Grip from Kings Gun Works. Kings version is an especially good design as both panels have an integral thumbguard at the top and their bottom ends are funnel-shaped for magazine speedloading.

Extra heavy grip panels that add up to half a pound to the weight of a pistol also are available. Those from Caspian, Wilson, Kings, and Brownells are solid pewter with checkering or other designs cast into their outer surface. They are about the same thickness as factory grip panels and available for standard and Commander-length frames. The Advantage Grip available from Jack Breskovich has an extremely thick steel liner on the underside of two wood grip panels. It's a great idea, but a bit too thick for a small hand.

328

This Bob Cogan comp gun has smooth wood grip panels.

Built by Dave Lauck, this custom Officer's ACP has grip panels with skip-line checkering coverage.

Kim Ahrends' smooth cocobolo grip panel on a C. W. Custom Officer's ACP.

The smooth inner surfaces of these Ahrends grip panels illustrate the striking figure of cordia wood.

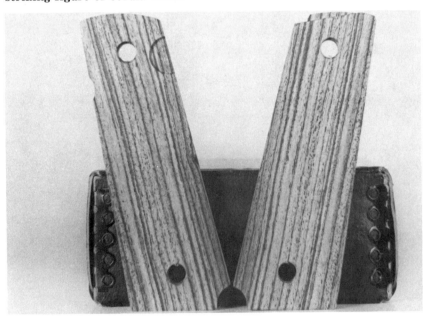

Inside surfaces of Ahrends grip panels carved from kingwood.

332

Fancy grip panel with full-coverage checkering on a Wilson Super Grade.

I use the solid metal grip panels when firing hundreds of rounds in a gun during load development. Their extra weight dampens recoil a bit and they protect the hand from flying shrapnel in the event of a blown case. They were once mildly popular among competitors in the action shooting games, but the introduction of compensated guns doomed their use for that application. A heavier grip does tame recoil, but does not reduce muzzle jump because the weight is added at the rear and below the axis of the bore, rather than out front and in alignment with the bore. Be that as it may, anyone who spends a lot of time developing heavy loads in Government Model pistols should own a pair.

Grip Panel Screws

Only a couple of things need to be said in this department.

First of all, on a full-blown, full-house, budget-blowing gun with every bell, whistle, trinket, and custom feature you might think of, the slots on the heads of both grip panel screws look best when both point precisely north and south. It's a little thing, one most shooters never notice, and they may not stay that way long as the moisture content of the wood fluctuates, but it's a subtle

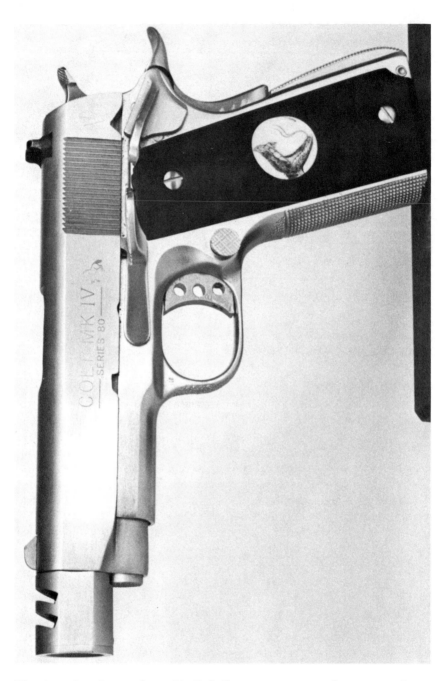

The smooth grip panel on this Bob Cogan compensated carry gun has a sterling silver plate inletted into its surface.

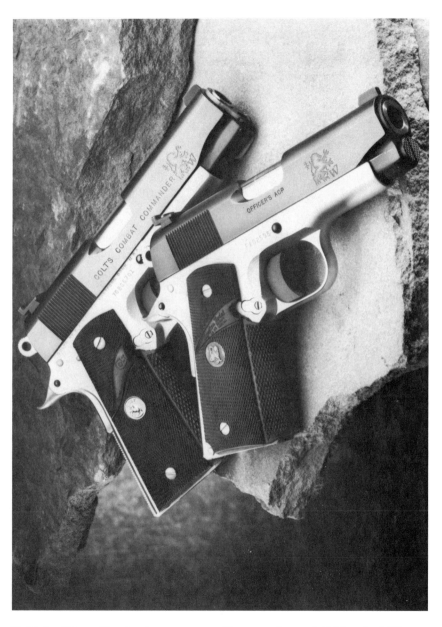

Built by Steve Woods, these custom Commander and Officer's ACP
carry guns wear Colt and Pachmayr rubber grips. *(Stephen Longley
photo)*

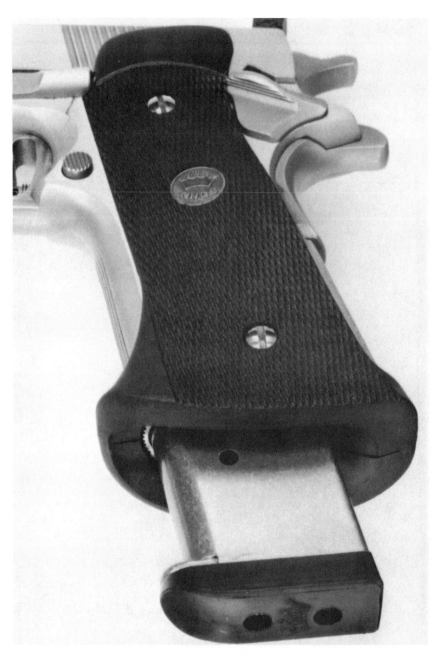

Made of a tough synthetic material, the Kings Speed Grip has an integral magazine well funnel at the bottom and thumbguard at the top.

336

The checkered grip panels on these Steve Woods guns are held in place with Wilson hexhead screws. *(Stephen Longley photo)*

Kings hexhead grip panel screws.

touch of class custom Government Model pistol connoisseurs really appreciate. Also, the screws on an expensive gun should have narrow slots like those available from Kings Gun Works. Screws with standard width slots are easier to bugger because most screwdrivers don't fit them as snugly as the narrow slots.

Secondly, custom hexhead screws probably are more expensive than they should be, but when a screwdriver slips in a slotted-head screw and plows a furrow along an expensive custom grip panel, they seem dirt cheap. They also tend to resist buggering better than their slotted-head cousins. On the opposite side of the coin, some say they don't look as good as those with slotted heads. I think they look better, but then, I prefer blondes, too.

16

Compensators

D EVICES designed to compensate for the muzzle jump of a firearm when it is fired have been around for many years. A very old one is the Cutts compensator which was designed for the Thompson submachine gun and went on to enjoy great popularity among shotgunners.

(Dave Lauck photo)

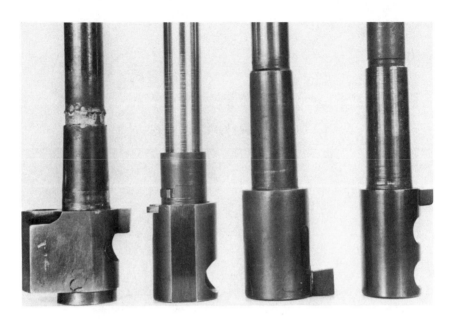

A collection of old compensators dating back to the early 1980s. The sleeve on the extreme left comp has broken loose from the barrel.

One of the first compensators manufactured for the Government Model pistol was introduced during the 1950s by Project Specialties Inventions of Warren, Michigan. Its design included expansion chambers, deflector plates, and ports that collected and diverted propellant gas as it emerged from the barrel's muzzle. Called the Maxi-Compensator, its maker advertised it as 40 percent effective in reducing recoil and muzzle rise. It was available in stainless or blued steel in three lengths—medium and long for competitive shooting, and a short one-incher for carry guns. Kings' No. 305 compensator is similar to that one.

According to my research, the compensator as we know it today did not get the undivided attention of those in the action shooting game until Arkansas pistolsmith J. Michael Plaxco won the IPSC nationals with a gun so equipped in 1982. During the following year Rob Leatham won both the IPSC National and World championships with a Wilson-built gun that wore the then-new ACCU-COMP "LE" (Leatham-Enos) single-port comp. Soon thereafter practically all of the top action game competitors were either shooting a compensated gun or wishing their competition wasn't. I believe 1981 was the last year a noncompensated gun won a major practical pistol match.

C. W. Custom compensators in the rough. Left one has an integral barrel sleeve. Right one has a separate barrel sleeve.

Compensators have become popular in USPSA/IPSC competition due to the fact that they decrease muzzle jump by adding weight at the muzzle of a pistol and by redirecting propellant gas. They also have become mildly popular on carry guns in the private sector and at least one law enforcement agency is rumored to be on the verge of adopting guns so equipped for special purpose applications.

Muzzle jump in an autoloader is caused by four factors: acceleration of the bullet through its barrel, the axis of its bore positioned out of alignment with the shooter's arm, the jet effect of propellant gas as it escapes at the muzzle, and momentum impinged on the frame by the slide as it slams to the rear during its firing cycle. When some of the propellant gas is redirected upward by the compensator, the jet effect pushes downward against the four opposing forces. There also are those who believe that since the gas slams into the vertical deflector plate(s) in a compensator, recoil also is reduced.

One thing is certain, the greater the volume of gas produced by the powder and the faster the gas exits the barrel, the more effective is any compensator in reducing muzzle jump. This important factor explains why the .45 ACP does not squeeze as much effectiveness from a compensator as the .38 Super, 9mm Parabellum, 9x23mm Super, and 9x21 with their relatively

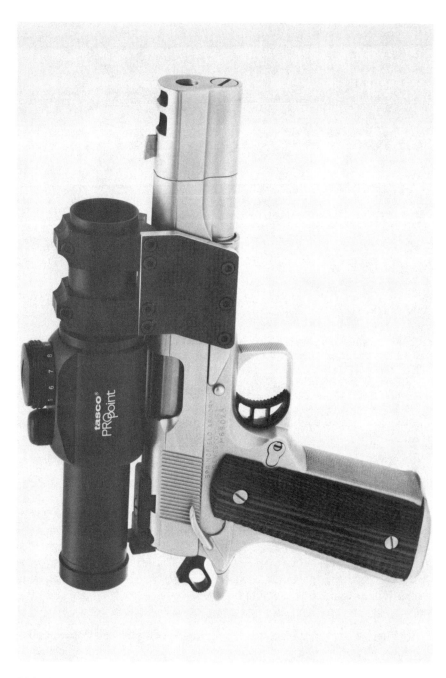

This Steve Nastoff competition gun has his Super Comp-IV full-profile compensator. *(ACRI Studio photo)*

Brian Enos shooting his optical-sighted Wilson Super grade in competition. *(*Front Sight *photo)*

light bullets, small bore diameters, and high muzzle pressure. In this respect, the 10mm Auto and .40 S&W sit about midway in effectiveness between the .45 on one side and the .38 Super and various 9mm caliber cartridges on the other. Install identical compensators (except for caliber) on identical custom guns in .45 ACP, 10mm Auto, and .38 Super; then fire Major power loads in them and muzzle jump will be the worst with the .45, least with the .38, and the 10mm will fall somewhere between the two. Even when the three cartridges are loaded with the same bullet weight (e.g., 150 grains) muzzle jump still will be less with the .38 Super. This is because a Major power load for the Super generates a higher level of chamber pressure, so pressure at the muzzle is higher as the bullet exits the barrel and enters the compensator. The higher the muzzle pressure, the faster the gas flows through the compensator.

There was a time when compensators were available from only a couple of sources, but that changed when the popularity of USPSA/IPSC competition spread like wildfire. Shops and companies that offer them are more abundant than fleas on a stray coon dog. A number of styles are available: full-profile, half-profile, with front sight, without front sight, barrel sleeve-type, barrel bushing-type, single-chamber, double-chamber, triple-chamber, quad-chamber,

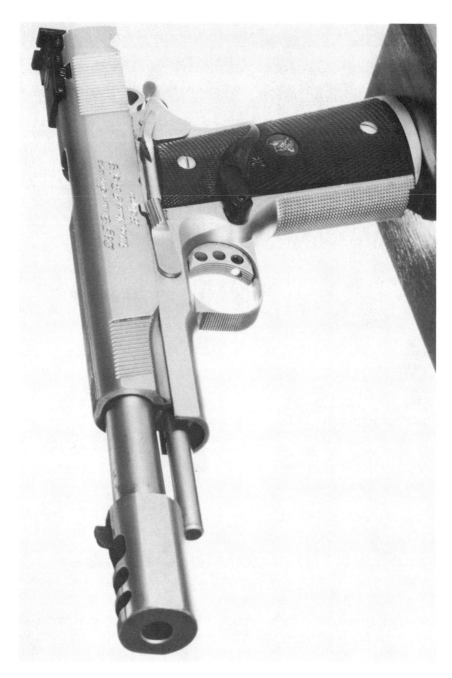

Don Fraley's competition gun with a triple-chamber, half-profile compensator.

Built by Ed Brown, this custom Colt Commander Mini-Comp with its
compensated barrel is a popular carry gun.

Ported barrel on an Al Capone Officer's ACP carry gun.

A compensator reduces muzzle jump by diverting some of the rapidly expanding propellant gases upward. *(Dave Lauck photo)*

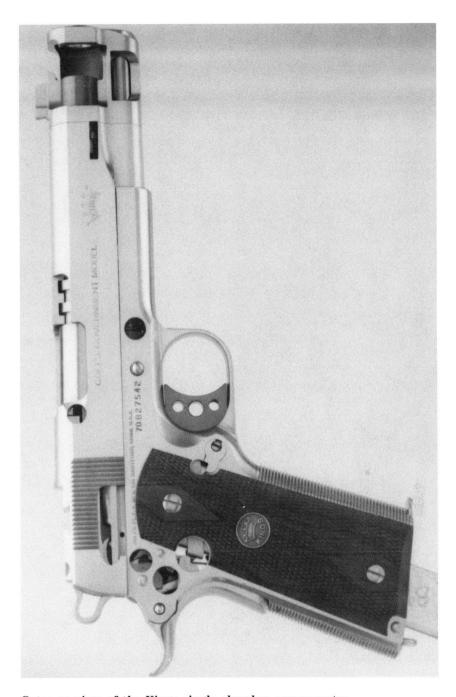

Cutaway view of the Kings single-chamber compensator.

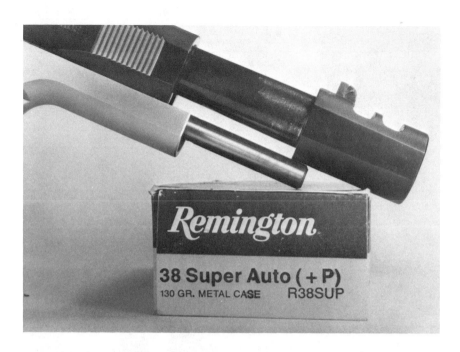

Jerry Barnhart shooting his compensated Wilson Super Grade in .38 Super. *(Colt photo)*

Steve Woods custom guns with half- and full-profile compensators.
(Stephen Longley photo)

A carry-comp gun built by Wayne Bergquist around a Caspian frame and Commander-length slide.

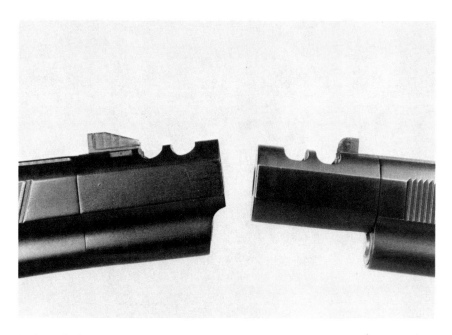

Left, a B.A.T. dual-chamber, full-profile compensator. Right, a Wilson dual-chamber, half-profile compensator.

you name it. They are available in blued steel, stainless steel, titanium, and aluminum with a steel liner. You can buy compensators alone or compensator kits containing a new match-grade barrel and all the accessories needed for installation. Some are intended only to be installed by competent pistolsmiths, others are described by their makers as prefitted or drop-in types.

The prices of compensators alone run from too cheap to be any good, to reasonable, to ridiculous. The prices of complete kits with custom barrels and all the trimmings range from about the cost of a dozen boxes of .45 ACP factory ammo to more than some of the autoloaders for which they are designed. The majority of comps and comp kits presently available are designed for the Government Model pistol, but a few shops are beginning to cater to owners of other autoloaders.

There are several basic styles of compensator systems. One type attaches to the slide with an integral barrel bushing that replaces the Colt-type bushing (among others, this type includes the Wichita, B.A.T., and Kings' No. 305). These are do-it-yourself types and rarely seen on a custom gun.

There also is the barrel-mounted type in which the barrel and compensator are threaded and held together with industrial strength Loctite or other

351

This Signature Grade .38 Super by C. W. Custom has a Brown Four-Star compensator.

The Wichita compensator replaces the barrel bushing rather than being attached to the barrel.

glue. Some compensators are made for barrels that utilize the Browning-designed barrel bushing. Others eliminate the barrel bushing by utilizing an integral reverse-taper threaded sleeve that extends back over the barrel, often reaching to just forward of the front locking lug. This type usually requires modification to the slide's front and for this reason is for installation by pistol-smiths only. Some compensators can be used with a bushing-type barrel or with a separate, nonintegral barrel sleeve designed to eliminate the bushing.

Possibly the most novel of designs is machined from a barrel blank of extremely large diameter by Jim Stroh. It's a Government Model barrel with an integral compensator. Or is it a compensator with an integral barrel? Whichever way you choose to describe it, Stroh considers his system one of the better ways to trap a mouse.

Another type of comp kit eliminates the bushing and the sleeve by utilizing an extremely heavy barrel with a special contour. The Centaur Quadra-Lok is the first I examined of this type, but various pistolsmiths now have their versions of heavy barrel designs.

Compensator kits that also include a barrel are often referred to by shooters as *drop-ins,* which implies that anyone capable of field stripping the Government Model pistol can install one. I find the description accurate in some cases, but misleading as minor fitting is required with some guns. One manufacturer says about 20 percent of the hundreds of guns in which his kit has been tried required minor fitting, but the one he sent me worked fine in three Colt Government Models with no modification.

Perhaps I'm just lucky, but only two of the barrel/compensator kits I have tried from various companies required some modification. The barrel in one kit wouldn't work until about .002-inch of metal was carefully removed with a file from the righthand side of its hood. The barrel in another kit fed round-nose bullets but its throat required a bit of polishing with my Dremel tool before it would digest loads with SWC bullets. The possible need for minor fitting also applies to the slide-mounted type. One kit I tried on five different slides wouldn't work until a bit of metal was removed from the bushing.

The so-called drop-in comp kits are designed to correct some of the extremely loose battlefield tolerance fit between Government Model component parts. In other words, their parts are intentionally manufactured toward the maximum side of the dimensional tolerance range so they will improve accuracy by eliminating some of the slop in mass-produced pistols. This is why they may not simply drop into some guns. On the more negative side, barrel fit seldom is as tight as with an oversized match grade barrel hand-fitted by a good pistolsmith.

Back a group of shooters who have tried various types of compensators into a tight corner and all probably will agree that although the slide mounted

The compensated barrel on this Steve Woods gun has been sleeved for added weight. *(Stephen Longley photo)*

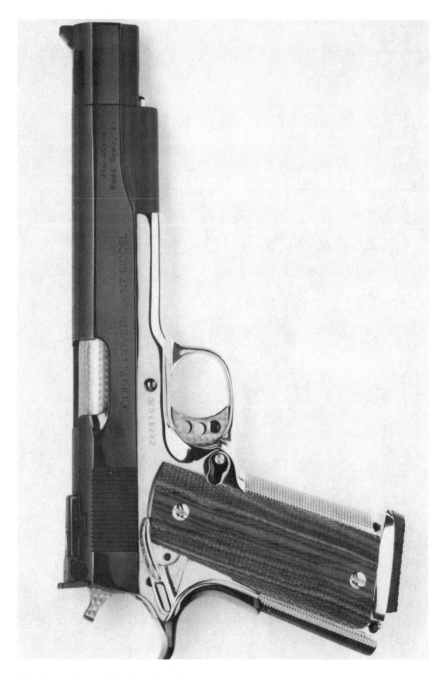

The barrel on this Jim Stroh competition gun has an integral
compensator and front sight.

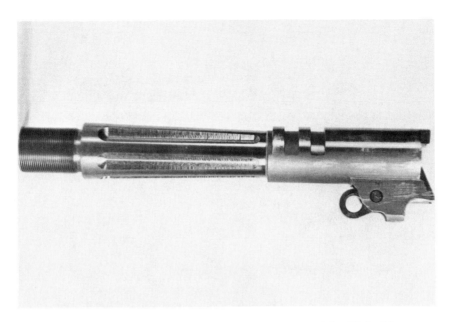

The muzzle of this C. W. Custom heavy-fluted barrel in CP 9x23mm Super has been threaded for a compensator.

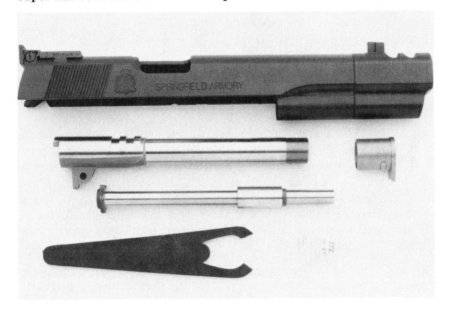

B.A.T. offers a complete top assembly kit consisting of a slide with sights, barrel, compensator, full-length recoil spring guide, open-front spring plug, and barrel bushing.

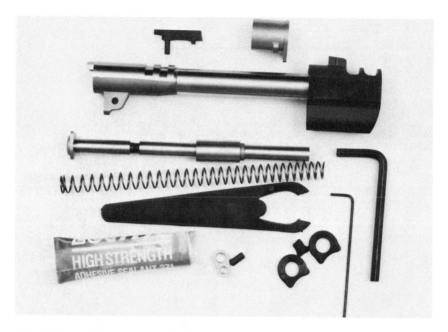

This Wilson kit contains a barrel, compensator, barrel bushing, two-piece full-length recoil spring guide, barrel link, shock buffers, extended ejector, hex wrenches and Loctite.

comp is far better than no comp, it is not as effective in reducing muzzle jump as the barrel-mounted type. The slide-mounted type is not as expensive, but one particular model does cost about half as much as complete barrel/compensator kits from other sources.

Moving on to the barrel-mounted compensators, some shooters who use the heavy barrel and sleeved barrel types are convinced that they are superior to the barrel bushing types. I'll let you in on a little secret (one that every pistolsmith with whom I have discussed it has admitted), both compensators have their advantages and disadvantages. However, if the difference in performance, reliability, durability, longevity, and accuracy between two guns of equal quality but with the different systems could be converted to TNT, you wouldn't have enough to blow a chipmunk's nose.

To date I have worked with four full-blown custom comp guns in .38 Super and .45 ACP which have proven to be 100 percent reliable over the long haul. Two have sleeve-type comp systems and the others have bushing-type systems. The two .38 Supers are the only comp guns I have clamped into my Ransom Rest that will consistently average two inches at 50 yards. One has a bushing-type system, the other has a barrel sleeve-type system. Take your pick.

358

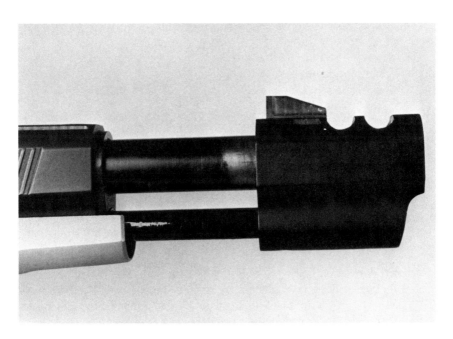

This B.A.T. dual-chamber Pro-Series V compensator is used with a bushing-type barrel.

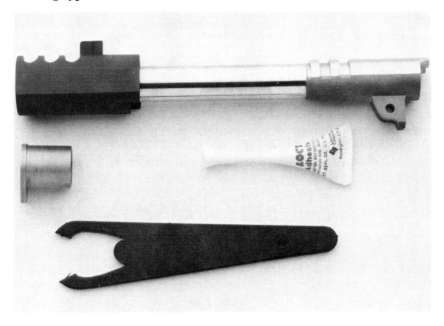

B.A.T. half-profile, triple-chamber compensator/barrel kit.

359

Compensators come in three basic shapes, full-profile, dual-profile, and half-profile. I know of no one who offers a drop-in kit with a full- or dual-profile comp due to the fact that installing this type is best left to a pistolsmith. Having this done usually costs a bit more than having a half-profile comp fitted because in order to eliminate the unsightly gap between comp and slide, the front of the slide has to be machined to a slight angle. On the more positive side, when a slide is so modified, any rounded corners caused by overly zealous polishing at the factory are eliminated. Of course, this modification can be made to the slide when a half-profile comp is fitted.

A full- or dual-profile comp usually costs a bit more because it is a bit more expensive to manufacture. Some shooters gladly pay the extra money because they think that style looks more like an extension of the slide rather than an add-on or afterthought. Others think the half-profile looks more trick and racy and happily spend the money saved somewhere else.

It would seem that due to its extra weight, a full-profile comp would be more effective than the half-profile type in dampening muzzle jump because it is heavier, but my young and tender hand says a compensator's ability to effectively redirect propellant gas is more important than a bit of extra weight. I have shot guns with full-profile comps that did not buck as much as some guns with half-profile comps, but I also have shot guns with half-profile comps that were much more controllable than other guns with the full-profile style. Truth is, I suspect that looks and price influence more shooters who buy compensators than all other factors combined.

A few months prior to writing this book I decided to illustrate my cleverness by performing tests that would objectively compare the effectiveness of compensators from eight different companies. They included the single-, double-, and quadruple-expansion chamber designs. I clamped a .45 caliber Government Model pistol into my Ransom Rest, installed one of the compensators, and measured how high above horizontal the muzzle lifted when Major power loads with three different bullet weights were fired. I then switched comps and continued on with the program until all of them were tested with the same loads. After burning up many hours in range time and a big pile of ammunition, I had all the notes and data ready to enlighten the shooting world.

Then I decided to really add clout and credibility to my test results by asking a number of shooters to try the various comps and rate them on an effectiveness scale of one through 10. Some were experienced practical pistol competitors, some were weekend plinkers, and others had never fired a Government Model pistol. In reviewing their opinions, it dawned on me that all those hours spent with the Ransom Rest were a total waste of time.

A Jim Garthwaite competition gun with his full-profile compensator.

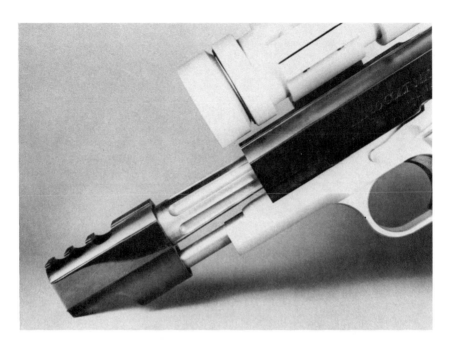

Chuck Warner's Triple Chamber Progressive (TCP), dual-profile compensator on his heavy fluted barrel. The integral rib matches the rib atop the Colt Gold Cup slide.

None of the shooters rated the compensators in the same order as my machine rest had rated them and practically every shooter picked a different one as the most effective. In fact, one shooter rated a comp second best while the machine rest had rated it dead last. The moral to this story? I can tell you which compensators seemed to be most effective in reducing muzzle jump in my Ransom Rest. I also can tell you which feels the most effective in my hand. But I won't do either because in addition to being misleading, such information is worthless. Don't buy a used car from anyone who tells you that a compensator that feels best to him will also feel best to you.

It should be noted that the gun used in those tests was chambered for the .45 ACP cartridge. Had it been in .38 Super or 9x21mm, the outcome would have been quite different, as there is a difference in effectiveness among compensator designs with those cartridges. With guns chambered for the Super and other 9mm caliber cartridges, muzzle jump is considerably less with a dual-chamber comp than with the single expansion chamber design. A compensator with three or four chambers will be slightly more effective than one with two chambers, but the difference is nowhere near as great as that between those with single and double chambers. In fact, it takes an

Two C. W. Custom competition guns. Top: Signature Grade .38 Super with half-profile compensator. Bottom: Double Eagle Plus with dual-profile compensator.

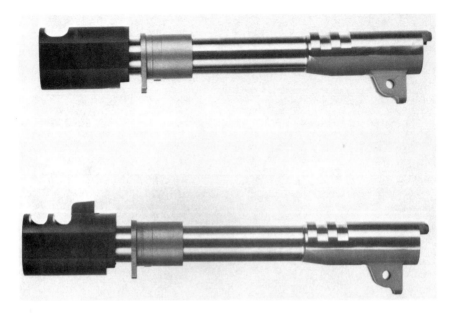

Wilson bushing-type barrels with single- and dual-chamber compensators. Top compensator is for use in a gun with the front sight mounted on the slide.

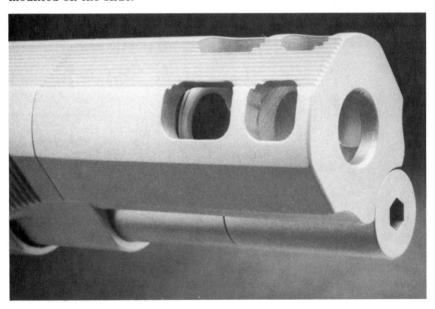

Steve Woods' third generation dual-chamber, four-port, half-profile compensator. *(Stephen Longley photo)*

364

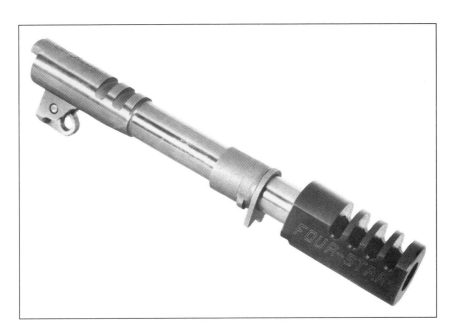

Ed Brown's match-grade barrel with his Four-Star compensator.

extremely experienced shooter to detect any significant difference in the effectiveness of guns in .38 Super with compensators of two-, three-, or four-expansion chamber designs.

So how do you decide which compensator is for you? The best way is to try various brands and styles owned by other shooters in your club before taking the leap. If that isn't possible, simply specify the one that best fits your budget, looks best to your eyes, or the one your pistolsmith prefers, and don't worry about it being more or less effective than the rest. Based on what I have seen and tried, there are no really bad compensators. I like some better than others and think some are better buys than others, but I could live happily ever after if I had to close my eyes and pick one from a covered basket. They all work to some degree.

A seldom-mentioned benefit realized when a compensator is installed on the Government Model pistol is increased life of the gun. The added weight of a compensator to the barrel and propellant gas pushing forward on the deflector wall(s) inside the comp delay unlocking until chamber pressure has dropped to a lower level. As a result, the slide travels fro and to with less violence. This is why a compensated gun uses a lighter recoil spring than a noncompensated gun. For example, when a 5-inch noncompensated 10mm is fired with full-power loads, it usually requires a 22- to 24-pound spring.

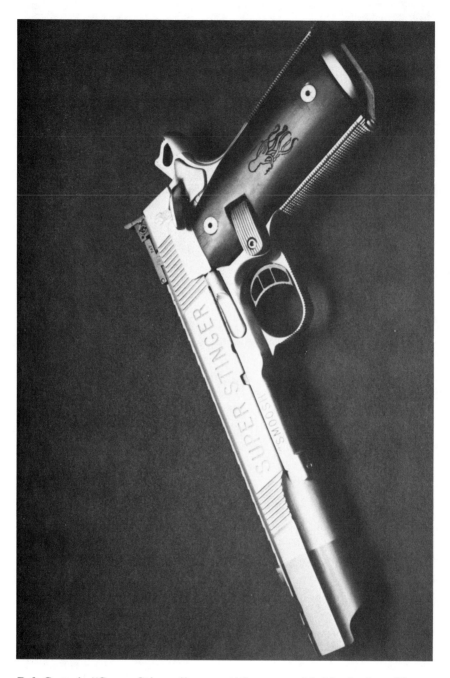

Bob Cogan's "Super Stinger" competition gun with his dual-profile compensator.

Install a comp on the gun and it probably won't cycle with a spring heavier than 16 to 18½ pounds.

For the benefit of those who could care less about competition guns, I must add that several pistolsmiths install compact compensators on carry and security blanket guns. When most are installed on a Commander, overall length of the gun is no greater than that of the Government Model. I don't care for a compensator on a carry gun, but other folks feel quite differently about the subject.

A question that occasionally creeps from the swamp is how much, if any, effect does a compensator attached to the muzzle of a barrel have on accuracy and velocity? Some shooters have the opinion that it will increase velocity and others say it will have a negative effect on accuracy. When performing the Ransom Rest tests previously described, I also chronographed several loads with each of the eight compensators installed and checked 10-shot accuracy at 50 yards. Not a single compensator had any effect whatsoever on accuracy or velocity.

How important a compensator is on a competition gun depends on the shooter. Sometime back a pistolsmith told me the "gadget" was of little value to the beginner and only top shooters could realize its advantage. I don't agree. The really good shooters with whom I have competed would win matches with or without compensated guns. On the other hand, I know one lady whose scores with the .45 ACP zoomed immediately after her husband had a comp installed on her gun. Another shooter usually placed among the top 10 percent in Limited class competition with his Gold Cup, but had never taken home a first place trophy. I loaned him a Gold Cup identical to his except for its compensated barrel and he won Unlimited class in the very next match. On the other side of the debate, another competitor I know places no higher in matches with a compensated gun than with a noncompensated gun. The moral to this story is—you'll never know until you try.

Workmanship

When a compensator is installed by a master class craftsman, it will look like an extension of the slide rather than an afterthought. Where the two parts meet, their lines, contours, and surfaces will match perfectly. Some manufacturers machine their compensators oversize so the pistolsmith can machine their surfaces down to exactly the same dimensions as the front of the slide. Those are the ones to be used on a top-grade custom gun. Quite often, a gun will leave the factory with the front edges of its slide slightly rounded by an overly zealous employee and his buffing wheel. A good pistolsmith corrects that when installing a compensated barrel.

A heavy compensated barrel enables B. J. Ratliff to control her .38 Super in competition. (Front Sight *photo)*

Pistolsmiths disagree on the correct relationship of the front surface of the slide and the rear surface of the compensator. Some opine that when the slide is fully forward in its locked position, its face should rest lightly against the rear of the compensator. Others say there should be a hairline gap measuring about .005 inch between the two. Regardless of who is correct, the fit between the parts must be uniform before it can be considered master quality work. If it's a top quality no-gap fit, you won't see any daylight between the two parts at the top or bottom. If it's a gap-type fit of equal quality, the space will be the same width at top and bottom.

The Schuemann Hybrid

Invented by Wil Schuemann and introduced to the handgunning world by Caspian Arms, the Hybrid compensating system consists of a rib attached to the top of a pistol barrel with a row of funnel-shaped holes or gas ports. The ports extend through the barrel's wall and into its bore; their number varies with the barrel length. A 5-inch barrel has five, a 4¼-inch barrel has four, and the rib for a 3¼-inch Officer's ACP barrel has three. When installed on an autoloader, a cutout must be machined through the roof of its slide for passage of the rib during the firing cycle. Slides with precut clearance

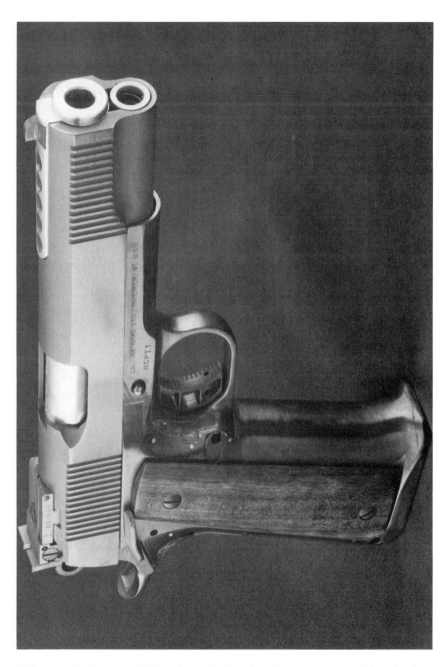

This gun built around the virtually handmade prototype of Caspian's high-capacity frame has a barrel with Hybrid muzzle jump compensator. *(Paul Hantke photo)*

are available from Caspian. The Hybrid counteracts muzzle jump by diverting propellant gas upward in the same manner as a compensator attached to the barrel's muzzle. The Hybrid, however, is more effective because it begins to divert the gas when chamber pressure is at its highest level. Additionally, a muzzle-attached comp diverts gas after the bullet exits the barrel. Gas is diverted by the Hybrid while the bore of the barrel is still sealed off or plugged by the bullet.

When first learning about the Hybrid, I was more than a bit skeptical about the claims made for it by its developer. After working with a couple of guns so modified and asking several of my shooting pals to also put them through their paces and express opinions, I changed my mind about some things, but not others. My friends and I unanimously agreed on one thing: muzzle jump with the Hybrid-equipped guns was considerably less than with identical noncompensated guns. This characteristic would be most appealing when applied to a carry gun built for someone who is sensitive to recoil.

For what it's worth, some of the fellows who tried the Hybrid thought it made a custom gun look trick and could hardly wait to have one built. Others thought it spoiled the otherwise clean lines of a custom gun. Some were strongly opposed to the idea of milling away so much metal from the slide.

I consider the Hybrid a good idea, but also recognize its shortcomings. For one, it reduces velocity by 50 to 75 fps. Metal fouling buildup caused by the passage of bullets also can present a problem. Lead spray from cast bullets has a tendency to accumulate in the ports. This lead buildup appeared to have no negative effect on accuracy, but it should be removed occasionally. When examining the bore with a 6x borescope, I noticed that copper fouling from jacketed bullets tends to build up at the sharp trailing or forward edge of each gas port. Unless the chunks of metal are removed from those areas, accuracy will begin to deteriorate after approximately 200 rounds. On a more positive note, the jacketed bullet fouling can be whisked away by thoroughly cleaning the barrel with a bore solvent made specifically for dissolving copper. Sweet's 7.62 and Kleen Bore No. 10 Copper Cutter are the best solvents I have found, but they are powerful stuff and best applied with surgical-glove-clad hands.

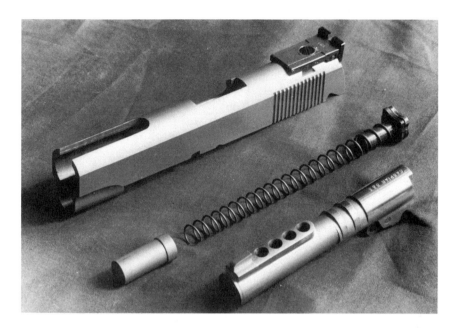

When a barrel with the Hybrid compensator is used, a clearance groove must be milled into the roof of the slide. *(Paul Hantke photo)*

17

The Switch-Top Guns

AS its name implies, the switch-top or switch-barrel gun can serve several roles and the ready availability of aftermarket slides and barrels makes the Government Model pistol an excellent candidate for such a project. The primary advantage is one of cost. Having a custom gun built with two or more top assemblies, or an extra barrel, is less expensive than having two or three complete guns built because the same frame is used with all. Another advantage is you will have two or more guns with a grip that feels the same. The balance of the gun may change when top assemblies are switched, but the feel of the grip will remain unchanged.

The disadvantage is inconvenience and the fact that switch-top guns often represent compromises some shooters aren't willing to accept. For example, if the package includes a slide with standard and compensated barrels, the front sight must be mounted on the slide whereas most competitors prefer the longer radius of a compensator-mounted sight. Many who participate in the various action shooting games also want an extended magazine release button with a reduced-power spring and an extended thumb safety with wide tab on a comp gun (features no carry gun should ever wear). Consequently, the magazine release and safety would need to be changed out each time the gun is required to serve a different role. Then there's the trigger. Most competitors want a lighter trigger than should be on a carry gun.

Despite their shortcomings, switch-top or switch-barrel combinations are relatively popular and some work out quite well. One of my Gold Cups is a good example. It started out as a custom gun with an original slide and a Heinie 5½-inch match-grade barrel in .45 ACP. I later added the following:

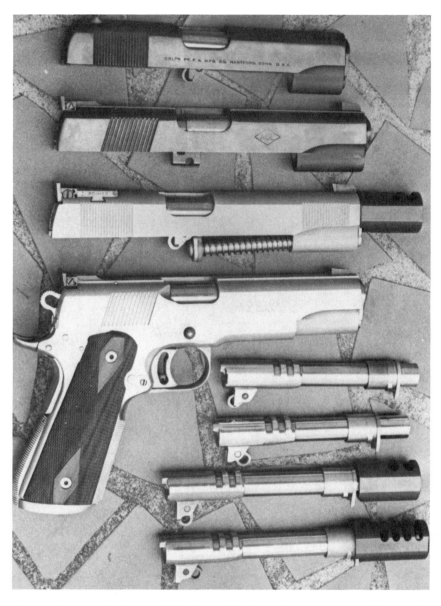

The author's switch-top Gold Cup with its various top assemblies and barrels, from top to bottom: (1) Colt Commander with Bar-Sto barrel in .45 ACP, (2) Colt ACE in .22 Long Rifle, (3) Colt Delta Elite with Heinie compensated barrel in 10mm Auto, (4) Gold Cup with its Heinie barrel in .45 ACP, (5) Bar-Sto 5-inch barrel in 10mm Auto, (6) Bar-Sto 5-inch barrel in .41 Avenger, (7) Heinie 5½-inch compensated barrel in .40 S&W, and (8) Brown 5½-inch compensated barrel in .45 ACP.

The author's C. W. Custom Combat Gold Cup switch-top gun with its
Heinie .45 ACP barrel.

The author's C. W. Custom switch-top Gold Cup with its Colt ACE top assembly in .22 Long Rifle.

The author's C. W. Custom switch-top Gold Cup with its Colt Delta Elite slide and Heinie compensated barrel in 10mm Auto.

The author's C. W. Custom switch-top Gold Cup with its Colt
Commander slide and Bar-Sto barrel in .45 ACP.

SSK Industries 5-inch barrel in .41 Avenger; Springfield Armory compensated barrel in .45 ACP for use with the Gold Cup slide; Colt ACE top assembly in .22 Long Rifle; Colt Delta Elite slide with two Heinie 5½-inch compensated barrels in 10mm and .40 S&W, and a Bar-Sto 5-inch barrel in 10mm for that slide; a complete Colt Commander top assembly with Wilson tritium night sights; and a Bar-Sto barrel in .45 ACP. This adds up to eight available options in one gun.

Here are some roles my switch-top, switch-barrel Gold Cup can play. With its 5-inch .45 ACP barrel and original slide, I can use the gun in Bullseye competition. The ACE top assembly can be used for ventilating tin cans and sharpening the hand and eye during practice sessions with paper targets. It's a nice gun for hunting small game as is, but within minutes I can attach a pistol scope with one of the grip-attached mounts and make the ACE conversion even better for that application. I also have an ACE assembly for one of my fullhouse .38 Super comp guns and find it an excellent way to practice USPSA/IPSC shooting with the .22 Long Rifle cartridge. You would be surprised what a brick-a-week practice program with discount house ammunition will do for your shooting skills.

I can use the gun with its 5-inch .45 ACP, .41 Avenger, or 10mm barrel for Tactical class IPSC competition, or switch to one of the compensated barrels in .45 ACP, 10mm, or .40 S&W and go for the Unlimited class gold. With either of the two 5-inch barrels, it's not a bad gun for home security or carry, but I really like it best for the latter application when it wears its Commander slide and barrel with Bill Wilson's night sights. I hunt wild hogs a great deal with hounds and for ending a chase with some fast and furious close-range shooting, the 5-inch 10mm barrel works quite well. The same goes for the 5-inchers in .45 ACP and .41 Avenger.

Some examples of what will and won't work follow.

A Series 70 slide will work on a Series 80 frame if the pistolsmith mills out a clearance notch in the bottom of the slide for the upper firing pin block plunger lever located in the frame. You obviously will not, however, have the benefit of the firing pin block of a Series 80 slide unless the pistolsmith installs its plunger, plunger spring, firing pin, and extractor in the Series 70 slide.

A series 80 slide will work on a Series 70 frame if the pistolsmith installs Colt's trigger bar and plunger levers for the firing pin block in the frame. You will then have the benefit of the additional Series 80 safety mechanism in a Series 70 frame.

A Colt Series 80 Government Model slide will work on the Double Eagle frame if the pistolsmith mills out a disconnector timing recess inside the right sidewall of the slide, same as on the Double Eagle slide. **WARNING! THIS**

IS AN EXTREMELY CRITICAL MODIFICATION AND IF DONE INCORRECTLY CAN BE DANGEROUS. The Series 70 slide also can be used if the pistolsmith mills out the disconnector recess and installs the Series 80 firing pin block mechanism which consists of a plunger, plunger spring, firing pin, and extractor.

The Commander slide will work on the Government Model frame, but its recoil spring tunnel will have to be shortened to about one inch. If this modification is not made, the slide will batter the frame's rail end even if a recoil buffer is used. I should add that the body of the Commander ejector is thicker than that of the standard Government Model in .45 ACP. Consequently, the disconnector timing rail in its slide is more narrow for clearance. When a Commander slide is installed on the Government Model frame, more daylight is left between the righthand side of its thinner ejector and the lefthand side of the timing rail. Most people would never notice, but I mention it because if a cartridge case should blow during firing, the wider gap between the two parts may allow more of the propellant gas to flow back into the shooter's face. Some gas usually will escape out through that area anyhow but the wider gap is likely to increase its volume.

I won't say the Officer's ACP slide will not work on the Government Model frame because as soon as I do, my mailbox will run over with letters telling me how wrong I am. I will say this, though. If the recoil spring tunnel of the Officer's ACP slide is shortened enough to work, it will be only about .400-inch long. The dust cover on the frame could be shortened, but it would then be too short for the standard-length slide.

Returning to what components work like a charm with each other, the Commander and Officer's ACP frames and slides are interchangeable.

As cartridge/slide matchups go, a 9mm slide works with the .38 Super, 9x21mm, CP 9x23mm Super, .41 Action Express, and other cartridges of similar rim diameter, but extractors with slightly different claw lengths may have to be used for .38 and 9mm. The .40 S&W slide works with the 10mm cartridge and vice versa. The .45 ACP slide works with any wildcat on that case, such as the .41 Avenger, .451 Detonics, 10mm Centaur, and .38-45. The .45 ACP slide also will work with the 10mm Auto and .40 S&W if a 9mm Parabellum extractor is used, and if a barrel is custom made for that application. A .40 or 10mm barrel shaped like the .45 ACP barrel would have to be made, as they do differ.

When barrels with the original style feedramp are installed, some pistolsmiths say the .45 ACP frame should be used only with barrels of that caliber. Others say 10mm Auto and .40 S&W barrels work quite well with the .45 ACP frame. My previously described switch-top Gold Cup supports the opinion voiced by the latter group, but it's best for your pistolsmith to decide. Frames made for the 9mm Parabellum will work with the 9x23mm, .38 Super, and 9x21mm.

One thing is certain, any frame will work with the various calibers if all the barrels have integral feedramps. You could start with a frame made for the .45 ACP or 9mm and use top assemblies in those calibers as well as .40 S&W, 10mm Auto, .38 Super, 9x21mm, or any other cartridge compatible with the Government Model pistol. With some guns, you might have to switch ejectors when going from the .45 ACP to a cartridge with a smaller rim diameter such as the 9mm Luger. Your pistolsmith should know for certain.

If tightening the slide to frame fit is a part of the custom package, all top assemblies should be fitted to the frame at the same time. If one is added later and has to be lapped to fit the frame, the lapping may loosen up the fit of the first slide, not to mention spoiling the frame's finish. Each upper assembly should have its own fitted slide stop. An identification code stamped or engraved on its inner surface indicates to which it belongs. Incidentally, two slide stops are made for the Government Model, one for the .45 ACP, .40 S&W, and 10mm Auto, and another for the .38 Super and 9mm Luger.

When ordering a switch-top gun, it is best to specify full-length recoil spring guides in all upper assemblies. This makes switching them much faster. Simply retract the slide, remove the slide stop, push the entire top assembly forward and off the frame, and everything stays together as a unit. Install another top assembly and you're back in business quicker than it took me to describe it.

Taking the switch-top concept even further, the Pachmayr Dominator and Springfield Armory S.A.S.S. single-shot conversions transform the Government Model into a good candidate for open-country hunting and metallic silhouette competition.

Even when a switch-top gun is not desired, the mixing and matching of slides and frames has become quite popular. Combine the Officer's ACP top assembly with the Commander frame and you have big-gun firepower with little-gun compactness. An especially popular combination is to use the Commander slide or a Government Model slide trimmed to the same length with a compensated barrel. The Commander slide also can be shortened to Officer's ACP length. Compensators used on those guns are considerably shorter than those installed on competition guns and usually are of single-chamber design. Called mini comps, carry comps, street comps, or whatever the individual pistolsmith chooses to call his version, the overall length of a compensated Commander is about the same as that of a noncompensated Government Model. The compensated Officer's ACP is about the same length as a non-compensated Commander.

Michael Morris, a friend of mine who is serious about practical competition, introduced me to an interesting idea in switch-top guns. During some of his practice sessions he installs a Colt Ace upper assembly on his comp gun and burns up about 4,000 rounds of discount house .22 Long Rifle ammunition each month. Michael practices on the same types of courses he shoots in competition. During other sessions he switches top assemblies and transforms his gun into a .38 Super. His brick-a-week exercises with the Rimfire keep his reflexes honed, his eye and trigger finger sharp, and yet it is considerably less expensive than shooting an equal amount of .38 Super handloads. I tried it and the system works so well I now do the same. Interestingly enough, I wrote about the concept in one of the gun magazines and before long several pistolsmiths announced the availability of fullhouse Government Model switch-top pistols built especially for USPSA/IPSC competitors.

The Switch-Bottom Gun

The introduction of high-capacity Government Model frames by Caspian, McCormick, and Para-Ordnance has made the switch-bottom custom gun mildly popular. It came about when competitors who already owned standard-capacity comp guns decided to have the top assemblies from those guns installed on one of the mucho firepower frames. One might logically think the old frame is no longer used and that probably is the case with some shooters. Others still prefer the handling characteristics of the old style frame for speed shooting where five or six rounds per string usually are plenty. Conversely, they also want the new style frame for USPSA/IPSC competition where its greater cartridge capacity can be an advantage. So, they use the standard frame for steel plate matches and switch to the high-capacity frame for hose 'em down-type practical pistol matches.

Warning

Switch-top and switch-bottom guns are fun and the concept can increase the versatility of a custom gun considerably. It is not something a shooter should blindly walk into without the assistance, advice, and recommendations of a qualified pistolsmith. In addition, the various combinations described herein have worked fine for the author, but due to variations from gun to gun, they may not always work.

18

Complete Disassembly

WITH the exception of removal of its ejector, slide latch/thumb safety plunger tube housing, grip panels, and grip panel bushings, the Government Model pistol is easily disassembled with no tools. The sequence can differ a bit, but one way of doing it follows.

Frame Disassembly

With the magazine removed and the gun unloaded, the upper assembly is removed from the frame. With the hammer at full cock, the thumb safety is removed from the frame by pulling it outward as it is moved from the *off* to the *on* position. The safety usually will come out freely as it begins to reach a halfway position between on and off, but may require a bit of back and forth jiggling as it is pulled outward. Removing the thumb safety releases the slide latch/thumb safety plunger spring for removal from its housing on the side of the frame.

IMPORTANT: The dual-opposed plungers are under spring pressure and if not caught with the hand, they may fly from their housing when the safety is removed.

With the hammer lowered, the shaft of the thumb safety is used to push out the mainspring housing crosspin from the frame's left side. The pin is located at the bottom rear corner of the frame and has a dimple in one end to prevent slippage as it is removed.

IMPORTANT: The hammer must be carefully lowered (rather than dropped) to its extreme forward position before the mainspring housing or

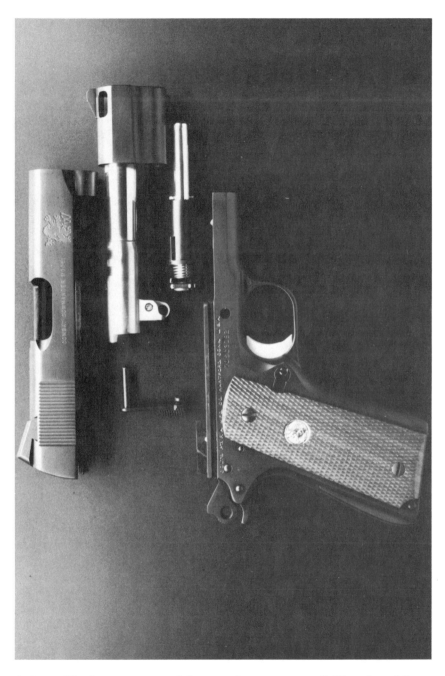

A Steve Woods compensated Commander carry gun field-stripped for cleaning.

With the hammer cocked, the thumb safety is easily removed.

The dual-opposed slide latch and thumb safety plunger is pulled from its housing on the frame's lefthand side.

The mainspring housing pin is best removed with this Brownells tool.

its retaining pin is removed. If the hammer is dropped with the slide removed, the thin shelf on the frame behind the disconnector can be damaged. With its crosspin removed, sliding the mainspring housing downward removes it from the frame, releases the grip safety for removal, and exposes the three-fingered sear spring which also is removed. If the housing is a bit stubborn about leaving the frame, cocking the hammer usually pops it loose unless it is rusted in place.

The shaft of the thumb safety is used to push out the hammer crosspin (from right side of frame), allowing the hammer and its strut to be removed. On a Series 80 gun, removal of the hammer crosspin also frees the upper firing pin block lever for removal. The crosspin holding the hammer and its strut together is pushed out with the firing pin.

The round shank of the hammer strut is used to push out the sear cross-pin (from right side of frame). If the shank of the strut happens to be square (as some now are), the firing pin is used to push out the crosspin. With the crosspin removed, the sear and disconnector are free to be pulled from the frame. On a Series 80 gun, this also frees the lower firing pin block lever for removal. On the Gold Cup, this also frees its sear depressor lever for removal.

The bottom of the grip safety is held in position by the mainspring housing.

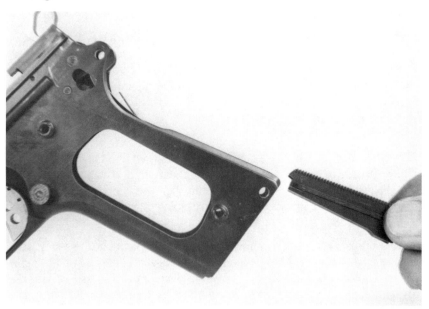

With the grip safety and mainspring housing removed, the hammer, sear spring, sear, and disconnector are removed.

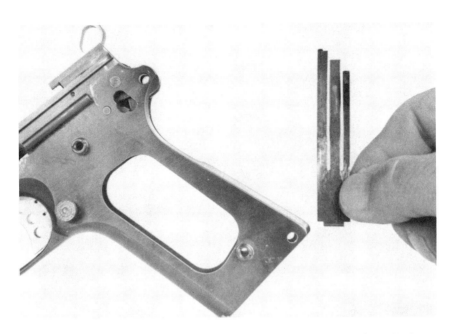

After the mainspring housing is removed, the sear spring is pulled from the rear of the frame.

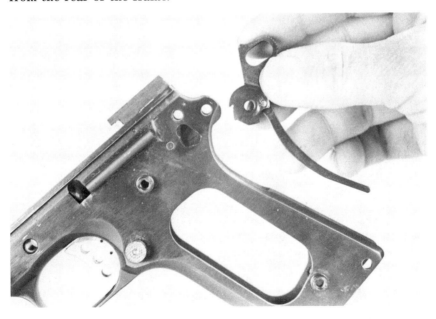

The hammer can be removed after its crosspin and the mainspring housing are removed.

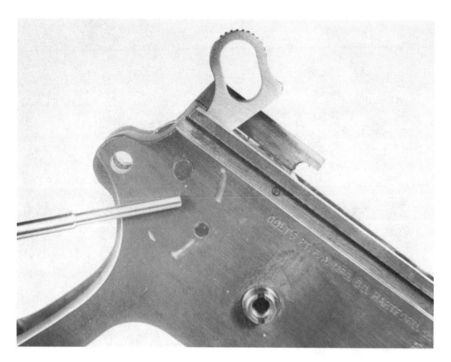

The hammer and sear crosspins are pushed out from the righthand side of the frame.

IMPORTANT: Attached to the rear of the Gold Cup sear is a tiny coil spring that is easily overlooked or misplaced during disassembly.

To remove the magazine catch from the frame, press its button inward with a finger and while holding it in that position, turn its slotted-head screw approximately 90 degrees counterclockwise with the bent end of the lefthand finger of the sear spring. The entire assembly can now be withdrawn from the righthand side of the frame. Don't attempt to force the screw. If it refuses to turn, ease off slightly on the pressure being applied to the release button while keeping counterclockwise tension on the screw with the screwdriver. If an oversize extension has been installed on the magazine catch button, it will have to be removed first. With the magazine catch assembly removed, the trigger can be withdrawn rearward and out of the frame.

Depressing the mainspring with the shaft of the slide lock and removing its retaining crosspin with the firing pin frees the spring, its strut cap, and its lower pin retainer for removal from their tunnel in the mainspring housing. **WARNING**: This spring is under extremely heavy tension and must be removed very carefully.

388

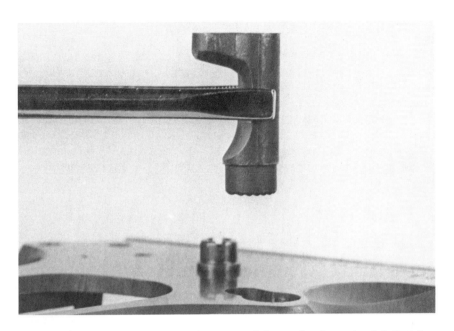

The magazine catch assembly is removed from the frame's righthand side.

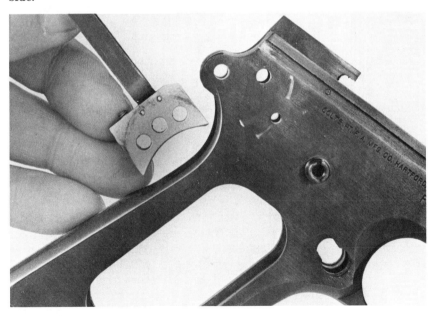

The trigger and its stirrup can be pulled rearward and from the frame after the magazine catch is removed.

Slide Disassembly

The shaft of the thumb safety is used to depress the firing pin for removal of its stop or retaining plate. The plate also retains the extractor. With the plate removed, the firing pin, firing pin spring, and extractor are free to be removed from the rear of slide. A push on the front end of the extractor with a finger usually will cause it to protrude from the rear of the slide far enough to be grasped for removal. If not, the firing pin can be used to push the extractor to the rear. If the claw of the extractor hangs on the front of its raceway at the breechface of the slide, an outward nudge with the tip of the firing pin will free it.

Series 80 Guns

Removing the firing pin and extractor from a Series 80 gun requires a slightly different procedure. Fully depress the spring-loaded firing pin block plunger at the bottom of the slide and while holding it in that position, push the firing pin as far forward as possible. While holding the firing pin forward, release the blocking plunger. The plunger will now hold the firing pin forward for easy removal of its stop plate. With the plate removed, a push on the blocking plunger releases the firing pin and its spring for removal.

WARNING: Since the firing pin is being retained under full spring pressure by the blocking plunger, it will fly from the gun when released and should be caught with a shop cloth or the palm of the hand.

The Series 80 extractor retains the firing pin block plunger in the slide and cannot be removed until the plunger is removed. To remove the plunger, slowly push the extractor rearward about .025 inch. This moves a retaining shoulder on the side of the extractor away from the plunger, allowing it and its spring to drop from the slide. The extractor can now be removed from the slide.

At this point the Government Model pistol has been disassembled by using its component parts as tools.

I have included the no-tools method of disassembly for its historical significance rather than its practical value. It can be done in a pinch, but the risk of scratching the finish of a gun is much higher than when the proper tools are used. The Government Model was designed to be disassembled in the field without the use of tools and for this reason most of its component parts fit together rather loosely. The fit of the hammer and sear cross-pins in the frame usually are so loose, they can be partially pushed out with a fingernail and then completely withdrawn with the thumb and finger. On the other hand, oversized crosspins often are installed in the higher-grade custom guns and they require punches of the correct size for removal.

After the firing pin retaining plate is removed, the firing pin, its spring, and the extractor can be removed.

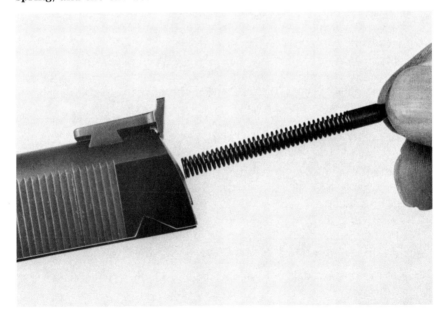

After the firing pin retaining plate is removed from the slide, the firing pin and its spring can be removed.

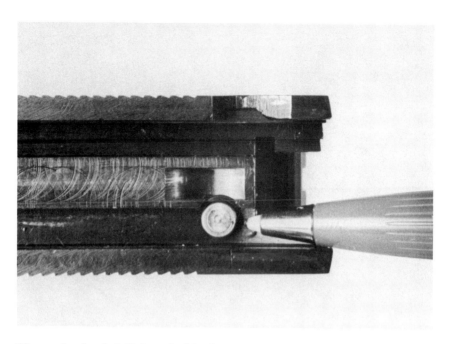

The spring-loaded firing pin block plunger in the bottom of a Series 80 slide.

On a gun that has not been properly maintained, its sear, hammer, and mainspring housing crosspins may be rusted firmly in place. The same also can apply to its extractor. Some pistolsmiths stake the hammer strut and barrel link retaining pins in place. Removing those parts obviously requires the skills of a trained professional.

Grip Panel Removal

If a custom gun has nice grip panels, they should be removed first during disassembly and placed out of the way to avoid damage. In climates with relatively high ambient humidity, wooden panels may have absorbed enough moisture to cause them to expand and grip the screw bushings in the frame rather tightly. Never insert a screwdriver or knife blade between the edges of the panels and the frame in an attempt to pry them loose.

One of the panels usually can be pushed loose by inserting a finger into the magazine well and pressing outward on its inner surface. If this fails, wrap the shank of a screwdriver with tape to prevent scratching the finish of the frame, insert it into the magazine well and gently pry or tap one of the panels loose. After one panel is removed, the inner surface of its mate is exposed

392

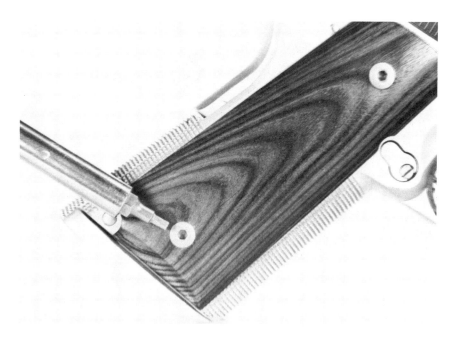

Removing the grip panels from the gun is the first step toward complete disassembly.

by the lightening cutout in the side of the grip frame. Light taps with the handle of the screwdriver on the inside of the panel will break it loose.

Helpful Reassembly Hints

Most firearms disassembly instructions end with "assemble in the reverse order," or something similar. Unfortunately, it's not always so simple because most of us find things far easier to take apart than to put back together. For this reason, I have included a few helpful hints that may eliminate a bit of frustration and head-scratching for other folks like me.

Frame Reassembly

The trigger goes back into the frame first. The magazine catch can now be installed. Insert it into the righthand side of the frame, turn its screw about 90 degrees clockwise, and the catch snaps into position.

The top end of the disconnector has a round shank with sharply beveled front and rear surfaces. Its bottom end is flat on the front side and beveled on the rear side. When inserting the disconnector, its top end will enter its

393

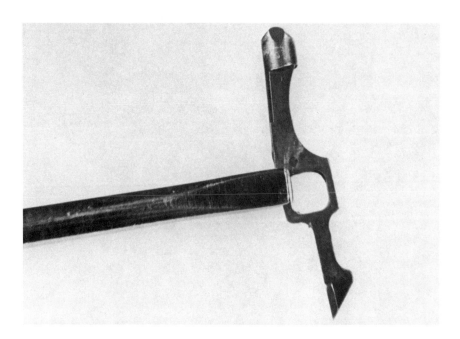

The disconnector as it rests inside the gun.

raceway in the frame only if the flat side of its bottom end is facing forward (toward the trigger) and its beveled side is facing rearward. Insert the disconnector and hold it in position by inserting an alignment pin (firing pin or hammer strut shank) through the sear crosspin hole from the right side of the frame.

The sear curves rearward to a relative narrow edge or hammer notch engaging surface at the top. At its bottom end is a flat surface with two legs projecting below it. With the front of the frame pointed down, lay the sear atop the disconnector (already installed) and then pull the alignment pin out far enough to allow the sear to drop farther onto the disconnector. Now push the pin through the retaining holes of the disconnector and sear and keep pushing until its end protrudes beyond the frame's left side. Now grasp the sear crosspin with the left hand, the alignment pin with the right, and push the latter from the frame with the former. The sear and disconnector are now held in position by their crosspin.

The Gold Cup Sear

Colt's Series 70 and 80 Gold Cup target pistols have two sear-related parts that do not appear on other guns. They are a tiny coil spring and a flat sear

394

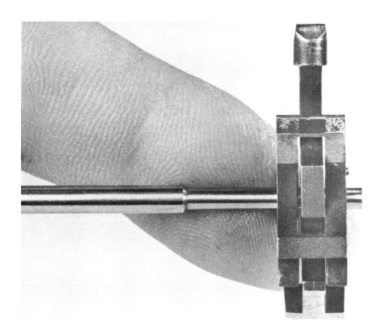

A rear view of the sear and disconnector together illustrates their relationship inside the gun.

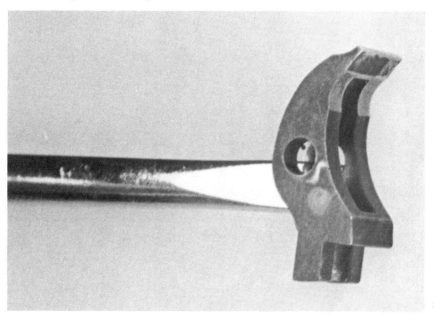

The sear as it rests inside the gun.

depressor lever. The lever has a crosspin hole through its top end and bent tabs on its lower front and rear edges. It is held in position by the sear crosspin and fits between the righthand side of the sear and the inside of the frame of a Series 70 gun. On a Series 80 gun, the lever fits between the sear and the lower firing pin block lever.

One end of the depressor spring fits into a recess in the rear flat of the sear; its other end bears against the rear tab of the depressor lever. These parts should not be left out of the gun during assembly as they increase sear engagement pressure against the hammer. This minimizes the possibility of sear bounce allowing the hammer to follow the slide during firing when the trigger is adjusted for a light pull.

Lower Firing Pin Block Lever

The lower firing pin block lever of the Series 80 gun is held in position by the sear crosspin. It is shaped somewhat like the profile of a bird's head, one with a long neck and beak. This can be the most frustrating part of all to install. When positioned correctly in the gun, its neck is pointed downward and its beak is pointed to the rear. It rests against the wall of the frame on the righthand side of the sear.

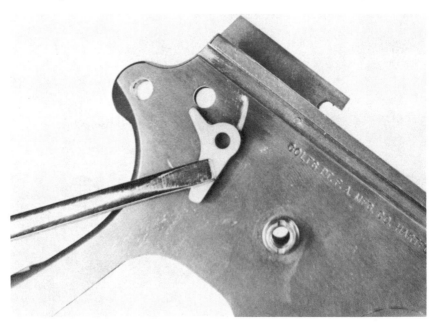

The lower lever of the Series 80 firing pin block is positioned in the gun with its "beak" pointed rearward.

396

I find it easier to first install the sear, disconnector, and their crosspin. Then while holding the frame left-side down, the crosspin is pulled out just far enough to allow the lever to squeeze between the end of the crosspin and the inside of the frame and be held in that position. While holding the lever with a tweezer, align its hole with the end of the crosspin and then push the pin all the way home. This procedure may work on the first attempt or it may take several tries, but when coaxed along with a generous application of "PPP" (patience, persistence, and perseverance), the lever eventually will rest in place beside the sear.

Hammer

The hammer, with its strut attached, is now placed into the frame and held in place with its crosspin.

Series 80 Upper Firing Pin Block Lever

The upper firing pin block lever is held in the frame on the righthand side of the hammer by the hammer crosspin. It is shaped like the profile of a long-nosed cartoon character wearing a long-billed cap. When positioned correctly in the gun, the nose and bill of the cap are pointed forward, with the latter lying exposed in a slot in the top of the frame.

This lever is easier to install after the hammer and its crosspin are in place. While holding the frame left-side down, push the crosspin from the frame just far enough to allow the lever to be squeezed between the end of the crosspin and the side of the frame. Slide the lever in beside the hammer and when its bottom hole is aligned with the end of the crosspin, it is pushed home.

Sear Spring

With the hammer strut swung up against the back of the hammer and out of the way, the sear spring is installed. It is the wide, flat spring with three fingers pointing up and a bent tab on its bottom end. The bottom tab fits in a slot inside the frame, almost in line with the bottom grip screw bushings. The lefthand, or longest, finger rests against the backside of the trigger stirrup. The middle finger rests against the disconnector's beveled surface. The righthand finger awaits installation of the grip safety. After the sear spring is installed, the mainspring housing is slid partially onto the frame to hold it in position while the grip and thumb safeties are installed.

The upper firing pin block lever on a Series 80 gun rests on the hammer crosspin in this position.

Grip Safety and Mainspring Housing

With the hammer down (fully forward), the grip safety is placed into the back of the frame. As the mainspring housing is pushed upward on the frame, the gun is tilted to and fro until the bottom end of the hammer strut is in alignment with the mouth of its spring tunnel. With the hammer strut aligned, the housing can be pushed all the way home. The mainspring housing crosspin is then installed with its dimpled end on the left side of the frame.

Dual-Opposed Plungers

This assembly consists of a coil spring with a metal plunger attached to each end. The front or slide stop plunger has a two-diameter shape and is smaller on its forward end than on its spring end. When installed in its housing on the lefthand side of the frame, the two-diameter plunger goes in first to rest against the slide latch when it is installed. The rear plunger is depressed and held inside its housing, and then released as the thumb safety is installed. The thin, narrow blade of a small pocketknife can be used, but it may scratch the frame. Much better is a small plastic gadget called a Widget, available from Brownells.

398

Thumb Safety

With the hammer cocked and the plunger depressed, the shaft of the thumb safety is pushed into its hole in the frame and through the hole in the top end of the grip safety. Pressing firmly inward on the safety while it is positioned about halfway between its on and off positions will push it all the way home. If it is an ambidextrous style, the left-side safety should be installed first.

Extractor and Firing Pin

The extractor is pushed into its tunnel in the slide with its claw pointed to the left. One end of the firing pin spring will fit tightly on the firing pin while the other will be a loose fit. The tight end goes toward the rear of the firing pin. Push the firing pin into its tunnel in the slide and while holding it there, slide the firing pin stop plate into position. The rounded end of the stop plate goes up. The firing pin and extractor are now locked into position.

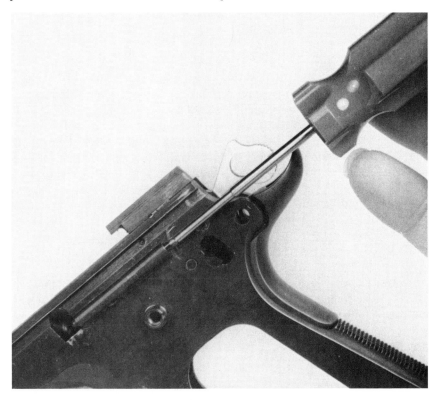

This tool (a safety detent depressor) from Brownells is used to depress the plunger in its housing when installing the thumb safety.

Firing Pin Block Plunger
(Series 80 Gun)

When in its proper position in the slide, the solid end of the firing pin stop plunger is pointed down and its cupped end is pointed up. One end of the small coil spring fits into the cupped end of the plunger.

Before installing the plunger, install the extractor and push it to its extreme forward position. A look into the plunger hole in the bottom of the slide reveals a retaining shoulder on the extractor that won't allow the plunger to completely enter. Carefully push the extractor to the rear until the shoulder disappears beneath the edge of the plunger hole. Now fully insert the plunger and its spring in the hole and hold them there while pushing the extractor fully forward. The plunger will now remain in the slide while the firing pin and its stop plate are being installed at the rear.

WARNING: If the plunger is not installed in the slide during reassembly, the gun will fire and function, but the firing pin block mechanism of the Series 80 is deactivated. This is neither recommended nor condoned by the author or the manufacturer of the gun.

Be Gentle

With few exceptions, every component part of the Government Model pistol was designed and is manufactured to be easily removed or replaced without application of force. A couple of exceptions that come to mind are the driven pins that hold the ejector and the Gold Cup rear sight in place. Everything else should slip smoothly into or out of the gun. I'm emphasizing this so you will remember that if a particular part seems stubborn about taking its place in the gun, you're probably trying to install it incorrectly. Never attempt to force a part into position. Be patient. Be gentle.

Preliminary Function Testing
(With Gun Unloaded)

Before loading and shooting the gun after reassembly, it should be checked for proper functioning while empty. To check for adequate sear engagement, cock the hammer and with both safeties in their off positions, push forward on the back of the hammer with about 20 pounds of force. The hammer should not drop.

To check the thumb safety for correct operation, cock the gun, push the safety to its extreme upward position (on), depress the grip safety, and pull on the trigger. The hammer should not drop. Then release the safety and pull the trigger. The hammer should drop.

To check the grip safety, cock the hammer, leave the thumb safety in its extreme downward (off) position and pull on the trigger without depressing the grip safety. Next, depress the grip safety and pull the trigger. If the hammer did not drop on the first check, but did on the second check, the grip safety is operating correctly.

To check the disconnector, cock the hammer, retract the slide about ⅛ inch, and while holding it in that position, pull the trigger. With the hammer lowered, hold the trigger back while retracting the slide and continue holding the trigger back while easing the slide forward to its locked position. If the hammer did not drop when either of those two checks was performed, the disconnector is operating correctly.

To check the firing pin block of a Series 80 gun, cock the hammer and press inward on the tail of the firing pin with a small nail or centerpunch. The firing pin should not move forward. While holding the hammer back, pull the trigger and hold it in that position while pressing inward on the tail of the firing pin. The firing pin should move forward.

It is important to remember that these are preliminary checks only; a gun should not be depended on until it is actually test fired at the range or other safe place. When test firing a gun at the range after reassembly, load only two rounds in the magazine and fire them. Repeat the two-shot procedure until 20 to 30 rounds have been fired. If the gun is not functioning properly and suddenly goes full auto, it can be controlled for a couple of rounds whereas this may not be possible with a full magazine.

Recommended Tools

Considering the small number of tool's required and their nominal cost, no Government Model owner has a good excuse for not owning the proper tools needed for disassembly. Without these tools one runs the risk of damaging a fine gun. Two screwdrivers are needed, one for the grip panel screws and another for the screw in the magazine catch. If the gun has an adjustable rear sight, a third screwdriver is required. If the grip panels have hex heads, the screwdriver count drops back to two. The blades of the screwdrivers should be hollow ground (like pistolsmiths use) rather than flat ground (like those found at the hardware store). The width and thickness of the blades should be a precise fit with the slots of the screws. Anything less and you will have buggered screws in short order.

Barrel bushing wrenches are made of either steel or a tough synthetic material. The steel wrench is not as easily broken, but is more likely to scratch the gun's finish. I highly recommend the synthetic version for use on custom guns. Two styles are available, open-end for guns with compensated barrels and closed-end for noncompensated guns. The former style of wrench can be used on the latter type of gun, but it is not as durable as the closed-end type. If you experience difficulty in finding the open-end type, simply purchase a closed-end wrench and convert it with a sharp pocketknife.

For removal of the various nondriven pins in the Government Model, nylon drift punches are best as they won't scratch the finish as will a steel punch. One of the best and least expensive routes is to buy the nylon front sight drift punches from Brownells (No. 080-478-000) and have a pistolsmith turn down one of their ends in a lathe for a close fit with the hammer and sear pins. Some pistolsmiths will furnish a couple of these punches with a custom gun upon request. The best thing I have found for pushing out the mainspring housing pin is Brownells' No. 662-545-000 tool. A steel roll pin punch is handy for removing the ejector, but it seldom has to be done. A small curved-nose, needlenose plier is handy for holding small parts in position during assembly, but a large, self-closing, flat-nose tweezer-like device called a hemostat works even better. Used by surgeons and pistolsmiths, mine came from Brownells (No. 360-060-000).

There will come a time in the life of every Government Model owner when the slide lock plunger will hang up in the retaining groove of the slide lock when it is being installed. The thin blade of a pocketknife will solve the problem, but is also likely to scratch the finish. A far better solution is the little plastic tool called a Widget from Wilson's. Even better is Brownells' safety plunger depressor tool (No. 583-120-101).

When rounding up hex wrenches of the correct sizes for removal of the screws from grip panels and scope mounts, insist on the best money can buy. They should be made of extremely hard steel. Cheap wrenches like those that come with scope mounts made for rifles by various companies usually are made to be used one time and thrown away. For this reason, they are quite soft. After a bit of use their shoulders become worn, causing them to slip and wallow out the heads of screws. After years of never being able to find the right size screwdriver or hex wrench for a job, I finally acquired a Brownells Magna-Tip Super Set and really don't know how I ever did without it.

Although not absolutely necessary, a small bench vise with padded jaws is quite handy as a third hand when removing or installing certain parts. Removing the mainspring from its housing is probably the best example.

When disassembling the gun, a parts box is an absolute necessity. As each part is removed, it is placed into the box. For that purpose, the large magnetic parts tray from Brownells (No. 568-710-000) can't be beat. It measures 10¼ inches long, 7¼ inches wide, ¾-inch deep, and its magnetized bottom won't allow even the smallest of metal parts to escape.

This magnetic parts tray from Brownells keeps parts from going
astray during disassembly.

It is best to disassemble the gun in an uncluttered area without carpet on the floor. If a spring or other small part escapes your grasp, it will be much easier to find in such an area. If you use your kitchen table for this purpose, remember that a spring's two favorite hiding places are beneath the refrigerator and the dishwasher.

If In Doubt, Don't Do It

I can remember a time when the chances of my attempting to completely disassemble a Government Model pistol were about as good as my taking a computer or rocket engine apart. Then I decided that in order to properly maintain the gun, it would have to be taken apart occasionally and it was a lot more convenient for me to do the job than sending it to a pistolsmith. So, I took the easy route by having a pistolsmith who specializes in working on John Browning's gun show me how it is done.

I'm saying all of this to emphasize that complete disassembly of a firearm is not a job for everyone and those who feel incapable of doing so should not be embarrassed. I found the procedure easy to learn, and I'm sure you will, too. If in doubt about your ability to do so safely, take the gun to a qualified pistolsmith. It is best to be safe and suffer a bit of inconvenience than to be sorry.

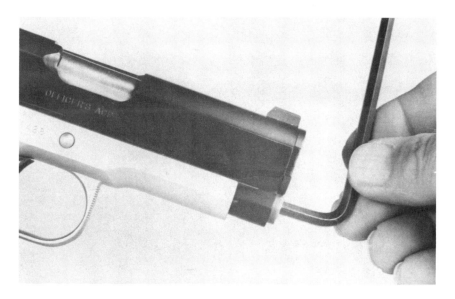

Field stripping a custom gun with a two-piece full-length recoil spring guide rod. (*Note:* This gun has a Wilson sleeved barrel and rear-entry recoil spring plug.)
Step 1: Loosen the rod a couple of turns before removing the top assembly from the frame.

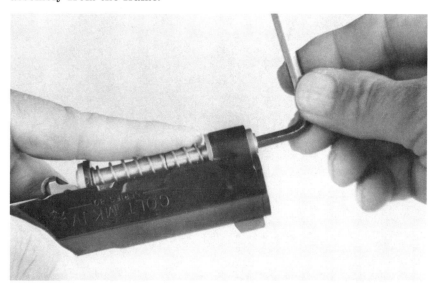

Step 2: After removing the top assembly from the frame, hold the recoil spring captive with a finger while unscrewing the rod's front section.

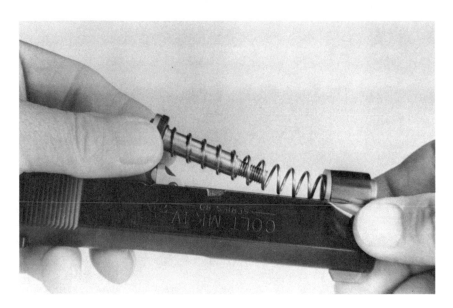

Step 3: Remove rear section of rod along with spring. Rear-entry recoil spring plug can now be removed.

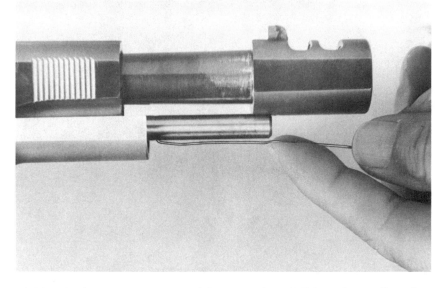

Field stripping a custom gun with a one-piece full-length recoil spring guide rod with takedown hole. (*Note:* This gun has a Wilson sleeved barrel and rear-entry recoil spring plug.)
Step 1: Lock slide back and insert end of bent paper clip in takedown hole in recoil spring guide rod.

406

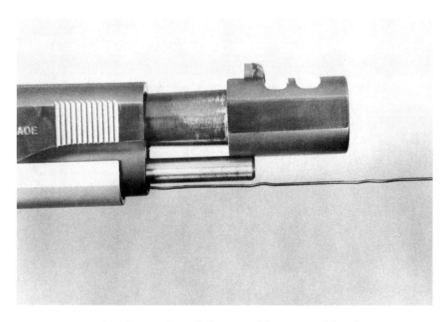

Step 2: Ease slide forward until its travel is arrested by the paper clip.

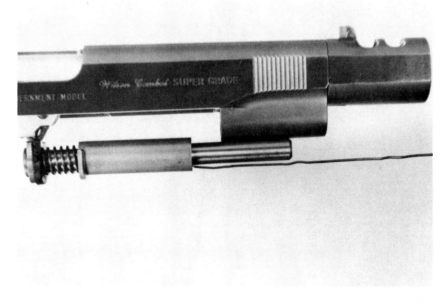

Step 3: Remove top assembly from frame and remove recoil spring, its guide rod, and its plug. Note that the paper clip is holding the spring captive and under tension.

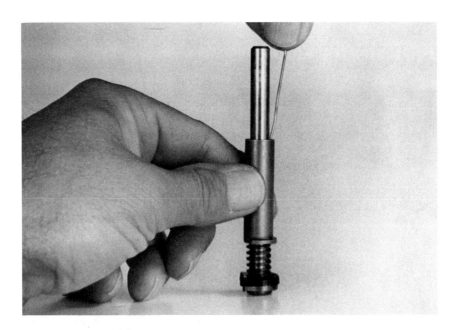

Step 4: Press down on recoil spring plug to remove paper clip. WARNING: Spring is under heavy tension.

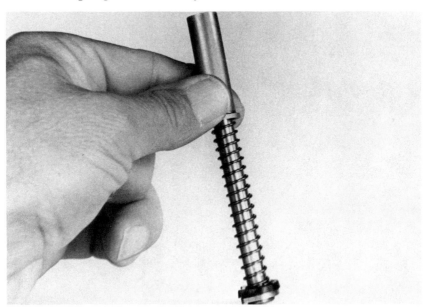

Step 5: With paper clip removed, recoil spring and its plug, and the shock buffer can be removed from the guide rod.

MODEL "O"

ELLIASON SIGHT

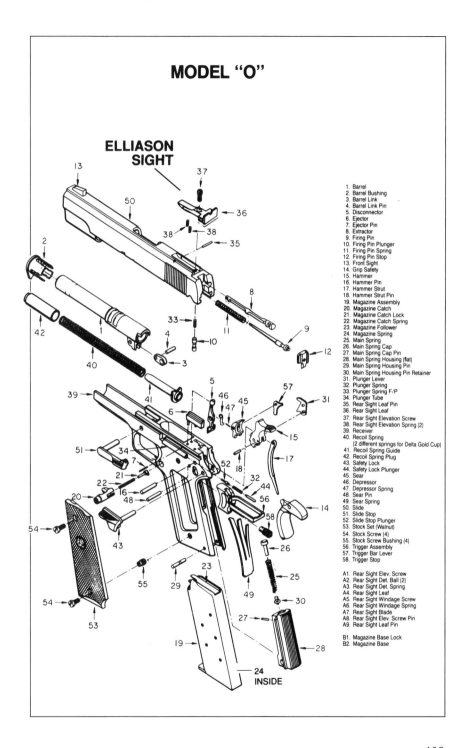

1. Barrel
2. Barrel Bushing
3. Barrel Link
4. Barrel Link Pin
5. Disconnector
6. Ejector
7. Ejector Pin
8. Extractor
9. Firing Pin
10. Firing Pin Plunger
11. Firing Pin Spring
12. Firing Pin Stop
13. Front Sight
14. Grip Safety
15. Hammer
16. Hammer Pin
17. Hammer Strut
18. Hammer Strut Pin
19. Magazine Assembly
20. Magazine Catch
21. Magazine Catch Lock
22. Magazine Catch Spring
23. Magazine Follower
24. Magazine Spring
25. Main Spring
26. Main Spring Cap
27. Main Spring Cap Pin
28. Main Spring Housing (flat)
29. Main Spring Housing Pin
30. Main Spring Housing Pin Retainer
31. Plunger Lever
32. Plunger Spring
33. Plunger Spring F/P
34. Plunger Tube
35. Rear Sight Leaf Pin
36. Rear Sight Leaf
37. Rear Sight Elevation Screw
38. Rear Sight Elevation Spring (2)
39. Receiver
40. Recoil Spring
    (2 different springs for Delta Gold Cup)
41. Recoil Spring Guide
42. Recoil Spring Plug
43. Safety Lock
44. Safety Lock Plunger
45. Sear
46. Depressor
47. Depressor Spring
48. Sear Pin
49. Sear Spring
50. Slide
51. Slide Stop
52. Slide Stop Plunger
53. Stock Set (Walnut)
54. Stock Screw (4)
55. Stock Screw Bushing (4)
56. Trigger Assembly
57. Trigger Bar Lever
58. Trigger Stop

A1. Rear Sight Elev. Screw
A2. Rear Sight Det. Ball (2)
A3. Rear Sight Det. Spring
A4. Rear Sight Leaf
A5. Rear Sight Windage Screw
A6. Rear Sight Windage Spring
A7. Rear Sight Blade
A8. Rear Sight Elev. Screw Pin
A9. Rear Sight Leaf Pin

B1. Magazine Base Lock
B2. Magazine Base

INSIDE

409

1911-A1 Pistol Disassembly:

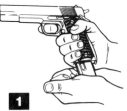

1

Magazine Removal and Chamber Check
a. Press the magazine catch and remove the magazine assembly.
b. Pull slide backwards and look inside chamber.
c. Check to be sure no cartridge is in chamber.

2

Recoil Spring Release
a. Press recoil spring plug with thumb.
b. Rotate barrel bushing clockwise.

3

Gently allow plug and recoil spring set to move forward. Do not remove set. It will keep the recoil spring guide in place.

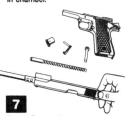

7

Barrel Removal
a. Rotate barrel bushing to the left side of the slide and remove it through the front.
b. Tilt the barrel link forward and remove the barrel through the front of the slide.

8

Firing Pin Removal
a. If necessary, the firing pin may be removed by pressing it while simultaneously pushing the firing pin and extractor stop downwards. This operation should be performed with a pin.
b. Remove the firing pin and its spring by pulling it by its tail.

9

Extractor Removal
Using a pin, (or the firing pin itself), pull the extractor by the groove where the firing pin stops runs.

BE SAFE! BE SURE PISTOL IS UNLOADED BEFORE BEGINNING DISASSEMBLY!

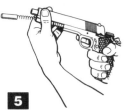

4

Slide Stop Removal
a. Pull slide backwards until the smallest slot on the left of the slide aligns with the top rear of the slide top.
b. Press the slide stop shaft on the right side of the slide, and remove the slide stop by the left side.

5

Slide and Components Removal
Pull the slide forward in its guides and remove the slide. The barrel, the barrel bushing, the recoil spring plug, the recoil spring and the guide will come with it.

6

Recoil Spring Components Removal
a. Remove guide through back side.
b. Recoil spring and its plug are removed through front side.

Reprint, *Springfield Armory, Inc.*

19

Maintaining the Custom Gun

NOT long ago in one of the gun magazines, the author of an article on a famous pistolsmith quoted the chap as being appalled at the number of custom guns that had malfunctioned at a recent major USPSA/IPSC match. For the sake of making a point and to avoid embarrassing the pistolsmith, let us call him Ted Twelvethumbs. Let me also add that the opinion of the author who penned the piece was right on target as Twelvethumbs' guns

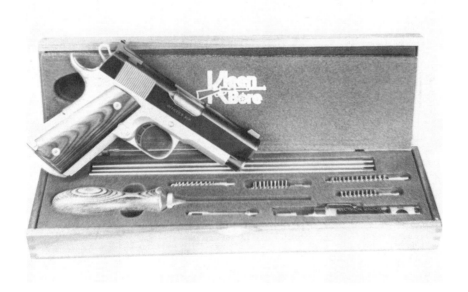

do have a worldwide reputation for quality. A gun simply doesn't leave his shop until he is personally satisfied beyond a doubt that it is 100 percent reliable. Whether or not Twelvethumbs went on to elaborate on his criticism of other pistolsmiths, I have no way of knowing, but the message seemed quite clear— those who put together the majority of guns used in the match were incapable of building in total reliability. That may have been true, but then again, the blame in some cases probably should have been tossed in another direction.

As fate would have it, about six months prior to my reading the article, another pistolsmith was at a match in which a competitor was using one of Twelvethumbs' gorgeous guns. The only problem was that it malfunctioned numerous times during the match. So, rather than placing the blame where it rightfully belonged, the competitor declared Twelvethumbs the most incompetent of pistolsmiths to all who would listen to his cries. It just so happened that the pistolsmith who was at the match overheard his moans and groans. He was absolutely shocked because Twelvethumbs was one of his mentors. To make a short story even more so, my pistolsmith friend agreed to take the gun and attempt to cure its ills. His prognosis? It was absolutely the filthiest gun he had ever taken apart. He later learned that its owner gave the gun a lick and a promise cleaning about every 5,000 rounds. As best as the pistolsmith could determine, the gun had close to 30,000 miles on it and had never been totally disassembled for a thorough cleaning.

Judy Garcia keeps her .38 Super running smoothly with proper maintenance. *(Front Sight photo)*

412

The moral to this story? A good pistolsmith can build total reliability into a custom gun, but its owner is responsible for keeping it running smoothly.

As all firearms designed for military use once were, the Government Model pistol is extremely durable, but like any machine, its useful life depends on how well it is maintained by its owner. Hundreds and possibly thousands of pistols have been reduced to scrap metal through the years by those who have not taken the time to understand the gun's requirements. On the brighter side, given proper care and the occasional replacement of minor component parts, John Browning's autoloader will outlast several generations of shooters.

Some owners of custom guns are hesitant about field stripping them for cleaning as often as needed for fear of harming the gun. The fact of the matter is, the Government Model was designed to be field stripped and even completely disassembled frequently. Shooting the gun while it is extremely dirty subjects it to far more wear and tear than carefully taking it apart and putting it back together. Think of a custom pistol as you would a high-performance automobile—the better you care for it, the longer it will last and the better it will perform.

Two things should be remembered about the accumulation of powder fouling in an autoloading pistol. First, powder is abrasive and an excessive buildup will accelerate wear between metal parts. Secondly, the longer propellant fouling remains on metal, the more solidified it becomes, so it is easier to remove it now rather than later. This can be demonstrated by wiping the fouling from a cartridge case immediately after it is fired and attempting to do the same with another case after it has worn a heavy coat of fouling for a week or so.

Removing the Gunk

I know some shooters who brag about the number of rounds they put through their gun without cleaning it, which is fine with me since they're wasting their money and not mine, but I consider a custom gun too expensive to mistreat. I keep a small cleaning kit in my range bag and clean a gun immediately after each shooting session, even if it has digested only a few rounds. The gun should be field stripped and a small cleaning brush dipped in solvent should be used to break up the accumulation of fouling on the slide's breechface as well as its locking lug recesses, rails, and raceways on either side of its disconnector timing rail. Particular attention should be paid to cleaning beneath the extractor claw. Accubore, Hoppe's No. 9, Birchwood Casey BC-1, and Shooter's Choice are good cleaning solvents, but Rem Oil and Break Free CLP work just as well, and also double as a lubricant.

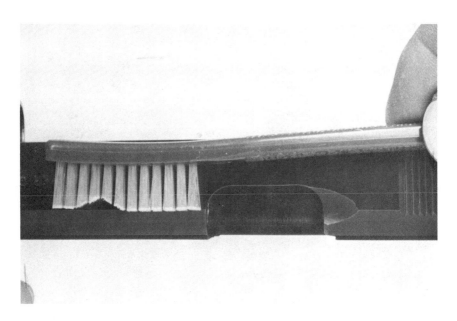

This nylon cleaning brush from Brownells is used to scrub gunk from nooks and crannies, but a toothbrush also will do the job.

The brush and solvent are used on the rails of the frame, its feed ramp, and the inner surface of its recoil spring housing. Narrow brushes designed specifically for this purpose are available from various commercial sources, but in a pinch, a toothbrush will get the job done. Dust and grit tend to accumulate in the frame's magazine well. It is easily removed with a Mag-Brush (available from Brownells), but a clean rag pushed through the chute with a cleaning rod also does the job.

If the barrel has an integral feed ramp, it receives a good brushing. The same goes for the barrel's underlug, the barrel link, and the transverse pin of the slide latch. The chamber and bore of the barrel are gently scrubbed with a tight-fitting bore brush with bronze bristles dipped in solvent.

After all the crud has been loosened by solvent, it is washed away with one of the quick-dry cleaners. Remington's Rem-Action Cleaner is a good one, as are Outers Crud Cutter and Birchwood Casey Quick-Scrub. Equally good cleaners that can be found in automotive supply shops are Sprayon #20747 Hi-Tech Safety Solvent and Degreaser, and Permatex Cleaner and Degreaser. These products come in a spray can and can be blasted into hard-to-reach areas to flush out the gunk after it has first been dissolved by a good solvent. They are nonflammable and leave no residue on the metal. Since their vapors should not be inhaled, I prefer to take the gun parts outside for this operation.

414

Brownells' Mag-Brush is used to clean out the magazine well funnel of a gun, and the interior of its magazine.

Getting the Lead Out

When shooting high-velocity cast bullet loads, lead has a tendency to accumulate in the chamber throat or leade of some barrels. If allowed to build up excessively, it can prevent the complete chambering of a cartridge. One of the best ways to remove it with a minimum expenditure of elbow grease is to use a device called the Lewis Lead Remover. Available from Brownells, it consists of a short cleaning rod with a receptacle on one end for holding a patch cut from extremely fine brass mesh. Being softer than steel, the patch won't harm the bore, but it is hard enough to scrape away the lead fouling in short order. The kit is available in .38, .41, .44, and .45 calibers and every pistol owner who shoots cast bullets should have one. The .38 caliber works with barrels chambered for the .38 Super, 9mm Luger, 9x21mm, and 9x23mm; the .41 caliber is the one to use in 10mm Auto, .40 S&W, and .41 Action Express barrels. Lead fouling can be whisked from the bore by feeding the barrel a dozen or so cartridges with jacketed bullets, but it won't always remove it from the chamber leade.

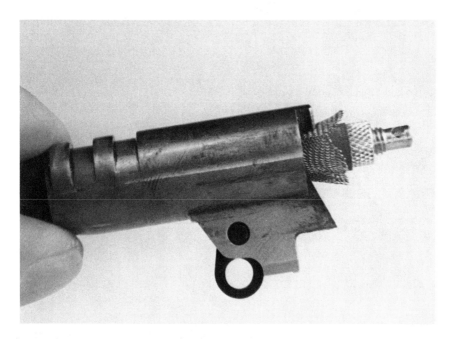

Available from Brownells, the Lewis Lead Remover is a must for those who shoot lots of cast bullets at high velocity.

Molten lead spray from cast bullets also has a tendency to build up on the interior surfaces of the expansion chambers of a compensator. I have yet to find an easy way for the average shooter to chase the lead away from this part of a gun. I know one chap who decided to melt out the lead with a propane torch. He did get the lead out, but the heat loosened the epoxy that held the compensator to the barrel. Although a bit expensive, the Outers Foul Out electrochemical bore cleaning system will make the inside of a compensator look like it has never seen a cast bullet. I know members of one gun club who pooled their resources to make buying the unit a bit easier on the family budget, just as they did when purchasing a chronograph and a progressive reloader. Here's how I use the Foul Out outfit for cleaning a compensated barrel.

The chamber end of the barrel is plugged and fiberglass tape is wrapped tightly around the outside of the compensator to contain the Lead Out cleaning solution in its expansion chambers. The barrel is clamped into a padded vise with its muzzle pointed up. It is then filled to the muzzle of the compensator with the cleaning fluid, the rod inserted, the electrical leads attached, and the unit switched on. If the compensator has an extremely heavy accumulation of lead, the rod will have to be removed and cleaned several times before the job is complete. It also takes longer to remove lead from the compensator than from the barrel because the deposits are farther away from the rod. Those who own the Foul Out rig obviously won't need the previously recommended Lewis Lead cleaner.

Perhaps this is a good place to mention that lead has an extremely difficult time accumulating inside the compensator of a gun wearing a finish called Black-T. The finish is so slick and nonporous that the lead spray cannot adhere to it. For more on this subject, see Chapter 8.

Removing Copper Fouling

Pistol barrels don't usually accumulate copper fouling from jacketed bullets as quickly as rifle barrels because they operate at considerably lower chamber pressures and velocities. Even so, high pressure loadings of the .38 Super, .40 S&W, 9x23mm, and 10mm Auto eventually will coat the bores of some barrels with streaks of copper. This especially is true if the bore is rough. If the fouling is allowed to build up to an excessive level, accuracy will begin to deteriorate. The Outers Foul Out device will remove the fouling, but if you don't have one, use of a bore cleaning solvent developed specifically for dissolving copper is the next best thing. I use Sweet's 7.62 solvent for this purpose because its high ammonia content dissolves copper in a jiffy. I have no personal experience with Shooter's Choice Copper Remover and Hoppe's Benchrest-9 Copper Solvent, but have received favorable reports on their effectiveness from others who have tried them.

Magazine Cleaning

Magazines that are dropped on the ground during speed reloads in competition should be disassembled and thoroughly cleaned after each match. Some magazines have a removable floorplate while others don't. It really doesn't matter because both types are easily taken down. Simply load the magazine about half-full of cartridges (or press the follower down with a wooden pencil), and insert a finishing nail or section of wire cut from a clothes hanger through the holes in its sides, just below the follower. The follower can then be shaken out the top of the magazine while its spring remains compressed. Removal of the nail or wire releases the spring so it can be lifted out through the top of the magazine. Dust, dirt, and other debris can then be wiped from the follower and spring. The inside surfaces of the magazine are cleaned with a Mag-Brush or a small rag wrapped around an old bore cleaning brush and pushed to and fro with a cleaning rod.

Stainless steel is one of the best things ever to happen to magazines, but many shooters still use the less-expensive blued steel variety. Salt-laden

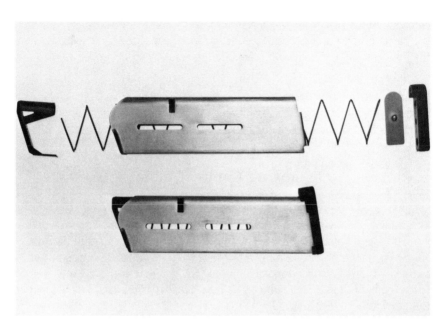

Wilson magazines are easily disassembled for thorough cleaning.

perspiration from the hands can cause rusting, even on the interior surfaces where it is deposited by cartridges handled by sweaty hands. An extremely thin coat of rust inhibitor on the surfaces of the magazine protects it from corrosion, but an excessive amount on the interior will attract lint and dust like a magnet. Applying several coats of automotive paste wax rather than oil to the interior and exterior surfaces of the magazine will prevent corrosion, yet won't attract dust and dirt. Any brand will do, but I use Turtle Wax because that's what I keep on hand for making my automobile shine.

While I'm on the subject, several coats of wax on the exterior surfaces of a blued steel gun will protect it from rusting. It also is the thing to use to prevent discoloration of a stainless steel gun. Simply apply a thin coat, let it dry, and buff it with a soft, clean cloth. Repeat the procedure three or four times and you have got a tough protective skin on a carry gun that won't stain clothing like an oil. I discovered how well this works sometime back while on a moose hunt on the Alaskan Peninsula. I applied several coats of wax to the blued steel of my Remington Model 700 and it survived several days of frog-drowning downpours without suffering a single spot of rust.

I prefer to completely disassemble a Government Model every 5,000 rounds or so to inspect all component parts for excessive wear, stress cracks, or breakage and replace whatever is necessary. On an autoloader with an extremely light trigger pull, the condition of the engaging surfaces of the sear and hammer should be carefully examined. If either surface is chipped or battered, it's time for the gun to visit its pistolsmith.

All component parts are thoroughly cleaned with solvent and then washed with one of the previously described degreasers. The firing pin, extractor, and disconnector tunnels are swabbed out with a cotton swab soaked in solvent and then flushed clean with the degreaser. The six-inch-long Cotton Tipped Applicators (catalog No. 885-861-500) from Brownells are ideal for this operation. The magazine housing and trigger raceway in the frame also are thoroughly cleaned.

Lubricants

If you were to examine two pieces of metal with a powerful microscope, you might be alarmed to see that what appears to the naked eye to be smoothly machined and polished surfaces actually are made up of sharp peaks and deep valleys. When those two pieces of metal are rubbed together, the peaks protruding from their surfaces collide and start to wear away. If an inferior grade of lubricant is applied to those surfaces, it coats the peaks and valleys, the same as one of the better products, but the comparison ends there. Heat

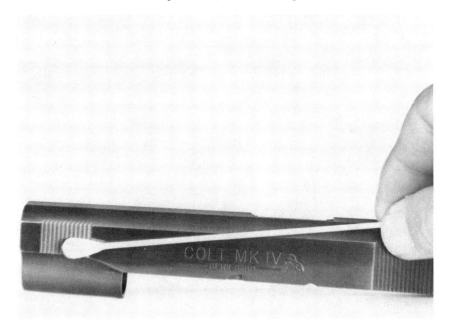

This extra-long cotton swab from Brownells is ideal for cleaning out the extractor and firing pin tunnels in the slide.

created by friction between the two moving parts quickly breaks down the cheap oil while the good stuff hangs in there like a pit bull. In addition, since the film strength of the discount house oil is low, raw metal is exposed to raw metal much quicker than with the oil that wears a white hat. Throw in some dust particles along with a bit of powder fouling, and wear is accelerated even more. Obviously there is a lot more to this lubrication thing than I have room to elaborate on, but you should be getting my drift by now—the best lubricant money can buy is dirt cheap when its cost is compared to that of a custom gun.

Some shooters tend to drown a gun in oil, while others go to the opposite extreme by neglecting lubrication. Frequent applications of an extremely thin coat of oil will make a gun run long and smoothly. This is extremely important on a custom gun because its component parts fit together tighter than the parts in a factory gun. I have listed a 30-point lubrication plan at the end of this chapter so going into further detail here would be repeating myself. Dozens of good lubricants are available, but those designed to withstand high temperatures are best for a competition gun as its barrel can get very hot during rapid fire and quickly burn away the lube in only a few rounds.

420

In this department, every pistolsmith seems to have his or her personal favorite. One I spoke with about the subject highly recommends Remington's Rem Oil to his customers. According to him, it displaces moisture, withstands high temperature, has an extremely high film strength, and keeps powder fouling and grime in suspension on the surface of metal for easier removal during cleaning. He also likes the microscopic Teflon™ particles in Rem Oil. Another pistolsmith is just as high on Break Free CLP while others tout such products as Kleen Bore Super Lube, Outers Tri-Lube, Firepower FP-10, and Pro-Long Anti-Friction Metal Treatment. I seriously doubt if you could go wrong with any of them.

When it comes to lubrication for the contact surfaces of the sear and hammer of an autoloader, I'm not a bit bashful about weeding out all but one. DuPont makes a Remington-brand product called Hinge & High-Pressure Grease (HHPG for short) which was developed for use in various types of firearms including high-grade, double-barrel shotguns. Usually available at gun shops, it is an extremely effective and long-lasting lubricant for carbon steel, stainless steel, titanium, and aluminum alloys. HHPG also protects metals from rusting and discoloration. They really should have called this stuff Trigger Job in a Jar. A toothpick is perfect for applying a tiny dab to small surface areas.

Regardless of what you hear or read, stainless steel does not possess the self-lubricating property of carbon steel. For this reason it has a tendency

Placing a dab of Remington Hinge & High-Pressure Grease on the sear with a toothpick is almost as good as pulling a trigger job from a jar.

to gall unless the right lubrication is used. For reducing wear between the rails of a stainless slide and frame, RIG +P Stainless Steel Lube and Remington Hinge & High-Pressure Grease are tough to beat.

Oil or grease should not be applied to any part of a self-defense gun if it is frequently exposed to a dusty environment. Excellent candidates for this application on the inside are Rem DriLube and Silicone Treatment from Remington and Dri-Slide. Protect all exterior surfaces with several coats of automotive wax, and you've got a gun that won't attract dust.

Long-Term Storage

Firearms owners who live in low-humidity areas don't often have a problem with rust, but in my neck of the woods, you can just about slice the humidity with a knife. An inexpensive way to prevent the rusting of a handgun during long periods of inactive storage is to cover it with a thin coat of RIG or Remington Universal Grease. Next, wrap it in a brown paper bag and then place it in a hard pistol case. Another good way to store a firearm is to place the gun in a plastic storage bag made specifically for that purpose. They are available from Brownells and Bianchi. Regardless of what measures are used to protect a gun while in long-term storage, it should be carefully examined every six months to make sure the rust protection is working.

Adjusting Extractor Tension

When a pistolsmith installs an extractor in a custom gun, it is polished, adjusted, and sometimes even slightly modified for reliable feeding of cartridges into the chamber and the extraction of fired cases. Ideally, the extractor will exert enough tension to hold each and every fired case it pulls from the chamber in precisely the same position as it rams their heads against the ejector's nose. If tension is insufficient, the trajectory arch of ejected cases will vary from shot to shot with some failing to exit the gun and causing a malfunction. If tension is excessive, the dented or distorted rim of a dinged case may not be able to slip beneath the extractor claw during the feeding cycle and prevent the cartridge from aligning with the chamber.

The amount of tension the extractor claw exerts on the rim of a cartridge will vary considerably among factory guns and can range anywhere from 20 ounces, or less, to 70 ounces, or more. Most custom guns I have checked ran somewhere between 15 and 40 ounces with most in the 20- to 30-ounce range. The important thing to remember is not how the tension exerted by the extractor of one gun compares with another, but how much tension the properly tuned extractor of a particular gun is exerting when the gun is feeding and ejecting perfectly.

A chemical included in the polymer mixture used in making the Bianchi Blue Bag protects a handgun from rusting for up to three years.

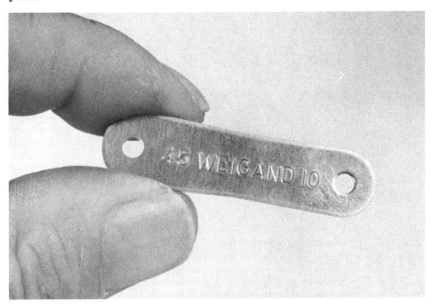

This Weigand extractor tension gauge is for .45 ACP and 10mm Auto guns.

An old pistolsmith's way of checking for adequate extractor tension is to remove the slide from the gun and push the rim of a hardball cartridge between the breechface and the claw of the extractor. If the extractor hangs onto the cartridge when it is released by the fingers, its tension is considered adequate. This method works fine for most guns, but some of the optical-sighted race-guns used in practical pistol competition often require a bit more sophistication.

A more precise method of measuring extractor tension is to use a gauge like the one available from Jack Weigand. The kit consists of two shim-type gauges with each of the four ends shaped for guns of various calibers. For example, the end of one gauge is used on guns chambered for the .45 ACP, while its other end is shaped for the .40 S&W and 10mm Auto. The second gauge takes care of the .38 Super, 9mm Luger, 9x21mm, and 9x23mm.

Each time a gun is field-stripped for cleaning, its extractor tension is checked as follows. One end of the gauge is pushed beneath the extractor and a trigger-pull scale or small fish scale used to measure the amount of force required to pull the gauge from beneath its claw. Let's say you have just had a new custom gun built or have had a new extractor hand-fitted to your old gun and it is operating perfectly. The first time you measure extractor tension with the Weigand gauge, your trigger-pull scale indicates 30 ounces. For several months you continue to get about the same reading each time the extractor is checked, and then its tension suddenly drops to 22 ounces. The gun might still be working just fine, but your trusty Weigand instrument is warning you that it may not continue doing so for many more rounds. So, you adjust the extractor (by carefully bending it) until its tension again reads close to the original 30 ounces. Now it is back where it was on the day your new gun arrived. If, after subjecting the extractor to many thousands of rounds, it requires adjustment more and more frequently, the time has come to have a new extractor hand-fitted to the gun.

Spring Replacement

All coil springs eventually lose some of their original tension from use with the recoil spring of the Government Model requiring the most frequent replacing. Several rules of thumb tell us when it should be done. According to one, the recoil spring should be replaced when it has been pounded two coils shorter than its original length. As other rules go, the spring should be replaced after a certain number of rounds have been fired.

The life of a recoil spring will vary considerably from gun to gun and from load to load. Feed any gun nothing but powderpuff bullseye loads and its spring will survive many more rounds than if the same gun is fed a steady diet of Remington's +P factory load. As a rule, recoil springs don't last as long in the Commander as in the Government Model, and the Officer's ACP eats them up faster than either of the guns with longer and heavier slides and barrels. Fire the heaviest of loads in two guns of the same caliber, one with a compensated barrel, the other without, and a spring usually will last about twice as many rounds in the comp gun.

I prefer to forego all the rules of thumb relative to recoil spring replacement and simply do it the lazy man's way by keeping a close eye on the condition of the shock buffer. Those who are not familiar with this inexpensive gun-saver can read all about it in Chapter 15. If a new spring is the correct weight for the gun and load, the slide won't even start making its mark on the shock buffer until 200 or 300 rounds are fired. Even then, the slide will only lightly kiss the buffer each time it slams to the rear until the spring loses some of its original tension. As the spring is pounded by more and more rounds and begins to lose a great deal of its tension, the amount of force delivered to the buffer by the slide will gradually increase and the buffer will eventually need to be replaced. Once the spring in a noncompensated gun has lost enough of its tension to require replacing the shock buffer more frequently than every 1,000 rounds, the spring is replaced. If the shock buffer in a gun with a compensated barrel has to be replaced more often than every 2,000 rounds, I know its recoil spring is due for retirement.

The author prefers to observe how long a Wilson shock buffer lasts when deciding if the recoil spring has lost enough of its original tension to need replacement with a new one.

When installing a recoil spring, don't forget that the end with the gripping coil goes to the rear, against the head of the spring guide.

How often the firing pin spring must be replaced is greatly influenced by how the gun is used. Some practical pistol competitors dry-fire their gun as much as 100 times each day which adds up to over 36,000 dry-firings from one Christmas to the next. When the hammer drives the firing pin forward with no cartridge in the chamber to arrest its travel, its spring is compressed to its limit, or goes solid if you want to get technical. In addition to beating the tension from the spring quite rapidly, it also batters its front coils. This causes no major damage to the gun, but the spring will need to be replaced about every 3,000 drops of the hammer. If the gun is seldom dry-fired, its firing pin spring should not require replacement more frequently than every 5,000 to 6,000 rounds.

Electronic Sights

Electronic sights like the Aimpoint, Tasco's ProPoint, and the Bushnell Trophy require very little maintenance, but they should wear lens caps when not in use to keep the dust away. The ocular and objective lenses should be kept clean. A small camel's hair brush will whisk the dust away without scratching them, and a liquid cleaner applied with soft tissue paper used for cleaning camera lenses should be used for removing fingerprints and grime. Those items are available at any camera supply shop. Scope-mount screws should be checked for tightness.

I like to keep spare batteries for each of the sights I use in my range bag. When replacing the battery, handle it with fingers clad in tissue paper or a piece of paper towel because skin oils and acids will cause the electrical contacts to corrode. Keep a sharp eye out for dings that begin to appear on the scope's bottom surface, just above the gun's ejection port. Dings are an indication that the extractor has lost some of its tension and is causing ejected cases to ricochet off the tube of the scope.

If the front of the scope is located close to the top of a compensator, its objective lens can become coated with propellant fouling and molten lead spray from cast bullets. A lens cleaner will remove the fouling, but the coat of lead is there to stay. To avoid the lead buildup, it is best to mount the scope as far to the rear as possible. This is one important reason why I prefer some scope mount designs over others. Attaching an extension tube to the front of the scope may shield its objective lens, but the tube should not extend out over the top of the compensator. On the other hand, an extension tube may channel even more fouling into the lens. The best way to avoid this problem when having a scope mounted on an old gun or having a new optical-sighted

426

The battery-powered Aimpoint sight on this C. W. Custom high-capacity Caspian in .38 Super requires little maintenance.

gun built is to specify to the pistolsmith that it will not be accepted if the scope is positioned within range of lead spray exiting the top of the compensator.

Spare Parts

You won't need many spare parts for a custom Government Model pistol, but those you will need to keep on hand are important because some are hand-fitted and a factory part may not work in the gun. In addition to spare springs and shock buffers, I like to have an extra firing pin in my range bag serving backup duty. The same goes for a spare firing pin stop or retaining plate. A spare extractor already hand-fitted to and fine-tuned for the gun also should be within reach. I've never had to replace a slide stop, but some pistolsmiths recommend keeping a spare on hand if the gun has a custom-fitted barrel. And, of course, don't forget spare batteries for the red-dot scope if the gun is wearing one.

The Shooter's Logbook

As a rule, I am not a highly organized person. In fact, if you were to walk into my office as I write this, you would probably reach for the telephone

427

and dial 911. I do, however, manage to keep a running record on my custom pistols.

Residing permanently in my range bag is a small 3x5-inch notebook with a section devoted to each of my guns. It contains information such as what recoil spring weights are correct for various loads in each gun, a running total of how many rounds have been fired in each gun, and the benchrest accuracy of each load. If it is a competition gun used with a light bullet load for steel plates and a heavier load for USPSA/IPSC matches, my logbook tells me how many clicks to adjust its sight when switching from one load to the other. Keeping a running total on the number of rounds fired tells me when it's time to completely disassemble a gun for a thorough cleaning, lubrication, and inspection of internal parts. By keeping up with and updating group sizes fired with a gun, I can tell when it is due for a trip to the pistolsmith for a major accuracy overhaul.

In the personal performance section of my logbook, I record the probable reason(s) why I shot poorly in a match as a reminder to concentrate on that aspect of my shooting during practice. If I finish at the front of the pack, I record the reasons I think I did so well in my logbook. Was my proficiency with the handguns actually unbeatable, or was it simply due to the fact that everybody else tripped and fell on their face during the match? Or was it because the fellows who usually beat me were somewhere else on that particular day?

Thirty-Point Lubrication Plan

	Frequent	Less Frequent	Lube
1. Locking lugs of barrel	X		A
2. Barrel link at retaining pin	X		B
3. Exterior of barrel	X		A
4. Locking lug recesses of slide	X		A
5. Rails of slide	X		A
6. Disconnector timing rail of slide	X		A
7. Exterior of recoil spring guide rod	X		A
8. Rear surface of spring guide head	X		A
9. Exterior of recoil spring	X		B
10. Exterior of recoil spring plug	X		B
11. Rails of frame	X		A
12. Disconnector bevel (upper)	X		B
13. Disconnector body		X	B
14. Disconnector bevel (lower)		X	C

428

Thirty-Point Lubrication Plan *(Cont.)*

	Frequent	Less Frequent	Lube
15. Hammer notch engaging surface of sear		X	C
16. Exterior of extractor		X	B
17. Exterior of firing pin		X	B
18. Exterior of firing pin spring		X	B
19. Firing pin block in slide (Series 80)		X	B
20. Exterior of mainspring		X	B
21. Top surface of mainspring cap.		X	C
22. Hammer crosspin		X	C
23. Sear crosspin		X	C
24. Mainspring housing crosspin		X	B
25. Thumb safety shaft		X	C
26. Slide lock shaft		X	A
27. Dual plungers and spring		X	B
28. Magazine catch spring and screw		X	B
29. Outside surfaces of trigger stirrup		X	B
30. Grip panel screw threads		X	B

Frequent: After every shooting session or match, or every 500 rounds.

Less Frequent: After each 5,000 rounds.

Lube Codes:
A. Light coat of oil.
B. Extremely light coat of oil.
C. Extremely light coat of Remington Hinge & High Pressure Grease.

IMPORTANT: If the Government Model pistol is frequently carried under extremely dusty conditions, a dry lubricant in lieu of oil or grease should be used on all the above lubrication points. Remington DriLube is highly recommended. It is an especially good choice for a carry gun as it doesn't stain clothing like oil.

20

How Much Does It Weigh?

$\mathbf{A}$T first glance, it would appear that when a handful of custom parts are added to a factory gun, its weight will increase substantially. This is not necessarily true. Some of the aftermarket replacement parts are considerably lighter than the factory parts. An extremely light custom hammer will weigh less than half as much as one made by Colt and other manufacturers. Other examples are lightweight triggers, hammer struts, firing pins, thumb safeties, and grip safeties. One of the lighter high-sweep grip safeties weighs less than the factory version and its installation requires removal of metal from the frame for even more overall reduction in weight.

An ever-increasing number of Government Model parts are being made of titanium. These parts weigh a bit more than half of those made of steel. To be more specific, if a steel part weighs one ounce, the same part made of titanium will weigh 0.5796 ounce.

Some aftermarket parts may weigh the same or slightly more than the factory parts they replace, but installing them results in a reduction in weight of the frame or slide. The Heinie high-profile rear sight, for example, weighs a bit more than a Colt low-profile sight, but when a pistolsmith mills away metal from the slide when installing it in a lowered position, overall weight of the slide with its new sight is reduced slightly or ends up about the same.

Other weight-reducing modifications commonly performed on the Government Model and its offspring are beveling the mouth of the magazine well, extending and checkering the frontstrap, squaring and checkering the trigger guard, checkering the heel of the slide, cutting additional grasping grooves

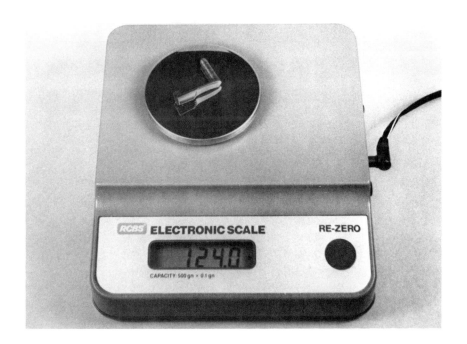

Some aftermarket grip safeties (like this one from Kings) weigh less
than Colt's factory version.

431

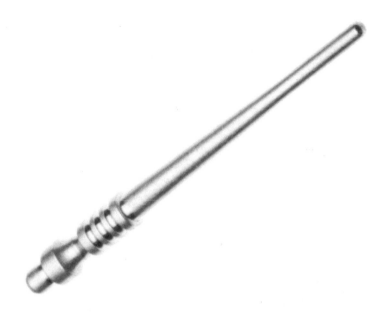

This Kings titanium firing pin weighs only 33 grains.

Removing metal from behind this Brown jig for the installation of a beavertail grip safety reduces the weight of the frame by a fraction of an ounce.

at the front of the slide, milling a flat down the top of the slide, lowering and flaring the ejection port, and serrating the top of the slide. Individually, those modifications decrease the weight of a gun by very little, but in combination they add up. It takes a lot of milling and whittling to remove an ounce of metal from the frame and slide of a Government Model pistol, but take off a little here and a little there, and before you know it, several ounces are lying on the floor of the pistolsmith's shop.

Even when what appear to be heavy parts are added to a gun, the increase in weight is quite small because the weight reduction modifications have a tendency to offset their additional heft. A good example is the huge Gun Craft magazine well funnel. It adds weight to the gun, but its installation requires shortening of the grip, which decreases the weight of the frame. So, you add a bit here and take away a bit there.

More drastic weight-reduction modifications are less common but, nonetheless, quite popular. Shortening the standard Government Model slide by one half inch and milling out lightening cuts in various nonstress areas will reduce its weight by over two ounces. On a big frame like the Para-Ordnance, a lightening cut here and another there can decrease its heft by three to four ounces. Fluting a heavy barrel also reduces weight. As a rule, these modifications are most often performed on competition guns, especially those carrying the additional weight of an optical sight and mount. When having a carry gun built, one does not have to resort to such extremes in order to come up with something weighing either a bit less than or about the same as what the gun weighed in its factory original form.

After red dot sights invaded the practical pistol game, competitors who had one installed on their old gun were faced with keeping its weight at a reasonable level. The excellent Aimpoint 5000 weighs six ounces without its extension tube. Adding the scope mount increases gun heft anywhere from one half to three quarters of a pound depending on mount design. A compensated gun that weighed, say, 42 ounces with its open sights would weigh well over 50 ounces with its battery-powered sight.

To decrease the weight of their optical-sighted guns, some competitors had the slide lightened. A bit of weight can also be shaved away by switching to lighter component parts. My old C. W. Custom compensated gun in .38 Super weighed 44 ounces with its open sights and Heinie full-length tungsten recoil spring guide. Removal of the open sights and installation of an Aimpoint 5000 in a Pegram mount increased its heft to 53 ounces. Replacing the tungsten spring guide with one of Jack Weigand's full-length polymer guides brought its overall weight back down to 50 ounces.

The least expensive way to decrease the weight of a custom gun is to use an aluminum alloy frame. Using Colt's lightweight Commander or Officer's ACP

Chuck Warner shortened and lightened the Caspian slide on this Para-Ordnance high-capacity gun to reduce its overall weight.

434

frame rather than steel as the basis of a custom carry gun will reduce the weight by 9½ to 10 ounces. The same applies to having a custom gun built for Unlimited class practical pistol competition. The Caspian high-capacity aluminum frame weighs a feathery five ounces which is less than 40 percent of what the steel version weighs. At least that's what my postal scale says the prototype weighs. Trim away just over eight ounces by going with an aluminum frame and you will decrease gun weight by about what an Aimpoint 5000 red dot sight and lightweight mount add to the gun.

By using a lightweight frame, a pistolsmith can build a high-capacity, optical-sighted gun with about the same weight as an open-sighted gun built on the standard-capacity steel frame. Since the typical competition gun is pounded by thousands of rounds of heavy loads each year, I believe the installation of a steel recoil block and Bob Krieger's Acc-U-Rail system is the way to go when building one around an aluminum alloy frame. Those items are described in Chapter 6. As amazing as it might seem, the Caspian high-capacity frame weighs exactly the same as the frame of Colt's lightweight.

Gun Weights

The following guns and component parts were carefully weighed on a postal scale or RCBS electronic powder scale. Each gun was weighed with one empty magazine. Actual weight will vary from gun to gun, even among those of the same model and caliber from the same manufacturer. I have weighed .45 caliber Colt Government Models fresh from their factory boxes and found their weights to vary by two ounces and more. The same goes for custom aftermarket parts, especially the larger ones. The various styles and brands of beavertail grip safeties can vary by as much as a quarter of an ounce.

Weights of the custom guns I have included as examples can be increased or decreased by referring to the section on custom parts weights. For example, if you want to know approximately what a Wilson Super grade in .38 Super will weigh after an Aimpoint 5000 sight is installed with a Weigand Stabilizer mount, simply add the weight of those two items to the weight I have shown for the gun. By the same token, if you already own a Super Grade and plan to have its top assembly installed on one of the high-capacity frames, you can project its heft by adding the weights of the new frame and various other parts to that of your top assembly. You also might find it fun to build an entire imaginary gun by choosing its component parts from the list and adding up their weights. At the very least this information may be of assistance as you write the specifications for your new custom gun.

The Para-Ordnance high-capacity aluminum frame weighs 5.25 ounces, or nine ounces less than a steel frame from the same company.

This CMC high-capacity synthetic/steel frame weighs 10 ounces.

436

Factory Gun Weights
(As Rated by Colt)

Model	Caliber	Weight *(ounces)*
Gold Cup	.45 ACP	39.0
Delta Gold Cup	10mm Auto	39.0
Combat Elite	.38 Super	38.0
Combat Elite	.45 ACP	38.0
Delta Elite	10mm Auto	38.0
M1991A1	.45 ACP	38.0
Government Model	.40 S&W	38.0
Government Model	.45 ACP	38.0
Government Model	.38 Super	39.0
Combat Commander	.45 ACP	36.0
Combat Commander	.38 Super	37.0
Lightweight Commander	.45 ACP	27.5
Officer's ACP	.45 ACP	34.0
Lightweight Officer's ACP	.45 ACP	24.0
Double Eagle	.45 ACP	39.0
Double Eagle	10mm Auto	39.0
D.E. Combat Commander	.45 ACP	36.0
D.E. Combat Commander	.40 S&W	36.0
D.E. Officer's ACP	.45 ACP	35.0
Lightweight D.E. Officer's ACP	.45 ACP	25.0

Custom Gun Weights
Gun: C. W. Custom Hi-Capacity Lite Unlimited*
Caliber: CP 9x23mm Super
Total Weight: 35.75 ounces

Custom Features

1. Colt Gold Cup .38 Super Elite slide (shortened and lightened)
2. Caspian high-capacity aluminum frame (19 + 1 rounds)**
3. Frame lightened
4. Stainless steel recoil block
5. Krieger Acc-U-Rails
6. C. W. Custom 5¼-inch barrel (bushing-type) with full-support chamber
7. C. W. Custom TCP-T titanium compensator
8. C. W. Custom T-Bone slide handle
9. Heel of slide checkered

10. Top of slide machined flat and serrated
11. Ejection port lowered
12. Wilson extended ejector
13. Wilson heavy-duty extractor
14. Weigand lightweight slide stop
15. CMC Commander-style titanium hammer
16. CMC titanium hammer strut
17. Caspian titanium firing pin
18. Wilson extended thumb safety (wide tab)
19. Caspian aluminum beavertail grip safety
20. Caspian extended magazine release
21. Caspian aluminum/steel trigger
22. Caspian wood grip panels
23. Weigand full-length polymer recoil spring guide
24. Wilson shock buffer
25. Bottom and front of trigger guard checkered
26. Frontstrap extended and checkered
27. Caspian aluminum mainspring housing checkered
28. Woods Competitor scope mount (lightened)
29. Aimpoint 5000 red dot scope

*Hi-Capacity Lite carry gun with a 5-inch noncompensated barrel and open sights should weigh 29.00 ounces.

**A Caspian prototype aluminum frame was used. Production frames may differ slightly in weight.

Gun: C. W. Custom Hi-Capacity Lite Limited
Caliber: .45 ACP
Total Weight: 32.20 ounces

Custom Features

1. Caspian slide (lightened)
2. Bo-Mar BMCS rear sight (lowered and melted)
3. Post front sight
4. Para-Ordnance high-capacity aluminum frame (13 + 1)
5. Stainless steel recoil block
6. Krieger Accu-U-Rail system
7. Barrett aluminum magazine well funnel
8. C. W. Custom 5-inch barrel (bushing-type) with full-support chamber
9. Heel of slide checkered
10. Slide machined flat on top and serrated
11. Grasping serrations at front of slide

12. Ejection port lowered and flared
13. Kings extended ejector
14. Wilson heavy-duty extractor
15. Weigand lightweight slide stop
16. CMC Commander-style titanium hammer
17. CMC titanium hammer strut
18. Caspian titanium firing pin
19. Wilson extended safety (wide tab)
20. Caspian high-sweep grip safety
21. Gun Craft extended magazine release
22. C&S checkered aluminum grip panels
23. C. W. Custom full-length titanium recoil spring guide
24. Wilson shock buffer
25. Bottom of trigger guard checkered
26. Frontstrap extended and checkered
27. Colt Commander aluminum mainspring housing checkered

Gun: C. W. Custom Signature Grade
Caliber: CP 9x23mm Super
Total Weight: 54 ounces

Custom Features

1. Colt Gold Cup .38 Super Elite slide, (shortened and lightened)
2. Para-Ordnance high-capacity steel frame (20 + 1) (lightened)
3. Krieger Acc-U-Rail system
4. C. W. Custom 5¼-inch barrel (heavy) with full-support chamber
5. C. W. Custom TCP compensator
6. C. W. Custom T-Bone slide handle
7. Heel of slide checkered
8. Ejection port lowered
9. Wilson extended ejector
10. Wilson heavy-duty extractor
11. Weigand lightweight slide stop
12. Gun Craft aluminum/steel trigger
13. CMC titanium hammer strut
14. Wilson titanium firing pin
15. Wilson extended safety (wide tab)
16. Brown beavertail grip safety
17. Wilson extended magazine release button
18. Gun Craft magazine well funnel
19. Wayland presentation grade grip panels

20. Wilson hexhead grip panel screws
21. C. W. Custom full-length titanium recoil spring guide
22. Wilson shock buffer
23. Bottom of trigger guard checkered
24. Frontstrap extended, recontoured, and checkered
25. Colt steel mainspring housing, checkered
26. Weigand Stabilizer scope mount
27. Aimpoint 5000 red dot sight

Gun: Wilson Super Grade
Caliber: .38 Super
Total Weight: 44.0 ounces

Custom Features

1. Colt slide
2. Colt steel frame
3. Wilson 5½-inch barrel (sleeved) with full-support chamber
4. Wilson Accu-Comp DP compensator
5. Bo-Mar rear sight (lowered and melted)
6. Top of slide serrated
7. Heel of slide checkered
8. Extra grasping grooves at front of slide
9. Ejection port lowered and flared
10. Wilson extended ejector
11. Wilson heavy-duty extractor
12. Wilson Commander-style hammer
13. Wilson titanium firing pin
14. Wilson extended, ambidextrous thumb safety (narrow tabs)
15. Wilson high-sweep beavertail grip safety
16. Wilson extended magazine release button
17. Wilson lightweight aluminum/steel trigger
18. Mouth of magazine well beveled
19. Wilson magazine well funnel
20. Wilson deluxe grip panels
21. Wilson full-length steel recoil spring guide
22. Wilson shock buffer
23. Bottom of trigger guard checkered
24. Frontstrap checkered
25. Mainspring housing (flat) checkered

Gun: C. W. Custom Officer's ACP
Caliber: .45 ACP
Total Weight: 35 ounces

Custom Features

1. Colt slide (internal lightening cuts)
2. Colt steel frame
3. Wilson 3½-inch barrel (sleeved)
4. Heinie rear sight (lowered)
5. Accent lines milled into sides of slide
6. Heel of slide checkered
7. Ejection port lowered and flared
8. Wilson heavy-duty extractor
9. Heinie Commander-style hammer
10. CMC titanium hammer strut
11. Wilson titanium firing pin
12. Wilson extended safety (narrow tab)
13. Brown beavertail grip safety
14. Checkering on factory magazine release button
15. CMC carbon fiber/titanium trigger (short)
16. Mouth of magazine well beveled
17. SASA mag well funnel with integral (flat) mainspring housing.
18. Ahrends cocobolo grip panels
19. Wilson hexhead grip panel screws
20. C. W. Custom full-length titanium recoil spring guide
21. Wilson shock buffer
22. Front of trigger guard flattened and checkered
23. Frontstrap extended and checkered
24. Backstrap checkered
25. Mainspring housing checkered

Gun: Wilson Standard Grade
Caliber: .45 ACP
Total Weight: 42.5 ounces

Custom Features

1. Colt slide
2. Colt steel frame
3. Wilson 5½-inch barrel (bushing-type)
4. Wilson hand-fitted barrel bushing
5. Wilson Accu-Comp DP compensator
6. Wilson No. 61 rear sight

7. Ejection port lowered and flared
8. Wilson extended ejector
9. Wilson heavy-duty extractor
10. Wilson Commander-style hammer
11. Wilson extended, ambidextrous thumb safety (narrow tabs)
12. Wilson beavertail grip safety
13. Wilson extended magazine release button
14. Wilson lightweight aluminum/steel trigger
15. Mouth of magazine well beveled
16. Wilson magazine well funnel
17. Wilson standard grip panels
18. Wilson hexhead grip panel screws
19. Wilson full-length recoil spring guide rod
20. Wilson shock buffer
21. Wilson No. 100 checkered frontstrap band
22. Mainspring housing checkered

Gun: C. W. Custom Double Eagle Plus
Caliber: .45 ACP
Total Weight: 45.0 ounces

Custom Features

1. Colt slide
2. Colt steel frame
3. B.A.T. 5½-inch barrel (bushing-type)
4. B.A.T. Pro-Series V compensator
5. Bo-Mar rear sight (lowered and melted)
6. Integral rib milled into top of slide and serrated
7. Heel of slide checkered
8. Extra grasping grooves at front of slide
9. Ejection port lowered and flared
10. Wilson extended ejector
11. Wilson heavy-duty extractor
12. C. W. Custom Commander-style hammer
13. SASA titanium firing pin
14. C. W. Custom beavertail backstrap
15. SASA extended, ambidextrous magazine release
16. Mouth of magazine well beveled
17. SASA magazine well funnel (with integral mainspring housing)
18. Wilson full-length steel recoil spring guide
19. Wilson shock buffer
20. Trigger guard recontoured and checkered (front and bottom)

442

21. Frontstrap extended and checkered
22. Steel mainspring housing checkered
23. Single action trigger pull tuned at 35 ounces

Gun: Dichiara/Jarrett International Grade
Caliber: .45 ACP
Total Weight: 44.3 ounces

Custom Features

1. Caspian slide
2. Caspian steel frame (standard capacity)
3. Bar-Sto 5½-inch barrel (sleeved)
4. Clark full-profile compensator
5. Bo-Mar rear sight (lowered and melted)
6. Top of slide serrated
7. Heel of slide serrated
8. Extra grasping grooves at front of slide
9. Ejection port lowered and flared
10. Caspian Commander-style hammer
11. Wilson extended, ambidextrous thumb safety (narrow tabs)
12. Caspian beavertail grip safety
13. Wilson extended magazine release
14. Wilson lightweight aluminum/steel trigger
15. Mouth of magazine well beveled
16. SASA mag well funnel (with integral mainspring housing)
17. Ahrends tulip wood grip panels
18. Clark full-length steel recoil spring guide
19. Wilson shock buffer
20. Trigger guard squared and checkered (front)
21. Frontstrap recontoured, extended, and checkered

Gun: C. W. Custom Signature Grade
Caliber: .38 Super
Total Weight: 44.0 ounces*
Total Weight: 53.0 ounces**
Total Weight: 50.0 ounces***

Custom Features

1. Caspian slide
2. Caspian steel frame (standard-capacity)
3. Caspian 5½-inch barrel (bushing-type)

4. Brown Four-Star compensator
5. Bo-Mar rear sight (lowered and melted)
6. Top of slide serrated
7. Heel of slide checkered
8. Extra grasping grooves at front of slide
9. Ejection port lowered and flared
10. Wilson extended ejector
11. Wilson heavy-duty extractor
12. CMC Commander-style titanium hammer
13. CMC titanium hammer strut
14. Caspian titanium firing pin
15. Brown extended thumb safety (wide tab)
16. Brown beavertail grip safety
17. Heinie extended magazine release
18. CMC carbon fiber/titanium trigger (long)
19. Mouth of magazine well beveled
20. SASA magazine well funnel (with integral mainspring housing)
21. Ahrends tulip wood grip panels
22. Brown hexhead grip panel screws
23. Heinie full-length tungsten recoil spring guide
24. Trigger guard squared and checkered (front and bottom)
25. Frontstrap extended and checkered
26. Backstrap checkered
27. Mainspring housing checkered
28. ProPoint red dot sight
29. Pegram ICBM mount

*Original weight with open sights and Heinie full-length tungsten recoil spring guide.
**Weight after Aimpoint 5000 red dot sight was installed.
***Weight after the tungsten guide rod was replaced with a Weigand synthetic rod.

Gun: Vais Warp Speed*
Caliber: .45 ACP
Weight: 34.0 ounces

Custom Features

1. Colt slide (skeletonized)
2. Colt steel frame (with lightening cuts)
3. Vais linkless barrel (heavy)
4. Vais single chamber compensator

444

5. Bo-Mar rear sight (lowered and melted)
6. Heel of slide serrated
7. Ejection port lowered and flared
8. Colt Commander hammer
9. Swenson extended thumb safety
10. Vais beavertail grip safety
11. Kings lightweight aluminum/steel trigger
12. Mouth of magazine well beveled
13. Colt factory wooden grip panels
14. Vais full-length recoil spring guide
15. Front of trigger guard checkered
16. Frontstrap checkered
17. Mainspring housing checkered

*Built by George Vais around 1980.

Gun: C. W. Custom Combat Gold Cup
Caliber: .45 ACP
Weight: 40.0 ounces

Custom Features

1. Colt Gold Cup slide
2. Colt Gold Cup frame
3. Heinie 5-inch barrel
4. Heel of slide checkered
5. Brown Commander-style hammer
6. Wilson extended thumb safety (narrow tab)
7. Brown beavertail grip safety
8. Colt magazine release button checkered
9. Mouth of magazine well beveled
10. SASA magazine well funnel (with integral mainspring housing)
11. SASA checkered walnut grip panels
12. Wilson full-length steel recoil spring guide
13. Trigger guard squared and checkered (front and bottom)
14. Frontstrap extended and checkered
15. Mainspring housing checkered

Gun: Wilson Burner
Caliber: .38 Super
Total Weight: 48.0 ounces

Custom Features

1. Colt slide
2. CMC synthetic/steel frame kit
3. Wilson 5½-inch barrel (sleeved) with full-support chamber
4. Wilson Accu-Comp DP compensator
5. Wilson lightweight slide grasping handle
6. Top of slide machined flat for scope mount clearance
7. Heel of slide checkered
8. Ejection port lowered and flared
9. Wilson extended ejector
10. Wilson heavy-duty extractor
11. Wilson lightweight Commander-style hammer
12. Wilson titanium firing pin
13. Wilson extended thumb safety (wide tab)
14. Wilson high-sweep beavertail grip safety
15. Wilson extended magazine release button
16. Wilson full-length polymer recoil spring guide
17. Wilson shock buffer
18. Wilson scope mount
19. Aimpoint 5000 red dot scope

Component Parts Weights

	Weight	
Part	*(Grains)*	*(Ounces)*
Barrels (with link and pin)		
Colt 3.50-inch, .45 ACP	1,268.7	2.90
Wilson 3.50-inch, .45 ACP (sleeved)	1,662.5	3.80
Colt 4.25-inch, .45 ACP	1,312.5	3.00
Colt 5.00-inch, .45 ACP	1,400.0	3.20
Wilson 5.50-inch, .45 ACP	1,575.0	3.60
Bar-Sto 5.00-inch, 10mm	1,750.0	4.00
Heinie 5.50-inch, 10mm	2,428.1	5.55
Colt 4.25-inch, .38 Super	1,575.0	3.60
Colt 5.00-inch, .38 Super	1,640.6	3.75
Heinie 5.50-inch, .38 Super	2,384.4	5.45
Colt 5.00-inch, .22 LR (SM ACE)	2,625.0	6.00

446

Component Parts Weights *(Cont.)*

Part	Weight *(Grains)*	*(Ounces)*
Barrel Bushings		
Solid, 5.00-inch barrel	172.7	0.39
Collet, 5.00-inch barrel	124.1	0.28
Solid, 4.25-inch barrel	122.8	0.28
Solid, 3.50-inch barrel	65.4	0.15
Barrel Sleeves		
C. W. Custom barrel sleeve (full-length)	305.7	0.70
Compensators		
C. W. Custom TCP, 9x23mm (titanium)	708.8	1.62
Wilson AccuComp DP, .38 Super	1,225.5	2.80
Heinie Premium, .38 Super	1,312.5	3.00
Heinie Premium, 10mm	1,268.8	2.90
Brown Four-Star, .45 ACP	1,356.3	3.10
B.A.T. Pro-Series V, .45 ACP	2,100.0	4.80
Firing Pins		
Colt, steel, .45 (Series 80)	67.5	0.15
Colt, steel, .38 (Series 80)	60.7	0.14
SASA, titanium, .45 (Series 70 or 80)	40.6	0.09
Wilson, titanium, .38 (Series 70 or 80)	36.0	0.08
Caspian, titanium, .38 (Series 70)	33.1	0.08
CMC, titanium, .38 (Series 80)	33.1	0.08
Firing Pin Block Components		
(Series 80)	50.1	0.11
Firing Pin Stops		
Colt No. 1	51.5	0.12
Colt No. 1, shortened for low-mount sight	40.5	0.09
Frames, Standard-Capacity		
Colt Government Model, steel	6,125.0	14.00
Colt Gold Cup, stainless steel (1)	4,768.8	10.90
Caspian Government Model, steel	6,037.5	13.80
Colt Commander, steel	5,468.8	12.50
Colt Commander, steel (1)	5,118.8	11.70
Colt Commander, aluminum alloy	2,187.5	5.00
Colt Commander, aluminum alloy (1)	1,837.5	4.20
Frames, High-Capacity		
Caspian, aluminum alloy	2,187.5	5.00
Para-Ordnance, aluminum alloy	2,296.9	5.25

Component Parts Weights *(Cont.)*

Part	Weight	
	(Grains)	*(Ounces)*
CMC, synthetic/steel	4,331.3	10.10
Caspian, steel	5,731.3	13.10
Para-Ordnance, steel	6,168.8	14.10
Para-Ordnance, steel (2)	5,906.3	11.50
Grip Panels, Pair		
Ahrends, GM, checkered cordia	515.3	1.18
Ahrends, GM, checkered kingwood	536.2	1.23
Ahrends, Officer's ACP, smooth cocobolo	543.4	1.24
Ahrends, GM, checkered cocobolo	584.8	1.34
Ahrends, GM, checkered dyamond wood	641.4	1.47
Wilson, GM, checkered synthetic	679.0	1.55
Wayland, Para-Ordnance, checkered cocobolo	793.8	1.81
C&S, Para-Ordnance, checkered aluminum	875.0	2.00
Caspian, pewter	4,156.0	9.50
Grip Panel Screws, Four		
Slotted head	60.0	0.14
Hexhead	54.2	0.12
Hammers		
Colt standard, steel	282.8	0.65
Colt Commander, steel	262.4	0.60
Heinie Commander-style, steel	221.7	0.51
Brown Commander-style, steel	225.0	0.51
Weigand Quick-Lock, steel	175.8	0.40
CMC, Commander-style, titanium	124.9	0.29
Hammer Struts		
Colt, standard, steel	57.9	0.13
Colt, Gold Cup, steel	52.3	0.12
CMC, titanium	28.6	0.07
Magazines		
Colt, factory	1,093.8	2.50
Wilson (with synthetic bumper)	984.4	2.25
Shooting Star (with synthetic bumper)	1,093.8	2.50
Caspian, high-capacity (with bumper)	1,596.9	3.65
Para-Ordnance high-capacity (with bumper)	1,400.0	3.20
CMC high-capacity (with bumper)	1,706.3	3.90

Component Parts Weights *(Cont.)*

Part	Weight (Grains)	(Ounces)
Magazine Bumpers		
Wilson, synthetic (.355" thick)	61.7	0.14
Heinie, synthetic (.625" thick)	107.4	0.25
B.A.T., brass (.500" thick)	875.0	2.00
C. W. Custom, brass (.500" thick) (checkered)	831.3	1.90
Magazine Catches		
Colt factory	89.8	0.21
SASA ambidextrous, Government Model	106.9	0.25
Para-Ordnance, synthetic	33.8	0.08
Para-Ordnance, steel (Gun Craft)	108.3	0.25
Caspian, steel (for high capacity frame)	106.2	0.24
Magazine Release Buttons		
Heinie, extended	35.3	0.08
Weigand, extended	98.3	0.22
Magazine Well Funnels		
Wilson	247.7	0.57
Gun Craft	647.5	1.48
Gun Craft, Para-Ordnance	721.9	1.65
SASA, Officer's ACP, flat (3)	875.0	2.00
SASA, Government Model, arched (3)	1,137.5	2.60
SASA, Government Model, flat (3)	1,093.8	2.50
SASA, Para-Ordnance, flat (3)	875.0	2.00
Mainspring Housings		
Colt, steel, flat	787.5	1.80
Colt, steel, arched	1,015.0	2.32
Colt, synthetic, flat	124.3	0.28
Colt, synthetic, arched	152.4	0.35
Colt, aluminum, flat (Commander)	269.3	0.62
Wilson, steel, flat, checkered	770.2	1.76
Caspian, aluminum, high capacity frame	258.6	0.59
Para-Ordnance, synthetic, flat	147.8	0.34
Recoil Spring Guide, Factory		
Colt Gold Cup, steel	169.9	0.39
Colt Officer's ACP, steel	133.2	0.31
Colt Delta Elite, synthetic	57.1	0.13
Para-Ordnance, synthetic	54.5	0.12

Component Parts Weights *(Cont.)*

Part	Weight (Grains)	(Ounces)
Recoil Spring Guide, Full-Length		
Weigand, polymer, 5.00-inch barrel	127.9	0.29
C. W. Custom, titanium, 5.00-inch barrel	407.0	0.93
Wilson, steel, 5.00-inch barrel	700.0	1.60
Wilson, steel, 4.25-inch barrel	568.8	1.30
Wilson, steel, 3.50-inch barrel	460.3	1.05
Heinie, tungsten, 5.00-inch barrel	1,443.8	3.30
Recoil Spring Plug		
Officer's ACP, factory, steel	71.6	0.16
Government Model, factory, steel	79.0	0.18
Wilson, open front, steel	79.1	0.18
Stroh, rear entry, steel	148.6	0.34
Wilson, rear entry, steel	155.7	0.36
C. W. Custom, rear entry, steel	163.8	0.37
Safety, Grip		
Colt, steel	468.8	1.07
Caspian, high-sweep, aluminum	195.3	0.45
Brown, high-sweep, steel	397.1	0.91
Wilson, high-sweep, steel	429.0	0.98
Safety, Thumb		
Colt, factory	153.7	0.35
Wilson, extended, narrow tab	146.9	0.34
Caspian, extended, narrow tab	208.6	0.48
Wilson, extended, wide tab	163.1	0.37
Wilson, extended, ambidextrous, narrow tabs	211.5	0.48
Brown, extended, ambidextrous, wide tabs	252.2	0.58
Scopes		
Aimpoint 5000	2,625.0	6.00
Tasco ProPoint PDP3BD	2,668.8	6.10
AA Ultra Dot	2,750.0	4.00
Scope Extension Tubes		
Aimpoint 5000	238.9	0.55
Tasco PDP3BD	139.1	0.32
AA Ultra Dot	107.4	0.25

Component Parts Weights *(Cont.)*

Part	Weight (Grains)	(Ounces)
Scope Rings (pair)		
Tasco ProPoint PDP3 (30mm)	1,109.6	2.54
Aimpoint 5000 (30mm)	830.4	1.90
AA Ultra Dot (1-inch)	701.2	1.60
Scope Mounts (with all screws)		
C.P.M.I	962.5	2.20
Woods Competitor	1,268.8	2.90
Weigand Stabilizer	1,356.3	3.10
Pegram ICBM	1,793.8	4.10
Sears		
Colt Gold Cup	41.2	0.09
Caspian	40.9	0.09
CMC	41.1	0.09
Springfield Armory	43.5	0.10
Colt standard, steel	43.8	0.10
Sights, Rear		
Colt, low profile	50.6	0.12
Colt, medium profile	71.0	0.16
Wilson, high profile	116.9	0.27
Millett, Series 100 (Gold Cup)	201.4	0.46
Bo-Mar, BMCS	420.4	0.96
Slides		
Colt Government Model	5,337.5	12.20
Colt Government Model, lightened	4,462.5	10.20
Colt Government Model, shortened ½ inch	4,550.0	10.40
Colt Delta Elite	5,381.3	12.30
Colt Commander, Pre-Series 70	4,593.8	10.50
Colt Commander, Series 70	4,965.6	11.35
Colt Commander, Series 80	4,900.0	11.20
Colt Officer's ACP	4,703.1	10.75
Caspian Government Model	5,315.6	12.15
Caspian Government Model, deluxe Bo-Mar cut	5,250.0	12.00
Springfield Armory Government Model	5,512.5	12.60
Slide Grasping Handles		
C. W. Custom "T-Bone"	150.1	0.34
Heinie	155.3	0.36

451

Component Parts Weights *(Cont.)*

Part	Weight (Grains)	(Ounces)
Slide Locks		
Colt	134.5	0.31
Weigand, lightened	125.4	0.30
Wilson, extended	143.8	0.33
Caspian, extended	154.5	0.35
Triggers, Standard Guns		
Colt Gold Cup, steel	261.6	0.60
Videki, Gold Cup, aluminum/steel	145.5	0.33
Colt Government Model, steel, long	241.5	0.55
Colt Government Model, synthetic/steel, long	91.0	0.21
Colt Government Model, steel, short	166.1	0.38
Wilson, GM, aluminum/steel, long	79.8	0.18
CMC, GM, carbon fiber/titanium, long	48.9	0.11
CMC, GM, carbon fiber/titanium, short	48.7	0.11
Triggers, High-Capacity Guns		
Caspian, aluminum/steel	94.4	0.22
Para-Ordnance, synthetic/steel	107.0	0.24
Gun Craft, Para-Ordnance, aluminum/steel	142.4	0.33
Gun Craft, Para-Ordnance, pivoting, steel	283.7	0.65

(1) Frontstrap extended and checkered; trigger guard squared (front only) and checkered (front and bottom); mouth of magazine well beveled, and modified for beavertail grip safety by C. W. Custom. Weight includes the ejector, four grip panel screw bushings, and the plunger housing.

(2) Frontstrap extended, recontoured and checkered; trigger guard checkered (bottom); mouth of magazine well beveled, and lightening cuts milled into the grip frame by C. W. Custom.

(3) SA Shooting Accessories unit with integral mainspring housing.

Note: The weights of component parts will vary slightly from gun to gun and from manufacturer to manufacturer, especially among larger parts such as the frame, slide, barrel, and grip safety.

Compensated Barrel Weight Comparison
(All 5½-Inch Barrels)

Barrel/Compensator	Type	Compensator Length (Inches)	Caliber	Total Weight* (Ounces)
(A) B.A.T. Pro-Series V	1/A	1.760	.45 ACP	8.75
(B) Brown Four-Star	2/A	1.935	.45 ACP	7.50
(C) Brown Four-Star	2/A	1.935	.38 Super	9.00
(D) Centaur Quadra-Lok	2/B	1.500	10mm Auto	8.50
(E) Clark Pin Master-H	1/C	1.515	10mm Auto	9.50
(E) Clark Pin Master-H	1/C	1.515	.45 ACP	8.00
(F) Heinie Premium	2/A	1.600	10mm Auto	7.75
(F) Heinie Premium	2/A	1.600	.40 S&W	7.80
(F) Heinie Premium	2/A	1.600	.38 Super	9.00
(G) Stroh Integral	2/B	1.600	.45 ACP	6.75
(H) C. W. Custom TCP**	3/C	1.900	9x23mm	9.90
(H) C. W. Custom TCP-T***	3/C	1.900	9x23mm	7.85
(H) C. W. Custom TCP-T***	1/A	1.900	9x23mm	8.10
(I) Wilson Accu-Comp DP	2/C	1.510	.38 Super	9.25
(I) Wilson Accu-Comp DP	2/A	1.510	.45 ACP	6.75

*Includes compensator, barrel, and barrel bushing or sleeve where applicable.
**Triple chamber progressive
***Titanium

Barrel Code: (A) B.A.T., (B) Brown, (C) Caspian, (D) Centaur, (E) Clark, (F) Heinie, (G) Stroh, (H) C. W. Custom, (I) Wilson.

Compensator Type Code: 1. full profile, 2. half profile, 3. dual profile.

Barrel Type Code: A. bushing, B. heavy, C. sleeved.

21

Government Model Cartridges

A S this book is written, the Colt Government Model pistol in its original form has been factory-chambered for six cartridges. In the order of their introduction by Colt, they include the .45 ACP, .38 Super, .22 Long Rifle, 9mm Parabellum (9x19mm), 10mm Auto, and .40 Smith & Wesson.

Wildcatters haven't exactly ignored John Browning's pistol, either. To name but a few, there's the .451 Detonics (Detonics Manufacturing Company), the .38-45 (Bo Clerke), Dean Grennell's interesting .38-45 Hard Head, the 10mm Centaur (Charles Petty), J. D. Jones' .41 Avenger, the .45 Colt Super (that Grennell fellow again). Cases for the Detonics, Hard Head, Avenger, and Super are formed from shortened .45 Winchester brass while the Petty and Clerke cartridges are simply the .45 ACP case necked down. Reloading dies and case forming dies (where needed) for the entire bunch are available from RCBS.

Then we have the CP 9x21mm +P+ and the 9x23mm +P+. The former cartridge was introduced for 9mm Luger-size autoloaders, but used in custom Government Model pistols by a few practical pistol competitors. The 9x23mm was designed to dethrone the .38 Super in the new breed of high-capacity Government Model pistols.

Let's now take a closer look at some of these cartridges.

The .45 ACP

This is the cartridge that made the Government Model pistol what it is today. In fact, without the .45 ACP, John Browning's pistol might have gone

Frank Garcia with two spent cases in the air and two more about to follow.

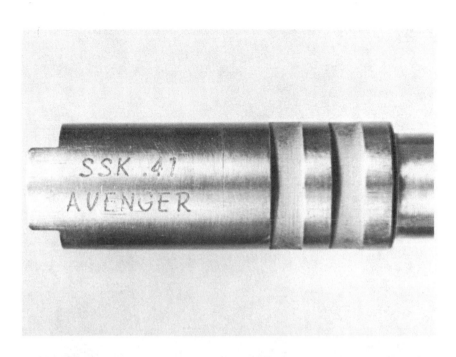

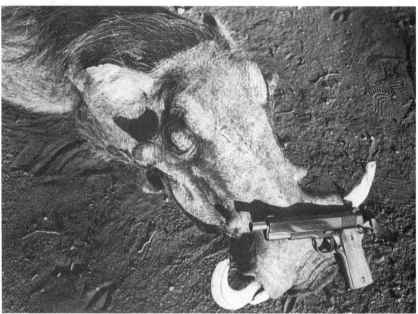

African warthog taken with a Colt Government Model in .41 Avenger. *(SSK Industries photo)*

down in history as just another gun among many, rather than the classic it eventually became.

The .45 ACP story began in 1906 when a rimless .45-caliber cartridge was designed at Frankford Arsenal for the Army's upcoming pistol trials of 1907. It had an extremely blunt-nosed 200-grain bullet loaded to a nominal velocity of 900 feet per second (fps). Cartridge historians will long debate the question of whether John Browning, Colt, or the U.S. Government came up with a similar cartridge called the .45 Automatic Colt Pistol, but the fact remains, it was chosen for the big Colt autoloader around 1911. The extractor groove of the .45 ACP case was wider than that of the earlier Frankford Arsenal case and its more streamlined 230-grain bullet was loaded to a nominal velocity of 800 fps.

For many years American ammunition manufacturers basically copied the original military loading of the .45 ACP with a 230-grain full-metal-jacketed (FMJ) bullet at 800 to 850 fps. Then lawmen who used the Government Model pistol began to request a more powerful load, one capable of penetrating a speeding automobile from bumper to bumper and stopping hoodlums inside from further flight. During the 1940s, Remington responded to the demand by introducing a load called the Metal-Penetrating Hi-Way Master. With its 173-grain bullet at 1,140 fps for 498 foot-pounds (ft-lbs) of energy, the new load represented an increase in punch of over 30 percent compared to the old 230-grain hardball load. If Remington were to reintroduce the old loading today, it would likely wear the +P headstamp.

Another step forward in the evolution of .45 ACP factory ammunition came during the early 1960s when Lee Jurras, owner of the Super Vel Cartridge Corporation introduced a new load with a 190-grain JHP at 1,060 fps for 473 ft-lbs. Whereas the old 230-grain FMJ bullet was noted for zero expansion, deep penetration, and minimal tissue damage, the new Super Vel bullet with its thin jacket, extremely soft lead core, and cavernous nose cavity usually expanded to almost twice its original diameter when fired from a 5-inch barrel.

The common use of lighweight bullets among bullseye shooters prompted Remington and Winchester to introduce match-grade .45 ACP loads at reduced velocities. Many years ago there was Winchester's Super-Match with its 210-grain bullet at 710 fps. Remington answered the challenge with its Targetmaster loading with a 185-grain semiwadcutter (SWC) at 870 fps. The Super-Match and Targetmaster loads are still available, but are now loaded with a 185-grain SWC at a nominal velocity of 770 fps. I have burned up many rounds of both loads in target pistols and consider them along with the Remington and Winchester 148-grain hollowbase wadcutter loadings of the .38 Special the most accurate centerfire handgun ammunition of any caliber available. Any handloader who can consistently equal their accuracy really knows his stuff.

Sharon Kimbrell double-taps her .45 ACP during a match while a range officer holds the timer.

The most powerful .45 ACP load available from a major manufacturer is Remington's 185-grain JHP +P. The Remington load has reached or at least come very close to reaching its advertised velocity of 1,140 fps in every 5-inch barrel in which I've tried it. When fired in the 3½-inch barrel of a Colt Officer's ACP, it exceeds 1,000 fps and generates close to 450 ft-lbs of muzzle energy. This is at least 25 percent more punch than other loads with the same bullet weight deliver from a 5-inch barrel. Thanks to its high impact velocity and huge nose cavity, the Remington bullet expands beautifully even when fired from a 3½-inch barrel.

The .45 ACP served military duty from 1911 until 1985 when the 9mm Luger was adopted by the United States armed forces. Its stint lasted much longer than any other rifle or handgun cartridge adopted by the United States military establishment. Some say the old .45's days are numbered and newer cartridges like the 10mm Auto and .40 S&W eventually will entirely replace it in the hands and hearts of America's handgunners. Others, who believe that firepower is the thing to have, gaze into their 9mm-size crystal balls and see a bleak future for the old .45 ACP. Then there are those of us who believe the bigger the bullet, the better the cartridge, and seven or eight rounds represents a strong enough argument if you know how to shoot.

The .38 Super

In 1929, Colt souped up the old .38 ACP cartridge and introduced it in the Government Model pistol as the .38 Colt Super Automatic. Had it been introduced during the 1980s or 1990s, it probably would have been called the .38 ACP +P, the same as was done with higher-pressure loadings of the .38 Special and .45 ACP. Until the .357 Magnum came along in 1935, the .38 Super was the most powerful handgun cartridge ever introduced by an American manufacturer, even surpassing in power cartridges of larger caliber such as the .44 Special, .44-40, .45 Colt, and .45 ACP.

The .38 Super has been available in the Government Model pistol longer than any other handgun and during the 1930s was offered in the National Match version as well. Later, during the 1980s, Colt built 750 Gold Cup pistols in this caliber, calling them the .38 Super Elite. The chambering still is available in Colt's Government Model and Combat Commander. Other pistols that are or have been available in .38 Super are the Springfield Armory Omega, the SIG/Sauer P220, the Victory MC5 imported by Magnum Research, and the 1911 Colt lookalikes from Llama and Auto Ordnance.

The .38 Super has long been plagued with a reputation for poor accuracy, but that had more to do with the gun than the cartridge. Rather than head-spacing the mouth of its case against a shoulder at the forward end of the

Jim Garthwaite custom Colt Officer's ACP in .45 ACP.

460

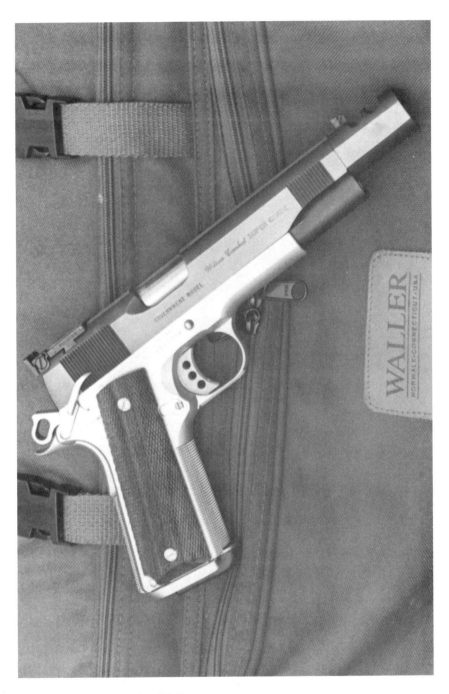

Wilson Super Grade in .38 Super.

chamber as was done earlier with the .45 ACP, Colt chose to headspace an extremely small segment of its narrow rim on an equally narrow shoulder cut into the rear surface of the barrel hood. Due to the somewhat generous manufacturing tolerance ranges of mass-produced guns and ammunition, the rim diameters of some lots of .38 Super cases are small enough to allow the cartridge to slip by its headspacing shoulder and sink deeply into the case. This causes a considerable variation in the amount of energy delivered by the firing pin to primers.

As if the .38 Super didn't already have enough accuracy problems, bore and groove diameters of its barrels have varied considerably among various manufacturers over the years. When it was introduced by Colt, nominal bullet diameter was established at .357 to .358 inch, the same as for the older .38 Long Colt and .38 S&W Special cartridges. The groove diameter of a 1930's vintage barrel I have measures .3574 inch; for obvious reasons today's .355-inch bullets would be less than accurate in it. SAAMI still lists the groove diameter tolerance range of .38 Super barrels as .355 to .359 inch. Then somewhere down the road, maximum specified bullet diameter was decreased to a nominal .356 inch, and the groove diameter of .38 Super barrels from some manufacturers followed suit. Today, bullets used by handloaders in the .38 Super range in diameter from .354 to .357 inch. The groove diameters of aftermarket barrels of current manufacturers I've checked ran from .354 to .356 inch, with most in the .356-inch range.

The barrels in Colt pistols of current manufacture have a headspacing shoulder at the front of the chamber and some guns are extremely accurate. Other Colt guns are not accurate simply because of extreme variations in chamber diameter. In a maximum dimension chamber, the rim of some cases will catch on the headspace shoulder of the hood while others will slip by it and headspace on the shoulder of the chamber. This is not a problem with the better aftermarket barrels with their minimum diameter chambers.

The .38 Super was once quite popular in law enforcement circles, but it has never come close to winning the hearts of American shooters as the .45 ACP has. There is one exception. After Rob Leatham won his first big match with the Super in 1984, it quickly went on to dominate the upper levels of practical pistol competition. In fact, the .38 Super became to USPSA/IPSC competitors what the 6mm PPC already was to benchrest shooters. It was the practical pistol competition favorite of the 1980s and lost very little of its popularity during the early 1990s. Whether or not other cartridges such as the 9x21mm and 9x23mm will eventually dethrone the .38 Super is a question yet to be answered.

In contrast to much of what you have just read about the accuracy of the .38 Super, when fired in a match grade, hand-fitted barrel, I find it to be the most accurate cartridge for which the Government Model has ever been

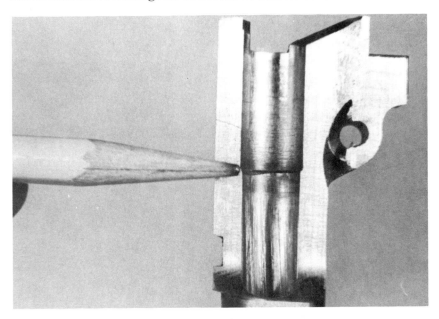

Sectioning this shot-out Wilson .38 Super barrel revealed its headspace shoulder at the forward end of the chamber.

463

Using a custom Government Model compensated gun built by Bill
Wilson, Rob Leatham was the first to win a major USPSA/IPSC match
with the .38 Super. *(Front Sight photo)*

factory chambered. I have no idea why, but this seems to especially hold true for compensated pistols. Of the many custom comp guns in .38 Super, 9mm Luger, 10mm Auto, .40 S&W, and .45 ACP with which I have worked, only four were capable of consistently keeping 10 jacketed bullets inside two inches at 50 yards from a Ransom Rest. All were in .38 Super.

While writing this book, I asked the following question of five of the top pistolsmiths in the country: "If you were to build a custom Government Model comp gun that would be pitted against custom guns built by other pistolsmiths and the builder of the most accurate gun would win a million dollars, what caliber would it be?" All five named the .38 Super.

The .22 Long Rifle

The .22 Long Rifle chambering was introduced in 1931 in Colt's ACE 22 variation of the Government Model pistol. In 1937, the Service Model ACE with a floating chamber that closely simulated the recoil of the .45 ACP load was introduced. The Service Model was designed by David "Carbine" Williams who was later responsible for designing the M1 Carbine for the U.S. Army. Colt also offered ACE conversion units on an on-again, off-again basis, but no longer does as this is written.

The Service Model ACE has never enjoyed a reputation for outstanding accuracy, probably because until recently pistolsmiths did not seem to take it seriously. It is, however, capable of good if not outstanding accuracy. I have a conversion unit that was hand-fitted to the frame of a compensated gun in .38 Super built by C. W. Custom. When fed Eley Tenex ammo on a calm, windless day, it will average four inches for 10 shots at 50 yards from a sand-bag rest. If someone like Bar-Sto ever decides to make match-grade barrels for it, I believe a custom .22 caliber Government Model pistol would be capable of averaging two inches or less at 50 paces with good ammunition.

Service Model ACE conversion units are still easy to find at gun shows and in trade publications, and usually are reasonably priced. Most cost about the same as having a custom aftermarket centerfire barrel installed. I don't believe this will hold true for long, unless Colt starts making them again. As more shooters who have custom Government Model pistols built discover how inexpensive and how much fun shooting .22 Rimfire ammunition in them can be, the supply is bound to dry up and prices will rise accordingly. I would really like to see Colt bring this one back with a match-grade barrel.

The 9mm Parabellum (Luger)

The 9mm Parabellum was introduced in 1902 in Georg Luger's famous autoloading pistol. The German navy adopted it in 1904 and in 1908 the

This C.W. Custom Colt ACE will average four inches for 10 shots at 50 yards with Eley Tenex.

466

German army followed suit. The stubby 9mm caliber often is described as the world's most popular handgun and submachine cartridge which is probably true since it has been adopted by most of the world's great military powers. In 1985, after using the .45 ACP for almost three-quarters of a century, U.S. military forces also adopted the cartridge and the Beretta M-9 (Model 92-F) pistol.

For several decades the 9mm Parabellum was less than popular in the United States because the majority of pistols available for it were military surplus imports. The situation began to change when Colt introduced its 9mm caliber lightweight Commander in 1949 and Smith & Wesson followed a few years later with its Model 39 autoloader.

During the 1980s, dozens of other United States manufactured autoloaders became available in 9mm and law enforcement agencies began the transition from revolvers to autoloaders. The FBI adopted the 9mm and for a short time it was considered the ideal self-defense cartridge for autoloading pistols. Then came the infamous 1986 Miami shootout which left two FBI agents dead and five severely wounded. As a result of that incident, the FBI eventually dropped the 9mm and adopted a reduced-velocity 10mm Auto loading with a 180-grain bullet at a nominal 950 fps.

The 9mm Parabellum will enjoy great popularity in the United States for many years, but among lawmen, it seems to be losing ground fast to the .40 S&W. The more powerful 9mm loadings deliver about as much energy, but the .40 shoots a fatter bullet which some experts consider an edge in stopping power. Autoloaders in 9mm do have a slight advantage in cartridge capacity, but this is important only to those who believe firepower can substitute for accuracy. In some guns, any firepower edge offered by the smaller caliber is slight. The magazine of the Glock 22, for example, holds 15 rounds of .40 caliber ammunition while the magazine of the Glock 17 holds two more rounds. The capacity of the standard Government Model magazine is eight for the .40 S&W, and nine for the 9mm Parabellum.

Interestingly enough, Colt appears to have dropped the 9mm option from the Government Model and all its variations as the 1992 catalog lists it only for the new All American 2000 double-action autoloader. I figured this was coming. Several years ago a Colt official informed me that the 9mm Luger was an extremely slow seller. In the Government Model and its variations, the .45 ACP was still No. 1 by a wide margin with the 10mm Auto and .38 Super in a distant second place. More recently, I was told that most buyers of Colt autoloaders were also ignoring the .40 S&W option.

A well-used C. W. Custom steel plate gun in 9mm Luger.

The 10mm Auto

The 10mm Auto is the most powerful cartridge ever introduced in the standard-size Government Model pistol. It was introduced in 1983 in an ill-fated autoloader called the Bren Ten which was built by a now-defunct company called Dornaus & Dixon. The Swedish firm of Norma developed the first factory load around D&D specifications which called for 170- and 200-grain bullets at respective muzzle velocities of 1,400 and 1,300 fps.

While in Sweden in late 1987, I met with Norma's chief ballistician, Sixten Holmquist who was involved in developing the 10mm cartridge from day one. According to Holmquist, in order to attain the muzzle velocities specified by D&D, the 10mm had to be loaded to a mean average chamber pressure of 37,000 psi, with a maximum pressure of 44,400 psi. Thus, the first lot of 10mm ammunition was loaded to those chamber pressures. Norma's advertising staff was so proud of those figures, they went ahead and had it printed on thousands of factory ammunition boxes, which, of course, later caused a bit of confusion.

To make a short story even shorter, the fellows at D&D quickly discovered that the first lot of ammunition was a bit too much for the Bren Ten handgun. They then instructed Norma to ease back the throttle when loading future lots of ammunition. This resulted in velocities falling short of the original 1,400 and 1,300 fps. However, since Norma had a warehouse full of 20-round boxes with the original performance data printed on them, the decision was made to continue using them even though the ammunition was considerably slower.

While in Sweden, I was able to obtain the latest ballistics specifications for Norma's two 10mm loads. At the time, both were being loaded to a mean average chamber pressure of 26,460 psi with a maximum in the neighborhood of 33,000 psi. When fired in the Norma 5-inch pressure gun, the 170-grain load clocked an average of 1,246 fps and the 200-grain load moved out at 1,115 fps. This was considerably slower than information printed on the factory boxes indicated, but still produced muzzle energies of 586 and 552 ft-lbs.

Based on what I have been told, it would appear that most 10mm ammunition is loaded by various United States manufacturers to a maximum chamber pressure of around 35,000 psi, which is about the same as for the 9mm Luger, .38 Super, and .40 Smith & Wesson. The *Hercules Reloader's Guide* seems to agree, as most loads are in the 33,000 to 35,000 psi range with no recommended load exceeding 36,000 psi.

The 10mm Auto has a reputation for being hard on pistols, but it is due to the fact that the Colt owner's manual says nothing about its special

Steve Woods custom Colt Delta Elite in 10mm Auto.

The ill-fated Bren Ten was the first handgun available in 10mm Auto.

requirements. The relatively large head surface area of the 10mm case, combined with the high chamber pressures to which it is loaded, increase slide velocity of an autoloader quite a bit compared to the .45 ACP. It only takes about 500 rounds of heavy loads in a Delta Elite to pound much of the tension from its dual recoil springs and its synthetic recoil spring guide often bites the dust at about the 1,000-round mark. The result is battering of the frame and slide.

To prevent the 10mm from eating up its home, and to live happily ever after with a Colt Government Model pistol in this caliber, the factory dual recoil springs should be replaced with a single 22- or 24-pound spring. The factory spring guide should be replaced with a full-length steel guide wearing a shock buffer. For a noncompensated gun, the recoil spring should be replaced about every 1,000 rounds. When feeding a compensated competition gun reduced velocity Major power loads for USPSA/IPSC competition, the spring won't usually need to be replaced until about the 2,000- to 2,500-round mark. Some comp guns will go 3,000 rounds on one spring.

I like the 10mm Auto and consider it a great cartridge for the Government Model pistol. The handloader can download it to slower velocities for plinking, paper-punching, and competition, or load it full throttle for bagging whitetails and wild hogs out to 50 yards or so. The 10mm does not, however, seem to be running roughshod over its competition like many crystal balls once predicted it would. This is probably due to the fact that on the opposing team is the .45 ACP, a cartridge many still consider the all-time greatest for personal defense use. Also, there is the .40 S&W, which is rapidly becoming the law enforcement cartridge by which all others are judged. Then we have the .38 Super and the 9x23mm Super, two cartridges that will never allow the 10mm to gain much of a toehold in practical pistol competition.

Conversely, when it comes to versatility, and to squeezing pure raw power from a Government Model pistol, the 10mm Auto leaves them all choking in its dust just beyond the starting gate of the cartridge race.

The .40 S&W

A joint-venture development between Winchester and Smith & Wesson, the .40 S&W was introduced in January 1990. It was designed in an effort to squeeze .45 ACP performance from 9mm Luger-size autoloaders. It does not, however, equal the .45 ACP in bullet diameter, nor does it produce as much punch as Remington's +P loading of the .45 ACP.

As odd as it might seem, Glock seems to have beaten Smith & Wesson to the draw by becoming the first company to actually produce .40 caliber guns. In March 1990, three months after he had learned of the .40 S&W's

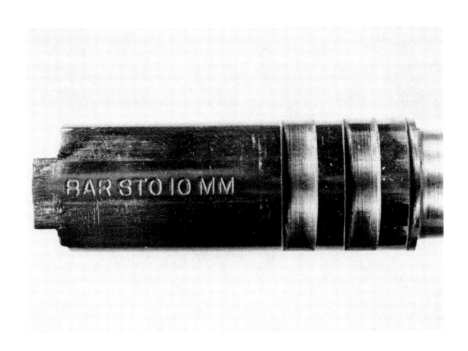

existence, the president of Glock took a prototype Model 22 to the South Carolina Law Enforcement Division (SLED) for testing. As a result, SLED adopted the .40 caliber Glock and the first guns were delivered in early May. This made SLED the first law enforcement agency in the country to put into service the new Model 22 pistol and its equally new cartridge.

Colt hopped aboard the .40 S&W bandwagon in 1992 by adding it to the Government Model's list of caliber options. Bluntly stated, one really has to try hard in order to come up with a logical reason for owning such a big pistol in this caliber. Like the 9mm Luger, it is a great cartridge for smaller autoloaders, but is shorter than it has to be for the Government Model. Full power factory loadings of the 10mm Auto deliver more punch than .40 S&W factory loads, and the various "10mm Lite" loadings duplicate .40 S&W performance. The same goes for handloads. You can load the 10mm faster than the .40 S&W, or ease back on the powder charge and duplicate its velocity. In my opinion, this makes the 10mm the more versatile of the two cartridges.

So, why would anyone want a little cartridge in a big pistol? I have no idea why those who handload would go the .40 S&W route, but then everybody doesn't load their own. Although the 10mm subsonic factory loads duplicate .40 S&W performance, only a few are available. In contrast, every major manufacturer of ammunition offers several .40 S&W loadings. For those who stick with factory loads and don't want or need the additional power and recoil

473

of the 10mm Auto, the .40 S&W is an excellent choice. In fact, the weight of a Government Model pistol makes the stubby little cartridge a powderpuff to shoot.

The .40 S&W is destined to become one of our all-time most popular handgun cartridges, but I believe it is seen at its best in autoloaders that are too small to take longer cartridges. There certainly is no law against owning a Government Model pistol in this caliber, but I prefer to move on up to the 10mm and leave the short cartridge for smaller guns. Of the various Government Model variations presently available, the Officer's ACP is probably the best candidate for the .40 S&W. Which brings up an interesting question: If Colt ever decides to do it, will the little gun be called the Officer's S&W?

The CP 9x21mm +P+

In practical pistol competition, a cartridge called the CP 9x21mm +P+ has become extremely popular among those who compete with custom high-capacity 9mm Luger-size pistols made by Springfield Armory, Glock, Smith & Wesson, and others. A few custom Government Model pistols also have been built in this caliber. It first became popular among IPSC competitors in Europe and was introduced to United States shooters in 1990 by a United States firm called C. P. Bullets. Unprimed cases and custom-loaded ammunition are available from C. P., and a couple of European firms offer it in factory-loaded form.

The 9x21mm case is nothing more than a two millimeter longer version of the 9x19mm Luger case. The actual length of virgin cases I have measured averaged .825 inch compared to .750 inch for 9mm Luger cases. Although it is a bit larger in diameter at the rim and base, the 9x21mm case is only slightly longer than the old 9mm Browning Long case which measures .800 inch. When loaded to Major power factor velocities for practical pistol competition, the 9x21mm generates extremely high chamber pressures which is to be expected since its net powder capacity is the same as that of the 9mm Luger and less than that of the .38 Super.

The 9x21mm was introduced to practical pistol competition soon after the USPSA banned the use of 9x19mm Luger Major-power loads in competition. This was done because tests performed by various United States handloading components manufacturers revealed that chamber pressures exceeded the SAAMI maximum. Since SAAMI did not have the 9x21mm on its list, the USPSA could not legally ban it from competition even though it generates the same chamber pressures as 9x19mm Luger Major power loads.

This somewhat controversial cartridge and the custom 9mm Luger-size autoloaders built for it have been called by many names. When first hearing

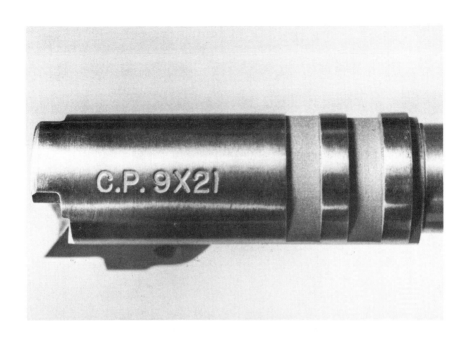

Billy Abbate shifting his high-capacity, optical-sighted gun in 9x21mm beyond warp speed during the Twist and Shout stage of the 1992 USPSA Area VI Championships.

about the cartridge, I dubbed it the 9x21mm LH (LoopHole), but the name didn't catch on. Paid professionals who are members of Team Smith & Wesson usually call it the .356 TSW, among other things. Others often refer to it as the 9mm PBF (Pistolsmith's Best Friend) because the chamber pressure to which it is loaded is extremely hard on some guns. When having a gun built around the Springfield Armory P9 and other 9mm autoloaders of similar size, most shooters ask the pistolsmith to include a pocketful of spare slide stops as they tend to snap like dry twigs with great regularity. In all fairness to the guns and the cartridge, I will add that this problem has just as much to do with how the barrel is fitted to the frame. At least one pistolsmith I know whipped the problem quite early, but some continue to struggle with it.

The 9x21mm should continue to enjoy popularity among those who use Unlimited class guns with magazines too short to handle longer cartridges. No doubt, it is the logical choice for 9mm Luger-size autoloaders and if I were to wake up one morning to find myself overcome with the urge to start using one in competition, the 9x21mm would be the cartridge for me. However, the standard-capacity Government Model pistol in 9x21mm will never make sense to me when the .38 Super accomplishes the same thing at lower chamber pressures. For custom Unlimited class guns built around the Caspian and Para-Ordnance high-capacity frames, the newer CP 9x23mm +P is a much better choice than its two millimeter shorter littermate.

One thing is certain, the 9x21mm is for expert handloaders only and when loaded full-throttle for the Government Model pistol, a barrel with a full-support chamber is highly recommended.

The CP 9x23mm Super +P

On the same day during the second week in March 1992, John Ricco of C. P. Bullets and I received the first chamber reamers made by Clymer for a new cartridge called the CP 9x23mm Super +P. I then sent the reamer to Chuck Warner of C. W. Custom to be used in chambering one of his heavy barrels for installation in a new Aimpoint-sighted gun built around a Para-Ordnance frame and Gold Cup slide. Shortly thereafter, I received a 9x21mm barrel from Ricco to be rechambered to 9x23mm and installed in one of my old .38 Super comp guns for load development purposes. I was ready to wring out the 9x23mm and develop load data for this book long before most people were even aware of its existence. But you know what they say about the best laid plains of mice and firearms writers, I had the guns long before a supply of cases became available.

The 9x23mm probably will be described by some as a rimless version of the .38 Super, but that's far from true. Those cartridges do share the same

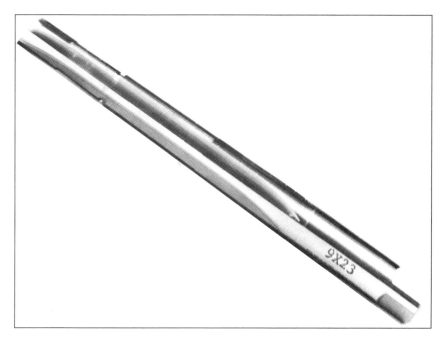

The author received one of the first 9x23mm Super chamber reamers from Clymer.

477

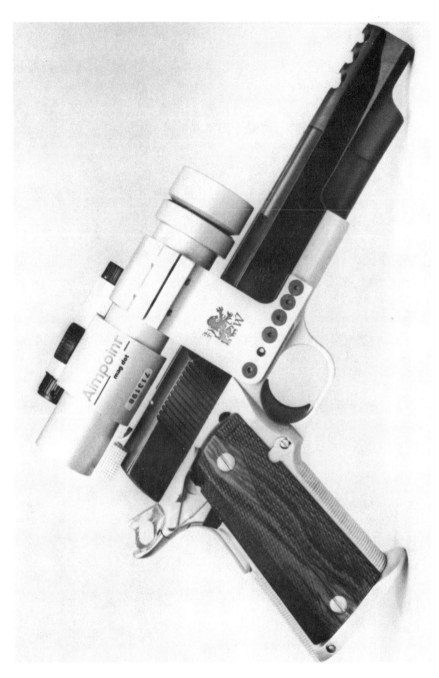

Built by Chuck Warner, this high-capacity job built around a Colt
Gold Cup slide and Para-Ordnance frame was the first gun built in
9x23mm Super.

maximum case length of .900-inch, and bullet diameter is the same, but from there on you are looking at two different cartridges. The .38 Super case is cylindrical with no taper from base to mouth and its .406-inch (maximum) rim diameter makes it a semirimmed design. Like the 9mm Luger case, the 9x23mm is rimless and tapers from base to mouth. The 9x23mm case has maximum rim and base diameters of .392-inch and tapers to a mouth diameter of .380-inch. Maximum base diameter (just forward of the extraction groove) of the .38 Super case is .384-inch, making it smaller than the 9x23mm case in that area by .008-inch.

One does not need a degree in nuclear fission to figure out that a barrel in 9x19 mm Luger, 9x21mm C.P., or .38 Super can be rechambered for the 9x23mm cartridge. Reamers with slightly different dimensions have been available from Clymer. Reamer "B" cuts minimum chamber base and mouth diameters. It is used for cutting a minimum-dimension chamber in a virgin barrel. The slightly larger "A" reamer (which John Ricco of C.P. has made standard) is used for chambering a new barrel and rechambering barrels with full-support chambers in .38 Super, 9mm Luger, and 9x21mm +P. The "A" reamer is best for rechamber jobs due to slight variations in actual chamber diameter that exist from barrel to barrel, plus the fact that a tapered 9x23mm reamer is used to clean out a cylindrical .38 Super chamber which can measure as much as .387 inch in diameter at its mouth. The 9x23mm reamer also cuts a .100-inch long freebore, compared to .060 inch which is standard for the .38 Super and 9x19mm Luger.

The smaller reamer usually will clean out the rear of 9x19mm, .38 Super, and 9x21mm chambers, but may or may not do the same up front. If it doesn't, a small shoulder can be left at the chamber's forward end or mouth. The larger reamer cleans up the entire chamber and yet the mere .002-inch difference in actual diameters cut by the two reamers is small enough to allow the use of the same full-length resizing die for cases fired in chambers cut with either reamer. Even so, in order to work the brass fired in an "A" chamber as little as possible during the resizing operation, I would rather have a full-length resizer cut specifically for it. Incidentally, Lee Precision made the first reloading dies for this cartridge.

Now for a warning to pistolsmiths who decide to rechamber customers' barrels for this cartridge. When a .38 Super chamber is reamed out with the 9x23mm reamer, some of the headspacing shoulder may remain on the barrel hood. If a .38 Super cartridge is mistakenly chambered, it could possibly headspace on the hood and fire when the trigger is pulled. If it does, the case will expand to fill the oversize chamber and in doing so, may rupture. If this happens, you have a blown gun. Even if the headspace shoulder is removed during rechambering, the extractor could conceivably hold a .38

Super cartridge tight enough against the breechface of the slide for the firing pin to ignite its primer. For that matter, the same could happen if a 9x19mm or 9x21mm chamber is reamed out to 9x23mm.

I am not trying to badmouth the 9x23mm Super. Quite the contrary, I consider it a fantastic idea for the new breed of high-capacity Government Model pistols. However, I am saying that if I were a pistolsmith, I wouldn't let a rechamber job go out the door before the old caliber markings are completely removed from the hood of the barrel and the hood restamped, rollmarked, etched, or engraved "CP 9x23mm Only."

Even though the 9x23mm case is larger in diameter at its base than the .38 Super, its powder capacity is a bit smaller. This is due to the great thickness of its wall just above the web of the case. The design adds lots of beef to a critical area, making it one of the finest cartridge cases ever designed for autoloading pistols. Starting loads shown for the .38 Super in various handloading manuals can be used when developing loads for the 9x23mm, but since its net boiler room area is a bit less, Major-power velocities will be reached with a bit less powder.

I would just as soon have the .38 Super in a standard capacity Government Model competition gun for several reasons. It works fine, feeds as smoothly as silk from a single-column magazine, and will reach Major power velocities at a bit lower chamber pressure than the 9x23mm. This is, however, rather a moot point since the standard capacity Government Model pistol is rapidly becoming obsolete for Unlimited class USPSA/IPSC competition, and the .38 Super is no longer classified as a Major-power cartridge for Limited class guns. The 9x23mm definitely gets the nod anytime the topic of conversation switches to an Unlimited class gun built on a high-capacity frame like the Caspian and Para-Ordnance because its rimless design is more compatible with their double-column magazines. As many pistolsmiths already have proven, the .38 Super works in those magazines when they are properly tuned, but I believe the rimless cartridge will work even better with less tuning required.

Assuming that the 9x23mm actually does get off and running, I predict a bright future for it. My crystal ball says everybody except those who get paid to shoot something else will switch to high-capacity Government Model pistols for Unlimited class practical pistol competition. I believe this extra-long 9mm will quickly become to competitors of the 1990s what the .38 Super was during the 1980s, and what the .45 ACP was before then. I don't see many people shooting any other cartridge in the new breed of custom high-capacity Government Model competition guns in the near future, unless Winchester (or Remington or Federal) decides to introduce a new factory-loaded cartridge by trimming the 9mm Winchester magnum case back to 24mm.

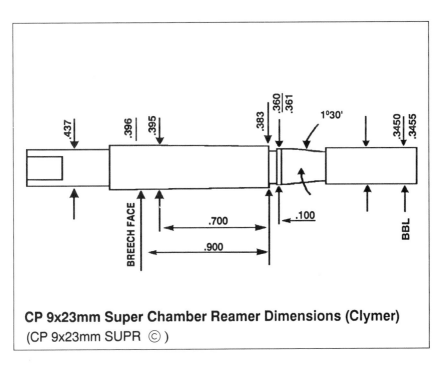

CP 9x23mm Super Chamber Reamer Dimensions (Clymer)
(CP 9x23mm SUPR Ⓒ)

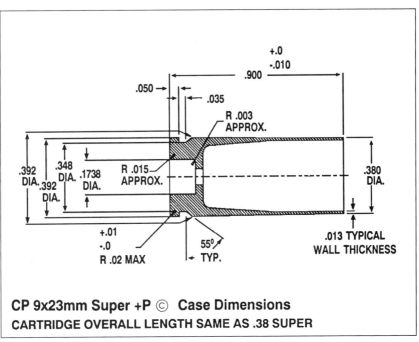

CP 9x23mm Super +P Ⓒ Case Dimensions
CARTRIDGE OVERALL LENGTH SAME AS .38 SUPER

481

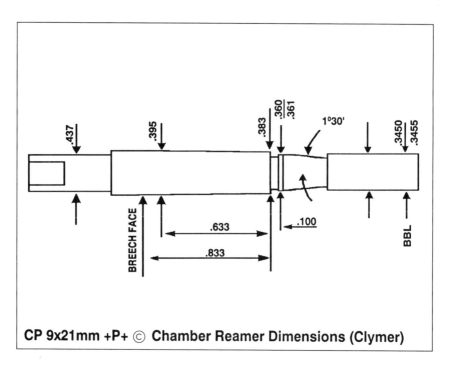

CP 9x21mm +P+ © Chamber Reamer Dimensions (Clymer)

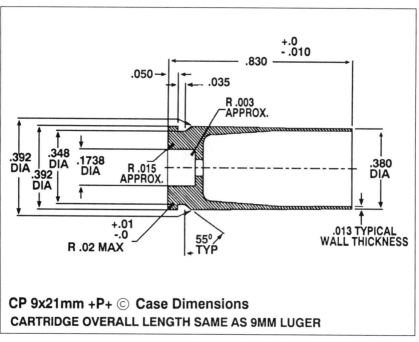

CP 9x21mm +P+ © Case Dimensions
CARTRIDGE OVERALL LENGTH SAME AS 9MM LUGER

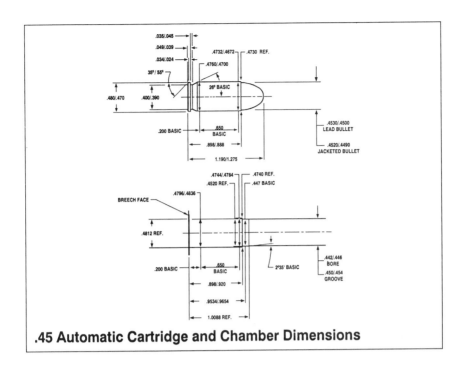

.45 Automatic Cartridge and Chamber Dimensions

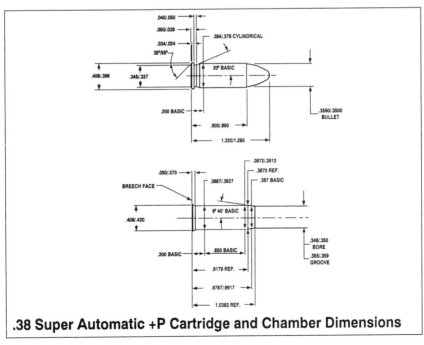

.38 Super Automatic +P Cartridge and Chamber Dimensions

483

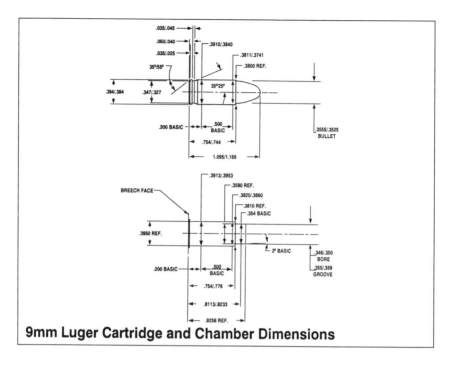

9mm Luger Cartridge and Chamber Dimensions

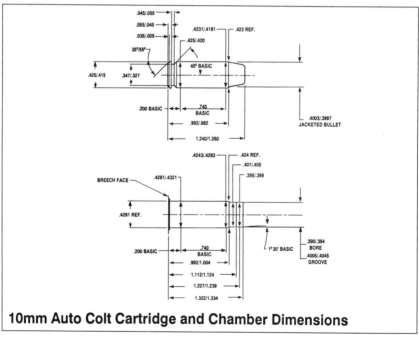

10mm Auto Colt Cartridge and Chamber Dimensions

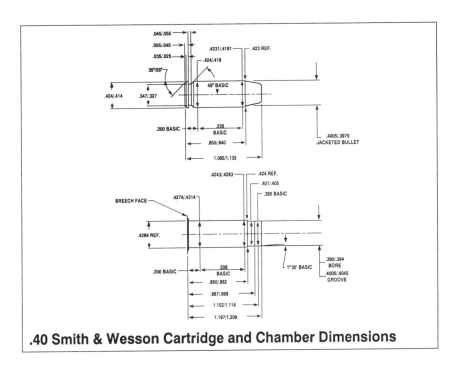

.40 Smith & Wesson Cartridge and Chamber Dimensions

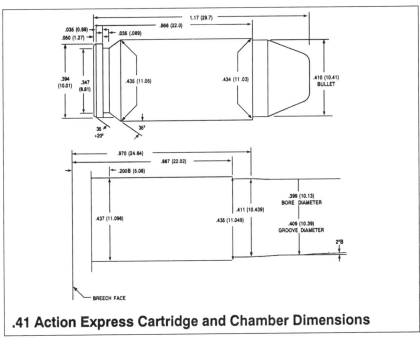

.41 Action Express Cartridge and Chamber Dimensions

22

Handloading for the Government Model

L IKE any autoloading pistol, the reliability of the Government Model is greatly influenced by its diet. Feed it junk handloads and reliability is gone. Feed it good factory loads or handloads, and it becomes one of the most reliable autoloaders ever designed. Contrary to popular opinion, ammunition produced by the average handloader is not better than factory-loaded ammunition. If the truth be known, only a tiny percentage of home-brewed loads produced by thousands of handloaders each year comes even close to equaling factory ammunition in quality. It can be done, but all too many handloaders have neither the patience nor the desire to do so.

Case Inspection

A thorough inspection of cases is the first step toward putting together top-quality handloads. When a case is work-hardended by expanding during firing and then sized back down during the handloading process, it eventually will split at the mouth and should be discarded. It also is best to keep different manufacturing lots of cases of the same brand separate as they can vary slightly in capacity from one lot to the next.

Various brands of cases also should be kept separate. In addition to slight differences in capacity among those from various manufacturers which can affect velocity, they also tend to vary in exact length. A relatively uniform overall length among cases is important because wide variations can affect primer ignition and therefore velocity uniformity. As a rule, when the same load is put up in cases that vary considerably in length, the short cases will

Handloads used in competition must be accurate and reliable.

produce lower velocities than the long cases. This is due to the fact that when their mouth headspaces on the headspacing shoulder of the barrel, the primers of the longer cases are positioned closer to the firing pin. The shorter the distance the firing pin must travel before striking a primer, the more energy it delivers to it. The more energy the firing pin delivers to the primer, the more uniformly the primer ignites the powder. By the same token, if the firing pin has to travel farther before impact, it will deliver less energy to the primer.

As a case is pounded with heavy loadings, its rim eventually will increase in diameter. A slight increase in rim diameter won't hurt anything as long as it does not exceed the SAAMI maximum, but the increase seldom takes place in a uniform manner. If flats, nicks, and gouges begin to appear on the rim, the case is ready for retirement. Cases with stretched primer pockets also should be discarded.

Case Cleaning

The handloader who deals with small quantities of cases can clean their exterior surface with a paper towel dampened with any good bore cleaning solvent. Those who load thousands of rounds each year will find life much

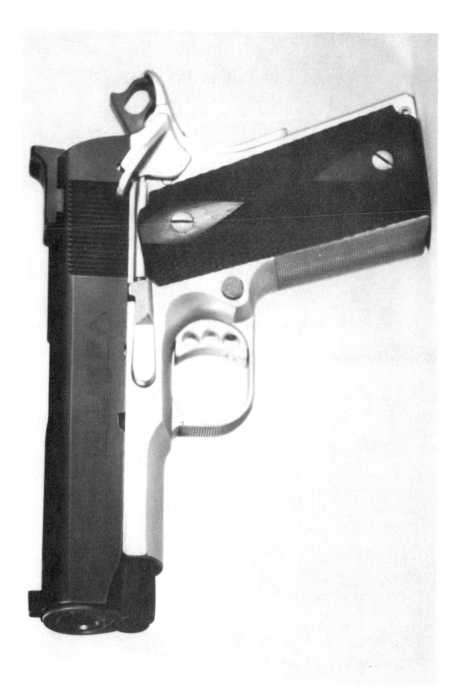

Jim Garthwaite fullhouse Officer's ACP carry gun.

Overworked with too many reloadings, this .45 ACP case blew in a barrel with a standard chamber.

Dillon's case and tumbling media separator is a great idea for those who turn out large quantities of ammunition on a progressive loader. *(Dillon Precision photo)*

easier if a good case tumbler is used. Tumblers are available with various case and polishing media capacities. The smaller units are better for apartment dwellers and others who are a bit cramped for space. I don't have a space problem so a king-size tumbler like Dillon's Magnum FL-2000 which holds 2,000 .38 Super cases and 42 cups of polishing media is more my style.

I handload more different calibers than the average handgunner and have several case tumblers. Each has its own inexpensive electrical timer which was purchased at a home appliance store. Powder fouling is much easier to remove shortly after a case is fired, so as soon as possible after a shooting session or match, I dump the cases into a tumbler, turn the timer to five minutes, and go on to more pressing matters. I continue doing this and when the tumbler contains a full load of cases, the timer is turned to 30 minutes and the entire batch receives their final cleaning.

Case/Media Separation

The small sifter-type case/media separators are fine for small batches of cases. The best thing to use for catching the polishing media as it drops through the bottom of the sifter is a square plastic kitty litter tub. This type of separator is too slow for large batches of cases. The best-designed separator I have found is from Dillon. Available in small and large sizes, it consists of a squirrel cage-type hopper with handle, suspended over a plastic tub. Simply dump media and cases from the tumbler into the hopper, turn the crank a few times, and the job is done. Cases remain in the hopper and the media collects in the tub with none on the floor. Great idea.

Bullet Diameters

As a rule, the correct diameter for a cast bullet is the same or somewhere in the neighborhood of .001-inch larger than the groove diameter of a particular barrel. In other words, if the groove diameter of a .45 ACP barrel is, say, .451-inch, the correct cast bullet diameter for it is from .451- to .452-inch. A .38 Super or 9x23mm barrel with a .356-inch groove diameter is likely to shoot best with a .356- or .357-inch bullet.

Bore and groove diameters for a particular caliber can vary considerably among the various manufacturers with less variation usually seen in custom barrels than in factory barrels. Determining the groove diameter of a barrel is easily accomplished by coating the bore and a lead bullet with a light film of oil and then pushing the bullet through the barrel with a wooden dowel. By doing this, you can avoid buying cast bullets of the wrong diameter.

Matching up the correct bullet diameter with a barrel is extremely important. A shooting pal of mine had a custom compensated gun in .38 Super

490

This Dillon FL-2000B tumbler has a capacity of 2000 9mm Luger cases. *(Dillon Precision photo)*

Sharon Kimbrel shoots Tru-Flight cast bullets in her .38 Super during practice, but switches to jacketed bullets from the same company for major USPSA/IPSC matches. *(Front Sight photo)*

built and it was quite accurate with most jacketed bullets. Then he tried cast bullet loads and the gun wouldn't hit the side of a barn. I put together batches of handloads with Remington Cases, Remington 7½ primers, AA-7 powder, and the Bull-X 147-grain flatnose bullet in three different diameters. Even when held securely in my Ransom Rest, the gun shot all over the paper with the .356-inch bullet, but started settling down when I tried the loads with .357-inch bullets. With an even larger .358-inch bullet, the gun became a tack-driver.

Here is another interesting observation. While working with many Government Model pistols of the various calibers, I have found that the smaller the caliber, the more critical cast bullet diameter becomes. I find the .45 ACP to be far more tolerant of undersized or oversized cast bullets than the .38 Super, with the .40 S&W and 10mm Auto less choosy than the .38 Super, but more choosy than the .45 ACP. When shooting jacketed bullets, I find just the opposite to be true: the .38 Super will tolerate greater diameter variations than the .45 ACP, and the 10mm Auto and .40 S&W are in between.

Cast Bullet Hardness

The higher the chamber pressure and velocity of the load, the more critical bullet hardness and lubricant quality become. This is why a .45 ACP load that gently pushes a 200-grain bullet along at 800 fps won't leave as much lead fouling in the barrel as a 150-grain load zipping along at 1,200 fps. You can get by with relatively soft bullets at low velocities, but as many practical pistol competitors have learned, they often won't produce acceptable accuracy at higher speeds.

In addition to being uniform in diameter, good cast bullets wear a top-quality lubricant, and they are hard enough to withstand the tremendous stress they undergo when fired at the higher velocities. When checking the relative hardness of a new brand or batch of commercially cast bullets, I can accurately predict how they will perform at high speeds without shooting a single one. If the bullets rate close to "9" on my Redding/SAECO relative hardness tester, they are sure to work. If they rate barely over an "8," they might work. If they fall below that rating in hardness, the bullets are definitely not good candidates for high-velocity loads.

Overall Cartridge Length

When extremely lightweight bullets are loaded in the various Government Model cartridges, overall cartridge length is less than with heavier bullets. Good examples are a 150-grain bullet in the .45 ACP, and a 145-grain bullet in the 10mm Auto. Some guns will feed short cartridges as smoothly as silk, but others will choke on them. Several of the jacketed hollowpoint bullets

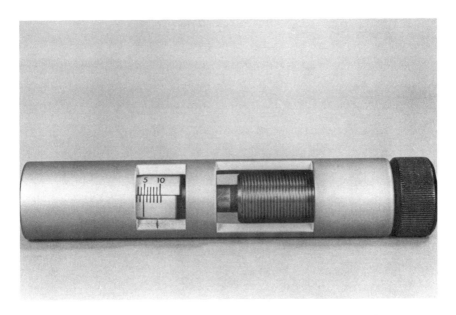

This Redding-SAECO device is helpful for checking the relative hardness of cast bullets.

also have a tendency to make some guns stop going bang after the first shot. The Speer 200-grain with its huge hollow nose cavity and relatively short overall cartridge length is one of few bullets that will expand at Officer's ACP velocity. On the negative side, with the possible exception of the Gold Cup, very few factory guns will feed short cartridges until a pistolsmith slightly modifies the barrel throat and adjusts the feed lips of the magazine so the rounds are presented to the chamber at a slightly different angle.

Case Mouth Tension

The trip a cartridge takes from the magazine to the chamber of an autoloading pistol is a rather violent one. The cartridge is sitting innocently in the magazine when suddenly the speeding slide gives it a tremendous boot in the rump. The acceleration from zero to pretty darned fast in less than a blink of the eye causes the heavy bullet to resist forward movement while the lighter case is eager to get ahead. If case mouth tension is too light, the bullet actually can creep deeper into the case at the very beginning of its journey. As the slide slams the cartridge forward, the nose of its bullet bounces off the feedramp and then ricochets off the roof of the chamber before it becomes aligned with the chamber. This also can drive the bullet deeper into the case.

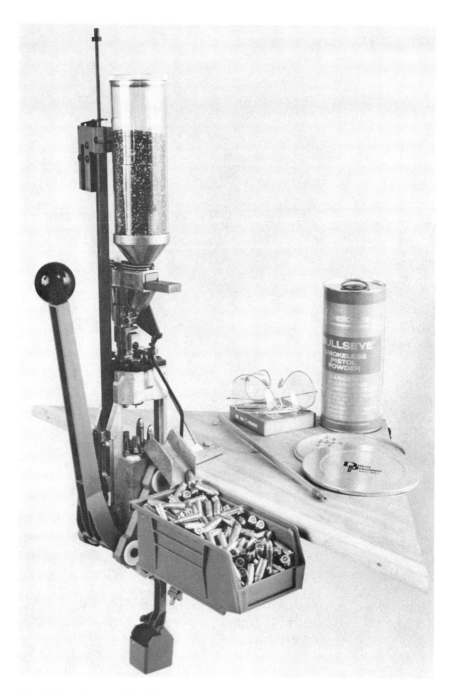

The Dillon Square Deal-B. *(Dillon Precision photo)*

494

A good taper crimp is required for preventing a bullet from being shoved deeper in the case during the feeding cycle.

A bullet has only to be seated slightly deeper into a straightwall case during the feeding cycle, for it to displace a large percentage of the combustion area. If this happens, chamber pressure skyrockets. According to technicians who developed load data for the *Speer Reloading Manual*, when the bullet of a 9mm Luger load that generates 28,000 copper units of pressure (CUP) is seated a mere .030-inch deeper in the case, chamber pressure increases to an extremely dangerous 62,000 CUP. The industry standard working pressure for the 9mm Luger is 35,700 CUP.

Since most straightwall autoloading pistol cartridges are designed to headspace on their case mouths, a roll crimp is out of the question. The next best thing is a taper crimp and I highly recommend this type of die for handloading all cartridges for autoloading pistols. Some handloaders get carried away with a taper-crimp die because they figure if a little crimp is good, a lot of crimp is better. Not so. Excessive crimping can affect accuracy with cast bullets and it shortens case life. It is best to taper-crimp the mouth of cases to the SAAMI maximum diameter shown in various handloading manuals. Those maximums also are listed for each cartridge in Chapter 23.

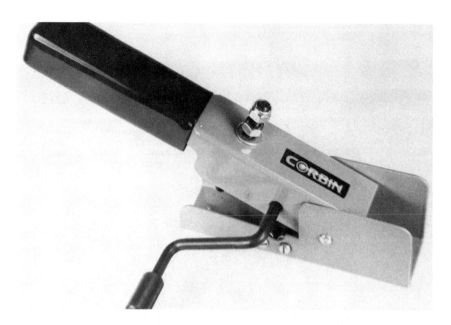

Short, lightweight bullets with their short bearing surface can be prevented from being shoved deeper into the case by applying a cannelure to the case with this Corbin tool.

(Left) Virgin case and (right) case with cannelure applied with Corbin tool.

The correct taper-crimp diameter of the mouth of a .45 ACP handload is .470 inch.

A good taper crimp die is a must for handloads used in autoloading pistols.

Final Inspection

Each loaded round should be examined for defects. Each round also should be gauged to make sure it easily enters the guns chamber. Gauges are available for this purpose, but none I have seen or tried are any better than simply using the barrel in which the ammunition will be fired. Simply remove the barrel from the gun and slip each round into the chamber. If a round won't go, you have caught a reject that probably would have tied up the gun during a match. Ideally, a cartridge should drop freely into the chamber and come to a stop with the surface of its head flush with, or only slightly below, the rear surface of the barrel hood.

Ammunition Storage

You can't beat a military surplus .50 caliber ammo can for storing ammunition. It is relatively inexpensive, and if in good condition its rubber seal will protect the ammo from dust and moisture for a long time. I store my cartridges loosely in an ammo can, but transfer a supply to RCBS 50-round plastic ammo boxes when checking my gear prior to a match. The boxes are handy and position the cartridges bullet down so I can visually make sure their primers are seated right-side up.

The barrel of a gun can be used as a gauge for checking handloads for smooth chambering.

498

The Progressive Press

The progressive reloading press is a wonderful invention and I would hate to have to live without one, but enough junk ammunition is produced with them each year to sink several battleships. The fault lies not with the various machines, but with their operators. Too many handloaders are more concerned with quantity than quality, and it shows at any shooting range or practical pistol match one decides to visit. Three of the more common problems shooters have with handloads are cartridges that won't chamber, primers seated upside down, and duds with no powder. The latter is such a common occurrence that the USPSA members' handbook tells competitors to keep a wooden dowel in their range bag to be used for pushing a lodged bullet from the barrel.

Until one reaches the level of accuracy required by benchrest shooters, there exists no difference in quality between ammunition properly loaded on a progressive or single-stage press, but the former does require more attention to detail and slightly bigger helping of common horse sense. A slower pace will do more to help handloaders turn out quality ammunition than anything else. When I operate a progressive press, my primary concern is to turn out the best ammunition possible on a single-stage press. I have never

Since most serious practical pistol competitors burn up thousands of rounds each year, they utilize various progressive presses for handloading their ammunition.

499

When turning out handloads on a progressive press, the author firmly
believes in quality rather than quantity.

The Dillon 550B.

timed myself to see how many rounds per hour are being loaded because quality rather than quantity is my number one priority. At the very most, I probably never exceed 250 to 300 rounds per hour with my Dillon 550B. This may seem turtle-slow to some handloaders, but I have yet experienced a gun malfunction during a match that could be blamed on my ammunition.

When loading ammo on a progressive, I keep a sharp eye on the powder-charging station to make certain each and every case gets its share of propellant. A gooseneck lamp clamped to the end of my loading bench is adjusted to shed plenty of light on the subject. Machines that have the charging station on the backside and out of sight require the attachment of a small mirror in addition to the light.

When operating my progressive press at less than full throttle, I can feel each primer being seated into a case. If one seats without a bit of resistance, I know the primer pocket is stretched and the case needs to be discarded. It is impossible to have such a sensitive touch when trying to break speed records.

A handy device for those who handload large quantities of ammunition, this Dillon cartridge counter will work on most progressive loaders. *(Dillon Precision photo)*

The RCBS Auto 4x4.

The Hornady Projector.

504

The RCBS Piggyback II.

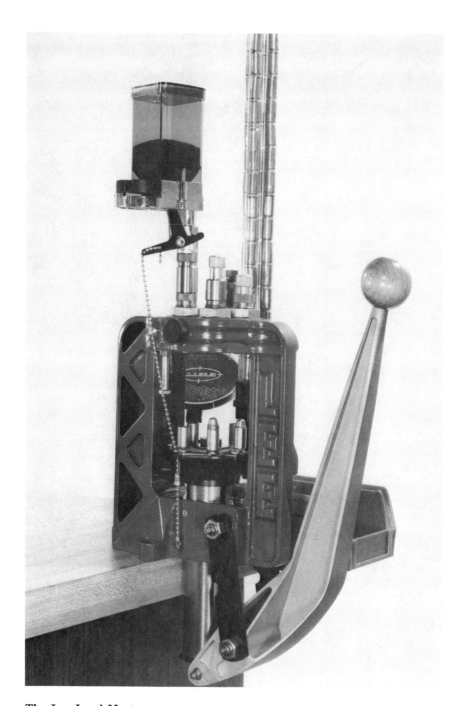

The Lee Load Master.

23

Load Data

A LL load data in the following charts are safe in the author's guns, but please be forewarned that due to the many uncontrollable variables involved in handloading, some loads may be excessive in other guns. It is for this reason that neither the author nor the publisher assumes any responsibility for the use of the data by other parties. All powder charges shown should be reduced by 20 percent. The loads are intended to be used in virgin cases and modern guns in excellent to new condition. If in doubt about using a particular load or loads in your gun, consult one of the handloading manuals available from various component manufacturers or the pistolsmith who built your gun.

Oehler Models 33 and 35P chronographs were used to measure bullet velocity. The velocity shown for each load represents a minimum of five rounds clocked 12 feet from the muzzle.

Light target loads may not generate levels of chamber pressure sufficient to operate the Government Model pistol with a standard recoil spring. For more on this subject, I refer you to this book's Appendix.

For the benefit of those who are into the various action shooting games, I have listed the power factor rating of most USPSA/IPSC competition loads for the various cartridges. Power factor (PF) is easily determined by multiplying bullet weight times muzzle velocity and dividing by a constant of 1000. For example, a 180-grain bullet at 1,000 fps has a PF rating of 180. A 200-grain bullet at 900 fps has the same rating. In order for a load to qualify as Major in USPSA/IPSC competition, it must rate a minimum of 175. The Minor power factor range is from 125 to 174.9.

507

I have not listed the muzzle energy of various loads. That information can be arrived at with an inexpensive pocket calculator by multiplying bullet weight times velocity squared and dividing by 0.000002218. For example, a 180-grain bullet at 1,000 fps would be 180 times 1,000 times 1,000 divided by 0.000002218 equals 399.2 foot-pounds of kinetic energy. Several other formulas work just as well, but this is the one I have become accustomed to using over the years.

Last, but certainly not least, handloading is as safe or as hazardous as the person doing it and should not be attempted by the careless or inexperienced. Before attempting to load your own, buy several handloading manuals and study their instruction sections until you become thoroughly familiar with the proper procedures. After doing so, you might want to read Chapter 22.

9x19mm Parabellum (Luger) High Performance Loads

Barrels: Bar-Sto 4¼ and Wilson 5-inch
Case: Remington
Primer: Remington No. 1½ Small Pistol
Overall Cartridge Length: Varied
Taper Crimp Diameter: .379-inch

	Powder		Velocity (fps) 4¼" Barrel	5" Barrel
Bullet	*(type)*	*(grs.)*	**Barrel**	**Barrel**
Cast Bullets				
Bull-X 122-gr. TFN	PB	4.3	1,131	1,164
Bull-X 122-gr. TFN	AA-2	4.5	1,124	----
Bull-X 122-gr. TFN	SR 4756	5.5	1,222	1,243
Bull-X 122-gr. TFN	AA-5	6.2	1,061	----
Tru-Flight 125-gr. BBTC	W231	4.0	1,010	----
Tru-Flight 125-gr. BBTC	WSF	4.7	1,018	----
Tru-Flight 125-gr. BBTC	W540	5.7	1,076	----
Tru-Flight 125-gr. BBTC	Blue Dot	8.0	1,291	1,347
Bull-X 125-gr. RN	700X	4.0	1,131	1,148
Bull-X 125-gr. RN	Bullseye	4.4	1,076	----
Bull-X 125-gr. RN	Red Dot	4.5	1,174	----
Bull-X 125-gr. RN	Green Dot	4.8	1,125	----
Tru-Flight 145-gr. BBRN	HS7	7.1	1,104	1,136
Tru-Flight 145-gr. BBRN	AA-7	7.2	1,088	----

Bullet	Powder (type)	(grs.)	Velocity (fps) 4¼" Barrel	5" Barrel
Bull-X 147-gr. TFN	W231	3.5	862	----
Bull-X 147-gr. TFN	WSF	4.1	926	----
Bull-X 147-gr. TFN	W540	5.3	1,019	1,063
Bull-X 147-gr. TFN	W571	5.0	1,028	----

Jacketed Bullets

Bullet	Powder (type)	(grs.)	4¼" Barrel	5" Barrel
Speer 88-gr. JHP	Blue Dot	9.0	1,364	1,419
Speer 88-gr. JHP	W231	6.1	1,318	----
Nosler 90-gr. JHP	HS6	8.0	1,384	1,422
Nosler 90-gr. JHP	AA-5	8.1	1,252	----
Hornady 90-gr. JHP	W231	5.7	1,218	----
Hornady 90-gr. JHP	HS7	9.2	1,330	1,457
Sierra 90-gr. JHP	Bullseye	5.0	1,362	----
Sierra 90-gr. JHP	Herco	6.9	1,411	1,466
Hornady 100-gr. FMJ-RN	AA-5	6.9	1,211	----
Hornady 100-gr. FMJ-RN	HS6	7.5	1,308	1,341
Speer 100-gr. JHP	HP38	5.5	1,312	1,354
Speer 100-gr. JHP	Blue Dot	9.3	1,339	----
Nosler 115-gr. JHP	CLAYS	4.0	----	1,132
Nosler 115-gr. JHP	700X	4.7	1,146	----
Nosler 115-gr. JHP	Blue Dot	8.5	1,174	1,218
Hornady 115-gr. JHP-XTP	Bullseye	5.1	1,137	----
Tru-Flight 115-gr. FMJ	HS6	6.9	1,215	1,244
Speer 115-gr. PHP	Green Dot	6.4	1,186	----
Speer 115-gr. PHP	Herco	7.0	1,315	1,361
Hornady 124-gr. JHP-XTP	CLAYS	4.0	1,104	----
Hornady 124-gr. JHP-XTP	HS6	6.9	1,088	----
Speer 124-gr. PSP	Blue Dot	8.3	1,124	----
Bull-X 125-gr. JSN	Herco	6.2	1,208	1,239
Tru-Flight 125-gr. FMJ	W571	7.5	1,076	----
Tru-Flight 130-gr. FMJ	HS6	6.6	----	1,127

Bullet	Powder (type)	(grs.)	Velocity (fps) 4¼" Barrel	5" Barrel
Hornady 147-gr. JHP-XTP	CLAYS	3.9	----	1,041
Hornady 147-gr. JHP-XTP	Green Dot	3.7	893	----
Hornady 147-gr. JHP-XTP	Herco	4.9	964	1,011
Hornady 147-gr. JHP-XTP	Blue Dot	5.5	878	----
Hornady 147-gr. JHP-XTP	AA-7	6.6	914	----
Speer 147-gr. PHP	Red Dot	3.4	851	----
Speer 147-gr. PHP	AA-2	3.8	911	----
Speer 147-gr. PHP	Bullseye	4.0	944	----
Speer 147-gr. PHP	AA-5	5.3	958	----
Speer 147-gr. PHP	Blue Dot	6.2	1,019	1,062
Speer 147-gr. PHP	AA-7	7.2	1,026	1,048

WARNING: These loads are safe in the author's guns, but due to the many uncontrollable variables involved in handloading that can have drastic effects on chamber pressure, may be excessive for others. All powder charges should be reduced by 20 percent for starting loads in other guns.

9mm Parabellum (Luger)
Light Target Loads

Barrel: Bar-Sto 5½-inch
Case: Remington
Primer: Remington No. 1½ Small Pistol
Overall Cartridge Length: Varied
Taper Crimp Diameter: .379-inch

Bullet	Powder (type)	(grains)	Velocity (fps)
Cast Bullets			
Bull-X 125-gr. RN	CLAYS	3.4	1,011
Bull-X 125-gr. RN	Bullseye	4.0	1,019
Tru-Flight 140-gr. SWC	AA-2	3.8	856
Tru-Flight 140-gr. SWC	AA-5	5.5	1,015
Bull-X 147-gr. TCFN	WSF	4.0	984
Bull-X 147-gr. TCFN	W540	5.0	954

Bullet	Powder (type)	Powder (grains)	Velocity (fps)
Bull-X 150-gr. SWC	W231	3.5	981
Bull-X 150-gr. SWC	AA-5	4.7	906

Jacketed Bullets

Bullet	Powder (type)	Powder (grains)	Velocity (fps)
Hornady 100-gr. FMJ	WSL	3.8	1,023
Hornady 100-gr. FMJ	Red Dot	3.8	1,019
Nosler 115-gr. FMJ	CLAYS	3.8	1,031
Nosler 115-gr. FMJ	HP38	5.0	1,022
Nosler 115-gr. FMJ	WSF	5.0	1,028
Bull-X 125-gr. JSN	CLAYS	3.6	1,044
Bull-X 125-gr. JSN	AA-2	4.6	1,020
Tru-Flight 130-gr. TCJ	HP38	4.6	1,015
Tru-Flight 130-gr. TCJ	Trap 100	5.0	1,032
Tru-Flight 147-gr. TCJ	CLAYS	3.7	1,019
Tru-Flight 147-gr. TCJ	WSF	4.3	984
Hornady 147-gr. JHP	HS6	5.0	1,010
Hornady 147-gr. JHP	Blue Dot	5.5	1,037

C.P. 9x21mm +P
USPSA/IPSC Major Power Competition Loads

Barrel: C.P. 5½-inch
Case: C.P. +P
Primer: Remington 7½
Overall Cartridge Length: Varied
Taper Crimp Diameter: .380-inch

Bullet	Powder (type)	Powder (grains)	Velocity (fps)	Power Factor	Chamber Pressure (CUP)

Cast Bullets

Bullet	Powder (type)	Powder (grains)	Velocity (fps)	Power Factor	Chamber Pressure (CUP)
C.P. 145-gr. RN	AA-5	6.8	1,221	177	35,540
C.P. 145-gr. RN	W540	7.4	1,258	182	35,720

Bullet	Powder		Velocity	Power	Chamber Pressure
	(type)	*(grains)*	*(fps)*	Factor	(CUP)

Jacketed Bullets

Bullet	Powder		Velocity	Power	Chamber Pressure
C.P. 135-gr. FMJ AA-5	7.7	1,329	179	41,080
C.P. 135-gr. FMJ W540	8.0	1,320	178	41,540
C.P. 150-gr. FMJ AA-5	6.8	1,182	177	37,560

WARNING: This load data was safe in the developer's guns, but due to the many uncontrollable variables involved in handloading that can have drastic effects on chamber pressure, may be excessive for others. All powder charges should be reduced by 20 percent for starting loads in other guns.

NOTES: This data was furnished by C. P. Bullets of Warminister, Pennsylvania. These loads should be used only in custom pistols built specifically for the 9x21mm +P cartridge and having barrels with the full-support chamber design.

C.P. 9x23mm Super +P
USPSA/IPSC Major Power Competition Loads

Barrel: C. W. Custom 5¼-inch
Case: Experimental*
Primer: Remington 7½ Small Rifle
Overall Cartridge Length: 1.260 inches**
Taper Crimp Diameter: .380-inch

Bullet	Powder		Velocity	Power
	(type)	*(grains)*	*(fps)*	Factor

Cast Bullets

Bullet	Powder		Velocity	Power
Bull-X 125-gr. RN	HS7	10.2	1,431	178
Tru-Flight 140-gr. SWC	HS7	9.0	1,306	182
Bull-X 147-gr. FN	HS7	8.6	1,241	182
Bull-X 150-gr. SWC	HS7	8.5	1,232	184
Bull-X 155-gr. SWC	HS7	8.3	1,205	186

Jacketed Bullets

Bullet	Powder		Velocity	Power
Bull-X 125-gr. JSN	HS7	10.2	1,400	175
Bull-X 125-gr. JSN	HS7	10.4	1,419	177
Bull-X 125-gr. JSN	HS7	10.6	1,460	183

Bullet	Powder (type)	(grains)	Velocity (fps)	Power Factor
Tru-Flight 130-gr. TCJ	HS7	10.0	1,302	169
Tru-Flight 130-gr. TCJ	HS7	10.2	1,370	178
Hornady 147-gr. FMJBT	HS7	8.7	1,204	176
Speer 147-gr. TMJ	HS7	8.7	1,223	179
Nosler 150-gr. IPSC	HS7	8.7	1,193	178
Sierra 150-gr. JFN	HS7	8.7	1,205	180

*The experimental cases used in developing this data may differ slightly in powder capacity from production cases should they eventually become available.

**Correct overall length for Para-Ordnance 20-round magazine.

WARNING: These loads were developed for custom barrels with a full-support chamber and should not be used in barrels with the standard Government Model chamber design. The powder charge/bullet combinations shown were safe in the author's gun, but due to the many uncontrollable variables involved in handloading that can have drastic effects on chamber pressure, they may be excessive for others. All powder charges should be reduced by 20 percent for starting loads in other guns.

.38 Super
USPSA/IPSC Major Power Competition Loads

Barrels: Wilson & Caspian 5½-inch
Case: Remington +P Nickel-Plated
Primer: Remington 7½ Small Rifle
Overall Cartridge Length: 1.280 inches
Taper Crimp Diameter: .380-inch

Bullet	Powder (type)	(grains)	Velocity (fps)	Power Factor
Cast Bullets				
Bull-X 147-gr. TCFN	Blue Dot	8.0	1,215	178
Bull-X 147-gr. TCFN	AA-7	8.6	1,212	178
Bull-X 147-gr. TCFN	HS7	8.6	1,220	179
Bull-X 147-gr. TCFN	AA-9	10.2	1,204	176

513

Bullet	Powder		Velocity	Power
	(type)	*(grains)*	*(fps)*	Factor
Bull-X 150-gr. SWC	Blue Dot	8.2	1,238	185
Bull-X 150-gr. SWC	HS7	8.4	1,211	181
Bull-X 150-gr. SWC	AA-7	8.5	1,207	181
Bull-X 150-gr. SWC	AA-9	10.0	1,215	182
Bull-X 155-gr. SWC	W540	7.0	1,174	181
Bull-X 155-gr. SWC	Blue Dot	7.0	1,159	179
Bull-X 155-gr. SWC	HS7	8.2	1,219	188
Bull-X 155-gr. SWC	AA-7	8.4	1,171	181
Bull-X 155-gr. SWC	AA-9	10.0	1,165	180
C.S. 160-gr. RN**	Blue Dot	6.9	1,155	184
C.S. 160-gr. RN	W540	7.0	1,153	184
C.S. 160-gr. RN	HS7	8.0	1,159	185
C.S. 160-gr. RN	AA-7	8.1	1,147	183
C.S. 160-gr. RN	AA-9	10.0	1,133	181

Jacketed Bullets

Bullet	Powder		Velocity	Power
Hornady 147-gr. FMJBT	HS7	8.5	1,214	178
Hornady 147-gr. FMJBT	AA-7	8.7	1,220	179
Hornady 147-gr. FMJBT	AA-9	10.3	1,212	178
Tru-Flight 147-gr. TMJ	HS7	8.5	1,207	177
Speer 147-gr. TMJ	Blue Dot	8.2	1,223	179
Speer 147-gr. TMJ	AA-7	8.7	1,194	175
Speer 147-gr. TMJ	HS7	8.7	1,202	176
Speer 147-gr. TMJ	AA-9	10.4	1,209	177
Nosler 150-gr. IPSC	Blue Dot	8.2	1,223	183
Nosler 150-gr. IPSC	AA-7	8.5	1,156	173
Nosler 150-gr. IPSC	HS7	8.7	1,196	179
Nosler 150-gr. IPSC	AA-9	10.5	1,214	182
Sierra 150-gr. FPJ	AA-7	8.5	1,188	178
Sierra 150-gr. FPJ	HS7	8.7	1,196	179
Speer 158-gr. TMJ	Blue Dot	8.0	1,163	183
Speer 158-gr. TMJ	AA-7	8.4	1,147	181
Speer 158-gr. TMJ	HS7	8.5	1,156	182
Speer 158-gr. TMJ	AA-9	10.0	1,144	180

Bullet	Powder (type)	(grains)	Velocity (fps)	Power Factor
Hornady 160-gr. FMJ-FN	Blue Dot	7.9	1,138	182
Hornady 160-gr. FMJ-FN	AA-7	8.4	1,140	182
Hornady 160-gr. FMJ-FN	HS7	8.4	1,133	181
Hornady 160-gr. FMJ-FN	AA-9	9.7	1,094	175
Sierra 170-gr. FMJ-RN	Blue Dot	7.8	1,062	180
Sierra 170-gr. FMJ-RN	AA-7	8.2	1,090	185
Sierra 170-gr. FMJ-RN	HS7	8.3	1,109	188
Sierra 170-gr. FMJ-RN	AA-9	9.7	1,094	185
Nosler 180-gr. NEFN	Blue Dot	7.6	1,031	185
Nosler 180-gr. NEFN	AA-7	7.9	1,044	187
Nosler 180-gr. NEFN	HS7	8.0	1,039	187
Nosler 180-gr. NEFN	AA-9	9.1	1,012	182

*With fully supported chambers.

**Competition Specialties bullet.

WARNING: These loads are safe in the author's guns, but due to the many uncontrollable variables involved in handloading that can have drastic effects on chamber pressure, they may be excessive in others. All powder charges should be reduced by 20 percent for starting loads in other guns.

.38 Super
High-Performance Loads

Barrels: Bar-Sto 4¼ and Wilson 5-inch
Case: Remington Nickel-Plated +P
Primer: Remington 7½ Small Rifle Primer
Overall Cartridge Length: Varied
Taper Crimp Diameter: .380-inch

Bullet	Powder (type)	(grs.)	Velocity (fps) 4¼" Barrel	5" Barrel
Cast Bullets				
Bull-X 155-gr. SWC	W540	7.0	–	1,134
Bull-X 155-gr. SWC	AA-7	8.0	–	1,187

Bullet	Powder (type)	(grs.)	Velocity (fps) 4¼" Barrel	5" Barrel
Bull-X 155-gr. SWC	HS7	8.1	1,184	1,203
Bull-X 155-gr. SWC	AA-9	10.0	–	1,210
C.S. 160-gr. RN*	W540	7.0	1,077	1,117
C.S. 160-gr. RN	HS7	8.0	–	1,110
C.S. 160-gr. RN	AA-7	8.0	1,086	1,122
C.S. 160-gr. RN	AA-9	10.0	–	1,107

Jacketed Bullets

Bullet	Powder (type)	(grs.)	Velocity (fps) 4¼" Barrel	5" Barrel
Speer 88-gr. JHP	Blue Dot	12.3	1,570	1,602
Speer 88-gr. JHP	AA-5	9.6	–	1,518
Speer 88-gr. JHP	Herco	9.7	–	1,566
Speer 88-gr. JHP	HS6	9.1	–	1,478
Speer 100-gr. JHP	HS6	9.3	–	1,447
Speer 100-gr. JHP	Blue Dot	10.5	–	1,422
Speer 100-gr. JHP	HS7	10.5	1,418	1,462
Speer 100-gr. JHP	AA-7	10.7	–	1,418
Nosler 115-gr. JHP	AA-5	8.3	–	1,307
Nosler 115-gr. JHP	HS6	9.1	–	1,319
Nosler 115-gr. JHP	Blue Dot	10.2	–	1,329
Nosler 115-gr. JHP	HS7	10.4	–	1,340
Nosler 115-gr. JHP	AA-7	10.5	1,310	1,333
Hornady 125-gr. JHP-XTP	HS7	9.5	–	1,315
Hornady 125-gr. JHP-XTP	Blue Dot	9.8	–	1,324
Hornady 125-gr. JHP-XTP	800X	9.9	1,282	1,307
Hornady 125-gr. JHP-XTP	AA-9	12.5	–	1,311
Sierra 130-gr. FMJ	Blue Dot	9.1	–	1,244
Sierra 130-gr. FMJ	AA-7	9.4	–	1,220
Sierra 130-gr. FMJ	HS7	9.8	1,219	1,251
Sierra 130-gr. FMJ	AA-9	12.0	1,252	1,270
Hornady 140-gr. JHP-XTP	HS7	8.9	1,150	1,184
Hornady 140-gr. JHP-XTP	AA-9	11.0	–	1,218
Speer 147-gr. PHP	AA-5	6.9	–	1,031
Speer 147-gr. PHP	HS7	8.7	1,082	1,110
Hornady 147-gr. JHP-XTP	AA-7	8.7	1,074	1,115
Hornady 147-gr. JHP-XTP	AA-9	10.2	–	1,068

Bullet	Powder (type)	(grs.)	Velocity (fps) 4¼" Barrel	5" Barrel
Hornady 158-gr. JHP-XTP	HS7	8.2	–	1,114
Hornady 158-gr. JHP-XTP	AA-7	8.2	1,049	1,078
Hornady 158-gr. JHP-XTP	AA-9	10.1	–	1,119
Hornady 180-gr. JHP/XTP	Blue Dot	7.6	977	1,008
Hornady 180-gr. JHP/XTP	AA-7	7.9	–	1,012
Hornady 180-gr. JHP/XTP	HS7	8.0	–	1,019
Hornady 180-gr. JHP/XTP	AA-9	9.1	–	984

*Competition Specialties bullet

WARNING: These loads are safe in the author's guns, but due to the many uncontrollable variables involved in handloading that can have drastic effects on chamber pressure, they may be excessive for others. All powder charges should be reduced by 20 percent for starting loads in other guns.

.40 Smith & Wesson
USPSA/IPSC Major Power Competition Loads

Barrel: Heinie 5½-inch
Case: Remington
Primer: Winchester WSP Small Pistol
Overall Cartridge Length: Varied
Taper Crimp Diameter: .420-inch

Bullet	Powder (type)	(grains)	Velocity (fps)	Power Factor
Cast Bullets				
Bull-X 145-gr. TFN	WSL	5.9	1,248	180
Bull-X 145-gr. TFN	W231	6.6	1,259	182
Bull-X 145-gr. TFN	Herco	7.0	1,236	179
Bull-X 145-gr. TFN	WSF	7.3	1,237	179
Bull-X 145-gr. TFN	AA-5	8.4	1,252	181
Bull-X 145-gr. TFN	W540	9.4	1,265	183
Bull-X 145-gr. TFN	Blue Dot	10.1	1,244	180
Bull-X 145-gr. TFN	HS7	10.2	1,233	178
Bull-X 145-gr. TFN	AA-7	10.3	1,231	178

Bullet	Powder (type)	(grains)	Velocity (fps)	Power Factor
Tru-Flight 155-gr. SWC	WSL	5.4	1,180	182
Tru-Flight 155-gr. SWC	W231	6.0	1,176	182
Tru-Flight 155-gr. SWC	WSF	6.9	1,174	181
Tru-Flight 155-gr. SWC	AA-5	7.8	1,192	184
Tru-Flight 155-gr. SWC	HS6	8.4	1,198	185
Tru-Flight 155-gr. SWC	W540	8.5	1,173	181
Tru-Flight 155-gr. SWC	HS7	9.3	1,173	181
Tru-Flight 155-gr. SWC	Blue Dot	9.6	1,201	186
Tru-Flight 155-gr. SWC	AA-7	9.9	1,194	185
Bull-X 175-gr. SWC	WSL	4.8	1,063	186
Bull-X 175-gr. SWC	HP38	5.0	1,071	187
Bull-X 175-gr. SWC	W231	5.1	1,054	184
Bull-X 175-gr. SWC	Herco	5.9	1,048	183
Bull-X 175-gr. SWC	WSF	6.0	1,077	185
Tru-Flight 175-gr. SWC	AA-5	6.7	1,077	188
Tru-Flight 175-gr. SWC	W540	7.8	1,076	188
Tru-Flight 175-gr. SWC	AA-7	8.3	1,023	179
Tru-Flight 175-gr. SWC	HS7	8.3	1,063	186
Tru-Flight 175-gr. SWC	Blue Dot	8.3	1,090	190

Jacketed Bullets

Bullet	Powder (type)	(grains)	Velocity (fps)	Power Factor
Sierra 150-gr. JHP	WSL	5.8	1,174	176
Sierra 150-gr. JHP	W231	6.3	1,197	179
Sierra 150-gr. JHP	WSF	6.9	1,169	175
Sierra 150-gr. JHP	W540	9.2	1,203	180
Sierra 150-gr. JHP	HS7	10.0	1,214	182
Sierra 150-gr. JHP	W571	10.2	1,211	181
Sierra 150-gr. JHP	Blue Dot	10.5	1,204	180
Hornady 155-gr. JHP	WSL	5.6	1,131	175
Hornady 155-gr. JHP	W231	6.0	1,144	177
Hornady 155-gr. JHP	WSF	7.2	1,161	179
Hornady 155-gr. JHP	W540	8.6	1,153	178
Hornady 155-gr. JHP	HS7	9.8	1,181	183
Hornady 155-gr. JHP	W571	9.9	1,192	184
Hornady 155-gr. JHP	Blue Dot	10.4	1,208	187
Tru-Flight 180-gr. TMJ	WSF	6.0	996	179
Tru-Flight 180-gr. TMJ	AA-5	6.3	991	178
Tru-Flight 180-gr. TMJ	HS6	6.9	1,002	180

Bullet	Powder (type)	Powder (grains)	Velocity (fps)	Power Factor
Hornady 200-gr. FMJ	HS6	6.2	911	182
Hornady 200-gr. FMJ	HS7	6.5	917	183

WARNING: These loads are safe in the author's guns, but due to the many uncontrollable variables involved in handloading that can have drastic effects on chamber pressure, they may not be in others. All powder charges should be reduced by 20 percent for starting loads in other guns.

NOTE: All loads that generated a power factor of 180 or higher in the 5½-inch Heinie barrel produced Major Plus velocities in the 5-inch Bar-Sto barrel of the author's Limited class gun.

.40 Smith & Wesson
Light Cast Bullet Target Loads

Barrel: Bar-Sto 5-inch
Case: Remington
Primer: Remington No. 1½ Small Pistol
Overall Cartridge Length: Varied
Taper Crimp Diameter: .420-inch

Bullet	Powder (type)	Powder (grains)	Velocity (fps)
Bull-X 175-gr. SWC	700X	3.5	811
Bull-X 175-gr. SWC	Red Dot	3.6	833
Bull-X 175-gr. SWC	AA-2	4.0	859
Bull-X 175-gr. SWC	WSL	4.0	868
Bull-X 175-gr. SWC	Bullseye	4.0	907
Tru-Flight 175-gr. SWC	CLAYS	4.0	887
Tru-Flight 175-gr. SWC	AA-100	4.1	886
Tru-Flight 175-gr. SWC	HP38	4.2	866
Tru-Flight 175-gr. SWC	WST	4.2	851
Tru-Flight 175-gr. SWC	W231	4.3	870
Tru-Flight 175-gr. SWC	WSF	5.2	908

10mm Auto
USPSA/IPSC Major Power Competition Loads

Barrel: Heinie 5½-inch
Case: Remington
Primer: Remington 2½ Large Pistol
Overall Cartridge Length: Varied
Taper Crimp Diameter: .420-inch

Bullet	Powder (type)	(grains)	Velocity (fps)	Power Factor
Bull-X 145-gr. TFN	WSL	6.6	1,252	181
Bull-X 145-gr. TFN	Bullseye	6.8	1,248	180
Bull-X 145-gr. TFN	Trap 100	6.9	1,260	182
Bull-X 145-gr. TFN	AA-2	7.0	1,235	179
Bull-X 145-gr. TFN	W231	7.3	1,253	181
Bull-X 145-gr. TFN	HP38	7.3	1,248	180
Bull-X 145-gr. TFN	WST	7.5	1,242	180
Bull-X 145-gr. TFN	WSF	7.9	1,241	179
Bull-X 145-gr. TFN	Unique	8.0	1,254	181
Bull-X 145-gr. TFN	Herco	8.1	1,248	180
Bull-X 145-gr. TFN	AA-5	9.1	1,254	181
Bull-X 145-gr. TFN	HS6	9.8	1,243	180
Bull-X 145-gr. TFN	W540	10.2	1,242	180
Bull-X 145-gr. TFN	Blue Dot	10.6	1,242	180
Bull-X 145-gr. TFN	AA-7	11.0	1,248	180
Bull-X 145-gr. TFN	HS7	11.2	1,255	181
Tru-Flight 155-gr. SWC	WSL	6.4	1,167	180
Tru-Flight 155-gr. SWC	HP38	6.5	1,183	183
Tru-Flight 155-gr. SWC	W231	6.5	1,177	182
Tru-Flight 155-gr. SWC	WST	6.9	1,170	181
Tru-Flight 155-gr. SWC	WSF	7.0	1,185	183
Tru-Flight 155-gr. SWC	AA-5	8.7	1,188	184
Tru-Flight 155-gr. SWC	W540	9.5	1,176	182
Tru-Flight 155-gr. SWC	Blue Dot	10.1	1,174	181
Tru-Flight 155-gr. SWC	HS7	10.3	1,172	181
Tru-Flight 155-gr. SWC	AA-7	10.3	1,169	181
CS 170-gr. SWC*	WSF	5.9	1,048	178
CS 170-gr. SWC	AA-5	6.3	1,052	178
CS 170-gr. SWC	HS7	8.3	1,061	180

Bullet	Powder (type)	(grains)	Velocity (fps)	Power Factor
Bull-X 175-gr. SWC	WSL	4.8	1,064	186
Bull-X 175-gr. SWC	W231	5.2	1,070	187
Bull-X 175-gr. SWC	AA-2	5.5	1,030	180
Tru-Flight 175-gr. SWC	WSF	5.9	1,039	181
Tru-Flight 175-gr. SWC	AA-5	6.3	1,034	180
Tru-Flight 175-gr. SWC	Blue Dot	7.7	1,022	178
Tru-Flight 175-gr. SWC	W540	7.8	1,056	184
Tru-Flight 175-gr. SWC	HS7	8.3	1,063	186

Jacketed Bullets

Bullet	Powder (type)	(grains)	Velocity (fps)	Power Factor
Nosler 135-gr. JHP	Blue Dot	12.1	1,359	183
Nosler 135-gr. JHP	HS7	12.9	1,356	183
Nosler 135-gr. JHP	AA-7	13.2	1,368	184
Sierra 150-gr. JHP	W231	7.1	1,206	180
Nosler 150-gr. JHP	HP38	7.1	1,217	182
Nosler 150-gr. JHP	HS6	10.0	1,251	187
Hornady 155-gr. JHP	HP38	7.0	1,164	180
Hornady 155-gr. JHP	W231	7.0	1,155	179
Hornady 155-gr. JHP	Unique	8.2	1,218	188
Hornady 155-gr. JHP	AA-5	9.8	1,204	186
Hornady 155-gr. JHP	Blue Dot	10.9	1,240	186
Hornady 155-gr. JHP	HS7	11.7	1,207	187
Tru-Flight 160-gr. TMJ	W231	5.8	1,103	176
Tru-Flight 160-gr. TMJ	WST	6.0	1,091	174
Sierra 165-gr. JHP	WSL	6.0	1,104	182
Sierra 165-gr. JHP	WSF	7.0	1,122	185
Nosler 170-gr. JHP	HP38	6.7	1,092	185
Nosler 170-gr. JHP	Trap 100	6.8	1,084	184
Nosler 180-gr. JHP	AA-2	6.2	1,011	181
Nosler 180-gr. JHP	AA-5	8.7	1,023	184
Speer 180-gr. PHP	Bullseye	6.4	1,018	183
Speer 180-gr. PHP	Herco	7.4	1,022	183
Hornady 180-gr. JHP	HS6	7.8	1,017	183
Hornady 180-gr. JHP	HS7	8.9	1,022	183

Bullet	Powder (type)	Powder (grains)	Velocity (fps)	Power Factor
Sierra 180-gr. JHP	HS6	7.9	1,021	183
Sierra 190-gr. FPJ	Blue Dot	9.5	968	183
Sierra 190-gr. FMJ	HS6	7.6	988	187
Speer 200-gr. TMJ	HP38	6.2	918	183
Speer 200-gr. TMJ	Trap 100	6.3	910	182
Speer 200-gr. TMJ	HS6	7.2	917	183
Speer 200-gr. TMJ	HS7	7.9	912	182
Hornady 200-gr. JHP	W231	5.2	924	184
Hornady 200-gr. JHP	Bullseye	5.3	907	181
Hornady 200-gr. JHP	AA-5	7.0	915	183

*Competition Specialties bullet.

WARNING: These loads are safe in the author's guns, but due to the many uncontrollable variables in handloading that can have drastic effects on chamber pressure, they may be excessive for others. All powder charges should be reduced by 20 percent for starting loads in other guns.

NOTE: All loads that generated a power factor of 180 and higher in the 5½-inch Heinie barrel produced Major Plus velocities in the 5-inch Bar-Sto barrel of the author's Limited class gun.

10mm Auto
High-Performance Loads

Barrel: Bar-Sto 5-inch
Case: Remington
Primer: Remington 2½ Large Pistol
Overall Cartridge Length: Varied
Taper Crimp Diameter: .420-inch

Bullet	Powder (type)	Powder (grains)	Velocity (fps)
Nosler 135-gr. JHP	HS6	9.5	1,411
Nosler 135-gr. JHP	AA-5	10.8	1,361
Nosler 135-gr. JHP	Blue Dot	12.6	1,410
Nosler 135-gr. JHP	HS7	13.5	1,436
Nosler 135-gr. JHP	AA-7	13.8	1,388

| Bullet | Powder | | Velocity |
	(type)	(grains)	(fps)
Sierra 150-gr. JHP	W540	10.5	1,306
Sierra 150-gr. JHP	Blue Dot	11.8	1,310
Sierra 150-gr. JHP	HS6	10.5	1,271
Sierra 150-gr. JHP	HS7	13.0	1,318
Sierra 150-gr. JHP	AA-7	13.0	1,284
Hornady 155-gr. JHP	HS6	10.3	1,289
Hornady 155-gr. JHP	W540	10.5	1,277
Hornady 155-gr. JHP	Blue Dot	11.5	1,311
Hornady 155-gr. JHP	HS7	12.0	1,276
Hornady 155-gr. JHP	AA-7	13.5	1,322
Tru-Flight 160-gr. TMJ	HS6	10.0	1,244
Tru-Flight 160-gr. TMJ	W540	9.7	1,262
Sierra 165-gr. JHP	Blue Dot	10.2	1,217
Sierra 165-gr. JHP	HS7	11.0	1,241
Sierra 165-gr. JHP	AA-7	13.0	1,230
Nosler 170-gr. JHP	WSF	6.6	1,132
Nosler 170-gr. JHP	HS6	9.8	1,139
Nosler 170-gr. JHP	Blue Dot	10.1	1,155
Nosler 170-gr. JHP	HS7	11.0	1,203
Nosler 170-gr. JHP	AA-7	13.0	1,210
Nosler 180-gr. JHP	WSL	5.6	1,014
Nosler 180-gr. JHP	W540	9.4	1,110
Sierra 180-gr. JHP	Blue Dot	10.0	1,117
Speer 180-gr. JHP	HS7	10.5	1,132
Hornady 180-gr. JHP	AA-7	11.0	1,084
Nosler 180-gr. JHP	HP38	5.5	971*
Nosler 180-gr. JHP	WST	5.5	964*
Nosler 180-gr. JHP	Bullseye	5.6	968*
Nosler 180-gr. JHP	AA-2	6.0	973*
Speer 200-gr. TMJ	Blue Dot	8.9	1,088
Speer 200-gr. TMJ	HS7	10.3	1,141
Speer 200-gr. TMJ	AA-7	11.3	1,110
Speer 200-gr. TMJ	AA-9	13.2	1,144

Bullet	Powder		Velocity
	(type)	(grains)	(fps)
Hornady 200-gr. JHP	WSF	6.2	955
Hornady 200-gr. JHP	W540	8.6	1,019
Hornady 200-gr. JHP	W571	9.3	1,023

*Duplicates the FBI light subsonic load.

WARNING: These loads are safe in the author's guns, but due to the many uncontrollable variables involved in handloading that can have drastic effects on chamber pressure, they may be excessive in others. All powder charges should be reduced by 20 percent for starting loads in other guns.

10mm Auto
Light Cast Bullet Target Loads

Barrel: Bar-Sto 5-inch
Case: Remington
Primer: Remington 2½ Large Pistol
Overall Cartridge Length: Varied
Taper Crimp Diameter: .420-inch

Bullet	Powder		Velocity
	(type)	(grains)	(fps)
Tru-Flight 155-gr. SWC	Red Dot	3.8	855
Tru-Flight 155-gr. SWC	Bullseye	4.0	838
Tru-Flight 155-gr. SWC	AA-2	4.1	856
Bull-X 175-gr. SWC	WSL	3.7	810
Bull-X 175-gr. SWC	Red Dot	4.0	785
Bull-X 175-gr. SWC	WSF	4.3	818
Bull-X 175-gr. SWC	Bullseye	4.4	817
Tru-Flight 175-gr. SWC	W231	4.5	793
Tru-Flight 175-gr. SWC	AA-2	4.7	931
Tru-Flight 175-gr. SWC	HP38	5.0	817

.41 Avenger
High-Performance Loads

Barrel: Bar-Sto 5-inch
Cases: Various .45 ACP and Shortened .45 Winchester Magnum
Primer: CCI 350
Overall Cartridge Length: Varied
Taper Crimp Diameter: .410-inch

Bullet	Powder (type)	(grains)	Velocity (fps)
.45 ACP Cases*			
Cast 185-gr. SWC	Bullseye	5.6	1,035
Cast 185-gr. SWC	Unique	7.0	1,015
Cast 185-gr. SWC	W231	6.0	1,033
Cast 185-gr. SWC	Blue Dot	10.0	978
Sierra 170-gr. JHP	Bullseye	5.0	676
Sierra 170-gr. JHP	Unique	7.0	944
Sierra 170-gr. JHP	W231	7.5	1,080
Sierra 170-gr. JHP	Blue Dot	10.0	886
Sierra 210-gr. JHP	Bullseye	5.0	716
Sierra 210-gr. JHP	W231	6.0	883
Sierra 210-gr. JHP	Unique	6.0	902
Sierra 210-gr. JHP	Blue Dot	10.0	963
.45 Winchester Magnum Cases**			
Cast 185-gr. SWC	Bullseye	7.0	1,171
Cast 185-gr. SWC	W231	8.0	1,183
Cast 185-gr. SWC	Unique	8.0	1,133
Sierra 170-gr. JHP	Bullseye	7.0	1,112
Sierra 170-gr. JHP	W231	8.0	1,154
Sierra 170-gr. JHP	Unique	8.0	1,059
Sierra 170-gr. JHP	Blue Dot	11.0	1,114
Sierra 210-gr. JHP	Bullseye	6.0	956
Sierra 210-gr. JHP	W231	7.0	947
Sierra 210-gr. JHP	Unique	7.0	939
Sierra 210-gr. JHP	Blue Dot	9.8	1,038

*.45 ACP case necked down to .41 caliber.

**.45 Winchester Magnum case shortened to .950-inch and necked down to .41 caliber

WARNING: These loads are safe in the developer's gun, but due to the many uncontrollable variables involved in handloading that can have drastic effects on chamber pressure, they may be excessive for others. All powder charges should be reduced by 20 percent for starting loads in other guns. Do not attempt to use loads developed in cases formed from .45 Winchester brass in .45 ACP cases.

NOTE: This load data was developed by SSK Industries, the developer of the .41 Avenger Wildcat, and not by the author. These loads should be used only in custom guns built specifically for the .41 Avenger.

.41 Action Express
High-Performance Loads

Barrel: Bar-Sto 5-inch
Case: IMI
Primer: CCI 300
Overall Cartridge Length: 1.155-inches
Taper Crimp Diameter: .432-inch

Bullet	Powder		Velocity
	(type)	*(grains)*	*(fps)*
Sierra 170-gr. JHC	Herco	7.5	1,171
Sierra 170-gr. JHC	Unique	7.2	1,119
Sierra 170-gr. JHC	AA-5	7.5	1,083
Sierra 170-gr. JHC	Blue Dot	9.5	1,122
Sierra 170-gr. JHC	HS7	10.0	1,155
Sierra 170-gr. JHC	AA-7	10.1	1,132
IMI Samson 200-gr. FMJ	Bullseye	4.5	910
IMI Samson 200-gr. FMJ	AA-5	6.5	973
IMI Samson 200-gr. FMJ	HS6	6.5	928
Hornady 210-gr. JHP/XTP	W231	5.0	961
Hornady 210-gr. JHP/XTP	Herco	6.0	1,017
Speer 210-gr. TMJ	800X	7.0	937
Speer 210-gr. TMJ	Blue Dot	7.8	910
Sierra 210-gr. JHC	AA-7	9.0	1,012

WARNING: These loads are safe in the author's gun, but due to the many uncontrollable variables involved in handloading that can have drastic effects on chamber pressure, they may be excessive for others. All powder charges should be reduced by 20 percent for starting loads in other guns.

.45 ACP
USPSA/IPSC Major Power Competition Loads

Barrels: Wilson and B.A.T. 5½-inch
Cases: Remington, IMI, and Winchester
Primer: CCI 300 Large Pistol
Overall Cartridge Length: Varied
Taper Crimp Diameter: .470-inch

Bullet	Powder (type)	(grains)	Velocity (fps)	Power Factor
Cast Bullets				
Bull-X 150-gr. BNWC	AA-5	10.7	1,181	177
C.P. 152-gr. SWC	HP38	7.9	1,218	185
Behn 155-gr. SWC	700X	5.8	1,154	179
Behn 155-gr. SWC	Bullseye	6.4	1,173	182
Behn 155-gr. SWC	AA-2	6.5	1,179	183
Behn 155-gr. SWC	Trap 100	7.5	1,160	180
Behn 155-gr. SWC	HP38	7.7	1,192	185
Behn 155-gr. SWC	AA-5	10.4	1,159	180
Tru-Flight 165-gr. SWC	Trap 100	7.2	1,151	189
Tru-Flight 165-gr. SWC	HP38	7.7	1,147	189
Tru-Flight 165-gr. SWC	AA-5	10.2	1,153	190
Tru-Flight 180-gr. SWC	Red Dot	5.4	1,006	181
Tru-Flight 180-gr. SWC	700X	5.4	1,012	182
Tru-Flight 180-gr. SWC	WSL	5.4	1,019	183
Bull-X 185-gr. SWC	Trap 100	5.5	983	182
Bull-X 185-gr. SWC	AA-2	5.6	1,004	186
Bull-X 185-gr. SWC	HP38	5.6	987	183
Bull-X 185-gr. SWC	WST	5.7	1,010	187
Bull-X 185-gr. SWC	Green Dot	5.8	993	184
Bull-X 185-gr. SWC	W231	5.9	1,014	188
Bull-X 185-gr. SWC	AA-5	8.9	1,017	188
Tru-Flight 200-gr. SWC	700X	5.1	922	184
Tru-Flight 200-gr. SWC	Bullseye	5.1	882	176
Tru-Flight 200-gr. SWC	Red Dot	5.2	915	183
Tru-Flight 200-gr. SWC	AA-2	5.2	890	178
Tru-Flight 200-gr. SWC	WSL	5.3	917	183
Tru-Flight 200-gr. SWC	WST	5.4	924	184

Bullet	Powder (type)	(grains)	Velocity (fps)	Power Factor
Bull-X 200-gr. SWC	Trap 100	5.3	912	182
Bull-X 200-gr. SWC	HP38	5.4	915	183
Bull-X 200-gr. SWC	Green Dot	5.5	904	180
Bull-X 200-gr. SWC	W231	5.6	916	183
Bull-X 200-gr. SWC	AA-5	8.2	911	182
Bull-X 230-gr. RN	AA-2	4.9	804	185
Bull-X 230-gr. RN	WSL	4.9	817	188
Bull-X 230-gr. RN	Bullseye	5.0	792	182
Bull-X 230-gr. RN	HP38	5.0	811	187
Bull-X 230-gr. RN	Trap 100	5.1	810	186
Bull-X 230-gr. RN	WST	5.2	810	186
Bull-X 230-gr. RN	Red Dot	5.2	819	188
Bull-X 230-gr. RN	W231	5.4	819	188
Bull-X 230-gr. RN	Green Dot	5.6	815	187
Bull-X 255-gr. SWC	700X	4.5	734	187
Bull-X 255-gr. SWC	Bullseye	4.6	727	185
Bull-X 255-gr. SWC	W231	5.4	744	190
Bull-X 255-gr. SWC	Herco	6.4	719	183

Jacketed Bullets

Bullet	Powder (type)	(grains)	Velocity (fps)	Power Factor
Hornady 185-gr. FMJ-SWC	WSL	5.4	988	183
Hornady 185-gr. FMJ-SWC	W231	6.5	1,015	188
Speer 185-gr. TMJ-SWC	Herco	6.8	1,021	189
Sierra 185-gr. FPJ	Unique	7.0	1,009	187
Speer 200-gr. TMJ-SWC	Red Dot	5.1	911	182
Speer 200-gr. TMJ-SWC	WSL	5.5	896	179
Speer 200-gr. TMJ-SWC	AA-5	8.6	912	182
Hornady 200-gr. FMJ-SWC	W231	6.0	925	185
Hornady 200-gr. FMJ-SWC	Herco	7.5	916	183
Speer 230-gr. FMJ-RN	AA-2	4.8	822	189
Sierra 230-gr. FMJ-RN	WSL	4.9	818	188
Nosler 230-gr. FMJ-RN	Herco	6.3	811	187
Nosler 230-gr. FMJ-RN	Unique	5.9	801	184
Hornady 230-gr. FMJ-RN	AA-5	7.4	817	188

WARNING: These loads are safe in the author's guns, but due to the many uncontrollable variables involved in handloading that can have drastic effects on chamber pressure, they may be excessive for others. All powder charges should be reduced by 20 percent for starting loads in other guns.

.45 ACP
High-Performance Loads

Barrels: Wilson 3½, Colt 4¼, Heinie 5-inch
Case: Remington
Primer: CCI 300 Large Pistol
Overall Length: Varied
Taper Crimp Diameter: .470-inch

	Powder		Velocity *(fps)*		
			3.50"	4.25"	5"
Bullet	*(type)*	*(grains)*	**Barrel**	**Barrel**	**Barrel**
Cast Bullets					
Bull-X 150-gr. BNWC	AA-5	10.7	1,052	1,088	1,167
C.P. 152-gr. SWC	HP38	7.9	1,104	1,148	1,207
Bull-X 185-gr. SWC	HS6	9.0	966	1,007	1,052
Bull-X 185-gr. SWC	AA-5	10.0	948	987	1,032
Tru-Flight 200-gr. SWC	Green Dot	6.0	906	968	1,018
Tru-Flight 200-gr. SWC	HS6	8.7	903	954	989
Jacketed Bullets					
Hornady 185-gr. JHP	Green Dot	6.5	937	1,018	1,052
Hornady 185-gr. JHP	HS6	8.9	922	979	1,011
Sierra 185-gr. JHP	Unique	7.7	953	988	1,036
Sierra 185-gr. JHP	AA-5	9.8(A)	969	1,012	1,097
Sierra 185-gr. JHP	AA-5	10.3(B)	1,011	1,067	1,139
Nosler 185-gr. JHP	Herco	8.3	962	1,004	1,047
Nosler 185-gr. JHP	Blue Dot	10.4	908	970	1,022
Hornady 200-gr. JHP	Red Dot	5.7	944	959	972
Hornady 200-gr. JHP	W231	6.6	915	937	1,009
Hornady 200-gr. JHP	AA-5	8.1(C)	771	–	862
Hornady 200-gr. JHP	AA-5	9.5(D)	921	977	1,016

Bullet	Powder (type)	(grains)	Velocity (fps)		
			3.50" Barrel	4.25" Barrel	5" Barrel
Speer 200-gr. JHP	Herco	6.7(E)	–	–	917
Speer 200-gr. JHP	Herco	7.5(F)	907	972	1,020
Speer 200-gr. JHP	HS6	9.0	902	957	988
Speer 200-gr. JHP	Blue Dot	10.2	876	968	991
Speer 225-gr. JHP	WSF	6.8	883	919	970
Speer 225-gr. JHP	Blue Dot	10.0	871	923	956
Sierra 230-gr. FMJ	Green Dot	5.4(E)	717	766	802
Sierra 230-gr. FMJ	Green Dot	6.1(B)	842	889	937
Nosler 230-gr. FMJ	HS6	8.2	706	768	811
Nosler 230-gr. FMJ	AA-5	8.5	724	771	810
Speer 260-gr. JHP	Herco	6.9	718	764	792
Speer 260-gr. JHP	HS6	8.0	748	812	860
Speer 260-gr. JHP	HS7	9.2	760	819	845

(A) Listed as maximum in the *Accurate Arms Loading Guide.*

(B) Listed as maximum in the *Sierra Reloading Manual.* Duplicates the performance of the Remington and Cor-Bon 185-grain +P factory loads.

(C) Listed as maximum in the *Hornady Handbook of Cartridge Reloading.*

(D) Listed as maximum in the *Accurate Arms* data manual.

(E) Listed as maximum in the *Hercules Reloader's Guide.*

(F) Listed as maximum in the *Speer Reloading Manual.*

WARNING: These loads are safe in the author's guns, but due to the many uncontrollable variables involved in handloading that can have drastic effects on chamber pressure, they may be excessive for others. All powder charges should be reduced by 20 percent for starting loads in other guns.

.45 ACP
Light Target Loads

Barrel: Heinie 5-inch
Case: Remington
Primer: CCI 300 Large Pistol
Overall Cartridge Length: Varied
Taper Crimp Diameter: .470-inch

Bullet	Powder (type)	(grains)	Velocity (fps)
Cast Bullets			
Bull-X 150-gr. BNWC	AA-100	4.6	822
C.P. 152-gr. SWC	Bullseye	5.0	954
Behn 155-gr. SWC	700X	4.3	927
Behn 155-gr. SWC	HP38	5.9	934
Tru-Flight 180-gr. SWC	CLAYS	3.6	748
Tru-Flight 180-gr. SWC	Bullseye	3.8	765
Tru-Flight 180-gr. SWC	HP38	3.9	754
Tru-Flight 180-gr. SWC	Trap 100	4.0	751
Tru-Flight 180-gr. SWC	HS6	5.8	778
Bull-X 185-gr. SWC	700X	4.0	758
Bull-X 185-gr. SWC	Red Dot	4.2	770
Bull-X 185-gr. SWC	Green Dot	4.6	751
Bull-X 185-gr. SWC	W231	4.1	760
Tru-Flight 200-gr. SWC	700X	4.1	768
Tru-Flight 200-gr. SWC	Red Dot	4.1	754
Tru-Flight 200-gr. SWC	Trap 100	4.4	755
Tru-Flight 200-gr. SWC	HP38	4.5	784
Bull-X 200-gr. SWC	WSL	3.5	781
Bull-X 200-gr. SWC	WST	3.5	755
Bull-X 200-gr. SWC	Bullseye	4.0	762
Bull-X 200-gr. SWC	W231	4.2	748
Bull-X 230-gr. RN	CLAYS	3.6	744
Bull-X 230-gr. RN	WSL	4.1	759
Bull-X 230-gr. RN	WST	4.3	744
Bull-X 230-gr. RN	700X	4.2	739
Bull-X 230-gr. RN	Trap 100	4.4	733

Bullet	Powder		Velocity
	(type)	(grains)	(fps)
Bull-X 230-gr. RN	HP38	4.5	750
Bull-X 230-gr. RN	Bullseye	4.6	748
Bull-X 230-gr. RN	Red Dot	4.7	738
Bull-X 230-gr. RN	AA-100	4.7	732
Bull-X 230-gr. RN	W231	5.0	755

Jacketed Bullets

Bullet	Powder		Velocity
Hornady 185-gr. FMJ-SWC	Bullseye	4.5	768
Hornady 185-gr. FMJ-SWC	WSL	4.8	755
Hornady 185-gr. FMJ-SWC	AA-100	5.1	769
Hornady 185-gr. FMJ-SWC	HP38	5.2	774
Speer 185-gr. TMJ-SWC	Red Dot	4.2	784
Speer 185-gr. TMJ-SWC	WST	4.5	750
Speer 185-gr. TMJ-SWC	Trap 100	4.6	758
Speer 185-gr. TMJ-SWC	W231	5.5	755
Hornady 200-gr. FMJ-SWC	Red Dot	4.6	774
Hornady 200-gr. FMJ-SWC	WST	4.7	789
Hornady 200-gr. FMJ-SWC	WSL	4.9	766
Hornady 200-gr. FMJ-SWC	AA-100	5.0	792
Speer 200-gr. TMJ-SWC	700X	4.8	761
Speer 200-gr. TMJ-SWC	Bullseye	5.0	744
Speer 200-gr. TMJ-SWC	Red Dot	5.1	753
Speer 200-gr. TMJ-SWC	HP38	5.5	760

WARNING: These loads are safe in the author's guns, but due to the many uncontrollable variables involved in handloading that can have drastic effects on chamber pressure, they may be excessive for others. All power charges should be reduced by 20 percent for starting loads in other guns.

Legend

AA: Accurate Arms
BBTC: Beveled-base truncated cone
BBRN: Beveled-base roundnose
BNW: Button-nose wadcutter
CLAYS: Hodgdon powder
800X: IMR "Hi-Skor" powder
FMJ: Full-metal-jacketed

FMJBT:	Full-metal-jacketed boat-tail
FN:	Flat nose
FPJ:	Full profile jacket
H:	Hodgdon
Herco:	Hercules powder
HP38:	Hodgdon powder
HS6:	Hodgdon powder
HS7:	Hodgdon powder
IPSC:	International Practical Shooting Confederation (NEFN style)
JHP:	Jacketed hollowpoint
L:	Lead
NEFN:	Nonexpanding flat nose
PB:	IMR powder
PHP:	Plated hollowpoint
PSP:	Plated softpoint
RN:	Roundnose
700X:	IMR "Hi-Skor" powder
SR 4756:	IMR "Sporting Rifle" powder
SWC:	Semiwadcutter
TCJ:	Totally copper jacketed (plated)
TFN:	Truncated flat nose
TMJ:	Totally metal jacketed (plated)
Trap 100:	Hodgdon powder
W:	Winchester
WC:	Wadcutter
WSF:	Winchester Super Field powder
WSL:	Winchester Super Light powder
WST:	Winchester Super Target powder

The Guns Used

The pistols used by the author in the development of load data were as follows:

9x19mm Parabellum

1. Colt Commander with Bar-Sto 4½-inch barrel.
2. Colt Government Model with Wilson 5-inch barrel.
3. C. W. Custom Steel Challenge with Bar-Sto 5½-inch compensated barrel.

CP 9x23mm Super +P

1. C. W. Custom high capacity Gold Cup with C. W. Custom 5¼-inch compensated barrel.
2. C. W. Custom Signature Grade with C.P. 5½-inch compensated barrel.

.38 Super

1. Colt Commander with Bar-Sto 4½-inch barrel.
2. Colt Government Model with Wilson 5-inch barrel.
3. Warner Signature Grade with Caspian 5½-inch compensated barrel.
4. Wilson Super Grade comp gun with Wilson 5½-inch compensated barrel.

.40 Smith & Wesson

1. Colt Delta Elite with Bar-Sto 5-inch barrel.
2. Dichiara/Jarrett International Grade with Heinie 5½-inch compensated barrel.

10mm Auto

1. Dichiara/Jarrett Carry Gun with Bar-Sto 5-inch barrel.
2. Dichiara/Jarrett International Grade with Heinie 5½-inch compensated barrel.

.41 Action Express

1. Colt Government Model with Bar-Sto 5-inch barrel.

.45 ACP

1. Warner Officer's ACP with Wilson 3½-inch barrel.
2. Warner Combat Gold Cup Commander with Colt 4¼-inch barrel.
3. Warner Combat Gold Cup with Heinie 5-inch barrel.
4. Wilson Combat with Wilson 5½-inch compensated barrel.
5. Warner Double Eagle comp gun with B.A.T. 5½-inch compensated barrel.

24

USPSA/IPSC Competition

THE phenomenal increase in interest in practical pistol competition has probably contributed more to the evolution of the custom Government Model pistol than any other factor. The publicity enjoyed by the sport also has generated more enthusiasm for custom pistols than anything else I can remember. It is for this reason that every pistolsmith who specializes in building custom Government Model pistols should support the sport by being a member of the United States Practical Shooting Association (USPSA). The orginization probably is responsible in some way for his being in business and for keeping his door open in the coming years.

I have tried most types of competitive shooting with rifles, shotguns, and handguns, and nothing has managed to keep my level of interest and enthusiasm as high as practical pistol competition. The thing I like best about the sport is its lack of repetitiveness. In most other shooting games, you know exactly what you will be doing before you get there and when you get there you'll do the same thing you did last week and the same thing you'll do next week. It's not that way with practical pistol matches. Seldom have I shot a particular stage design in more than one match, and seldom have all the tactics I've used in one match served as well (or as poorly) in another. To me, not knowing what to expect is a big part of the fun in this type of competition. This is why I call it the Sporting Clays of pistol competition.

My all-time favorite type of course is classified by the USPSA as a surprise stage. In contrast to those classified as semisurprise and published, you have absolutely no idea what to expect until you open a door or step from behind a barricade to confront the targets. Nothing I have managed to

Mike Morris is the range officer keeping tabs on Mac McEachern as
he shoots at distant targets from behind a wooden barricade.

Practical pistol competition is fun because it is nonrepetitive. At the
sound of the buzzer, this competitor will drop the magazine, draw his
pistol, and engage the targets.

536

Mac McEachern shooting paper targets and Pepper poppers with a range officer watching over his shoulder.

John Dixon, the 1991 individual IPSC world champ. *(Front Sight photo)*

find in any other shooting sport equals the challenge (and sometimes frustration) of racing against the clock to analyze the situation on the spot, come up with the right tactics, and then initiate them successfully. Sometimes you come up with the right game plan. Other times you don't. That, to me, is what makes it so much fun.

Since I enjoy shooting all types of firearms, I find the variety of club-level USPSA competition most appealing. I have competed in matches in which everyone used autoloading pistols and in matches where autoloaders were pitted against revolvers. Naturally, the fast-shooting guns with their greater cartridge capacity usually win. I have shot three-gun matches (my favorite) to determine who is best overall with the handgun, the rifle, and the shotgun. One of the more unusual shoots I've participated in was called an any-gun match. In addition to being fun, it proved that under practical conditions, most handgunners are badly outclassed by those who come to the party with a scattergun, and under most circumstances, a good man with a rifle is better than a good man with a shotgun.

Trying my hand at practical pistol competition has changed my mind about several things, one being the practicality of the highly modified autoloaders used by many shooters in the game. Before trying those types of guns, I was convinced that silly gadgets like a magazine well funnel, an extended magazine release, or a beavertail grip safety on the Government Model represented nothing more than unnecessary bells and whistles sold by people who try to convince the average shooter that wins can be bought with money rather than earned with practice and sweat. I was wrong.

As I eventually discovered, some of those aftermarket goodies were developed by and being sold by top-level competitors who have been there and back enough times to know what it takes to win. They picked up the ball where John Browning left it back in 1911 and ran like the wind. While doing so, they managed to transform a homely old workhorse into the most handsome, best handling, and most shooter-friendly thoroughbred ever created by the hands of mortal man. Other autoloaders make as much noise as a custom Government Model pistol, but nothing else feels as good to the hand or is so appealing to the eye.

Despite my fondness for and all the publicity enjoyed by fullhouse custom compensated guns, I am happy to point out what may not be so obvious to those who have yet to pop a cap in a match at their local gun club. Given a fair shake, a good shooter with a mildly modified gun will always triumph over a poor shooter with a custom gun that cost half as much as the family automobile. In other words, shooter ability is far more important than the cost of a gun.

Donna Burch makes her .38 Super Unlimited class gun sing a happy song. *(Front Sight photo)*

Jim Harris shooting his .45 ACP caliber Marlin carbine with an extended magazine in one stage of a three-gun match.

Brian Enos shooting the Journalist in Kuwait stage at the 1991 USPSA Nationals. (Front Sight *photo*)

Chuck Warner Limited class Gold Cup in .45 ACP and Unlimited class compensated gun in .38 Super.

Don Fraley Unlimited class gun.

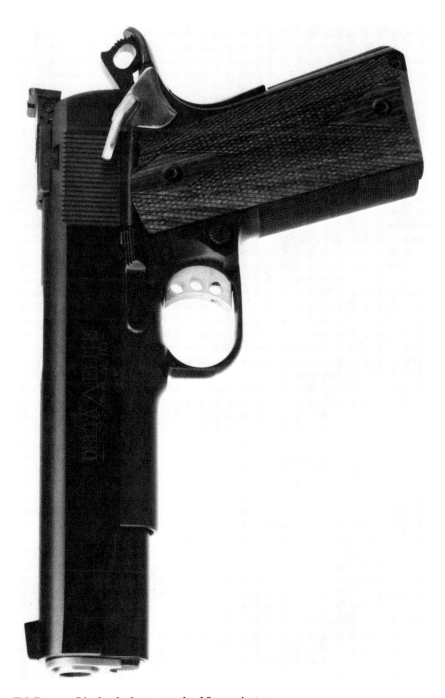

Ed Brown Limited class gun in 10mm Auto.

Don Fraley Limited class gun.

As practical pistol competition goes, there are those who opine that a custom gun is for the big league shooter and the average guy won't benefit from owning one. I totally disagree. After observing a number of competitors ranging from beginners to those in Master class, I believe custom modifications benefit a shooter with little to no experience more than those with a lot of experience. The experienced shooter has learned to quickly adapt and will place well in competition regardless of the gun he or she shoots. The inexperienced shooter needs all the help he can get.

An inexperienced shooter will progress much quicker with a gun that feels friendly to the hand. If we take two inexperienced shooters, give one a factory gun and the other a mildly modified custom gun, and introduce both to practical pistol competition on the same day, it will be a tossup as to who will win the first few matches. Assuming that the two shooters are equally talented and both practice the same amount of hours between matches, there eventually will come a time when the fellow with the custom gun will start showing his heels to the factory gun shooter on a regular basis. If both stay in the game long enough, the factory gun shooter eventually will creep up on the custom gun shooter, but he'll have to work hard to do it. You don't have to have a custom gun to be good, but having one probably will make you good a lot quicker.

Now don't mistake what you have just read. One does not have to own a fullhouse compensated gun to be competitive in practical pistol competition. It wasn't always that way, or at least that's how many shooters felt back when no separate classifications for custom guns existed. Some felt that from the day the compensated barrel was introduced in competition, the equipment race grew to the point where the initiation fee was scaring new shooters away from the game.

In 1992, USPSA officials silenced a lot of grumbling in the trenches by dividing competition guns into two classifications. In a nutshell, competitors who use guns with compensated barrels and optical sights compete in Unlimited class while those who use guns without those two items compete in Limited class. It's a bit more complicated than that, but the two classes should keep the majority happy. Those who believe practical pistol competition has matured into a competitive sport can have their custom guns with all the bells and whistles. On the other side of the trail, those who still consider practical pistol shooting nothing more than a way of honing their defensive skills can live happily ever after with factory guns or with custom guns limited to fewer modifications than are allowed in Unlimited class.

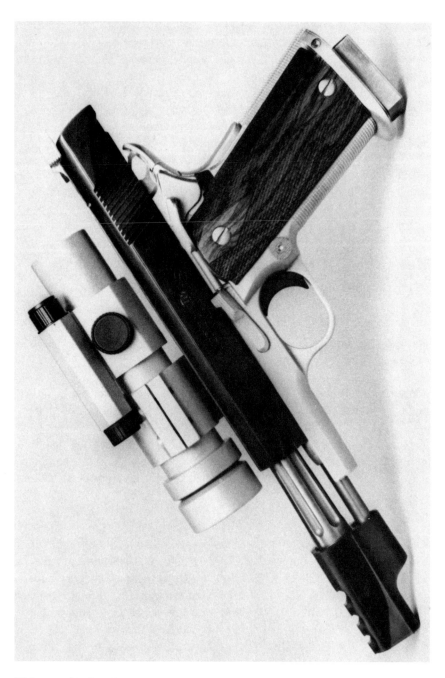

This gun is chambered for the 9x23mm Super. Built by Chuck Warner, it appears on the cover of this book and is described in the Appendix.

Steve Woods Limited class gun. *(Stephen Longley photo)*

Steve Woods Unlimited class gun. *(Stephen Longley photo)*

Springfield Armory Custom Shop Limited class gun.

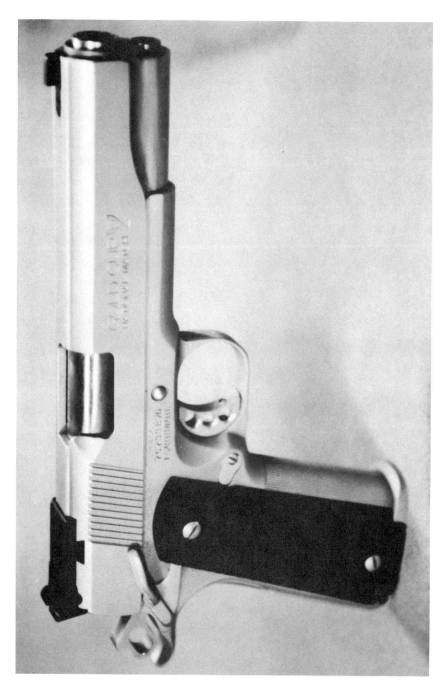

Jim Garthwaite Limited class Gold Cup in .45 ACP.

The Beginning

It is difficult to determine exactly when what is now commonly referred to as practical pistol competition was born, but its roots reach much deeper into the history of shooting sports than is often thought. As far back as the 1920s, the National Rifle Association was sponsoring a police training school at Camp Perry where lawmen practiced and competed on a coarse of fire called Hogan's Alley. As a lawman walked along the street, a concealed range official operated levers that caused cardboard hoodlums and sometimes their hostages to suddenly appear in the windows and doorways of sham buildings. Another interesting target consisted of a cardboard silhouette of an automobile. The officer's score was based on elapsed time and the number of A-Zone hits made on bad guys. Bullet holes in the gas tank and tires of the paper auto raised his score, but those in "nonvital areas" counted against him. Of course, his score dropped some more if targets that represented hostages had bullet holes in them. All of this will sound quite familiar to today's practical pistol competitor.

Practical pistol competition was mainly used as a training aid for lawmen until southern California shooters started playing the game during the 1950s. Various clubs in that state formed the Southwest Pistol League (SWPL) in an effort to get the sport better established. The SWPL published a booklet entitled *Standard Pistol Courses of the Southwest Pistol League,* made it available to other clubs, and practical pistol competition began to slowly spread throughout the United States. Some of the basic courses of fire in that booklet went on to become classics still being used at hundreds of clubs around the world.

Jeff Cooper first promoted the sport in his writings and then later became the driving force behind a shooting organization that would eventually become a household word among those who believed handgun evolution began and ended with Colt's Government Model pistol. In 1976, Cooper and representatives from several foreign countries met at Columbia, Missouri, to form the International Practical Shooting Confederation (IPSC), of which Cooper was elected the first president. By the end of 1977, 18 countries were members, including the United States, Canada, Australia, New Zealand, Austria, Norway, the United Kingdom, Rhodesia, Belgium, Denmark, South Africa, Finland, Southwest Africa, France, Germany, Sweden, the Netherlands, and Switzerland. As this is written in early 1992, the number of IPSC member nations is climbing toward 40.

In the beginning, all individual clubs of every member nation were directly affiliated with IPSC, an organizational structure that quickly became unmanageable as clubs around the world were added to the roster. By mid-1977, the United States alone had more than two dozen affiliated clubs in 15 states from

Dave Lauck built this gun for concealed carry by a lawman who prefers the Government Model pistol and the .45 ACP cartridge.

Dan Ruff just before .38 Superizing a few targets during a USPSA match. *(Front Sight photo)*

coast to coast. During that year, it was proposed that individual clubs should affiliate with their national administrative bodies, and those bodies should in turn affiliate with IPSC. Some member countries instituted the idea immediately, but it would be several years before the United States followed suit. In May 1983, the first edition of The International Practical Shooting Confederation and the United States Region of IPSC rule book was printed for distribution to members of the newly formed United States Practical Shooting Association.

The USPSA has enjoyed tremendous growth since its inception, due in large part to the devotion and hard work of its president, Dave Stanford, and his staff. A retired Seattle police sergeant, Stanford took over the reigns of the fledgling organization in 1984 when it had less than 1,500 members. By 1992, USPSA membership was at 12,000 active members in well over 350 clubs across the country—and still climbing.

The USPSA/IPSC Minor-Major Power Factor

The minimum handgun cartridge power factor accepted for registered USPSA competition is 125. The power factor of a load is calculated by multiplying bullet weight (in grains) times muzzle velocity (in feet per

Dave Stanford, retired president of the USPSA, shooting his old compensated .45 ACP (Front Sight *photo*)

second) and dividing by a constant of 1,000. If, for example, your 9mm Parabellum handload is producing 1,200 fps with a 115-grain bullet, 115 times 1,200 divided by 1,000 equals a power factor of 138 which exceeds the minimum by a comfortable margin of 13. To find the velocity needed for a particular bullet weight, divide the power factor by the bullet weight and multiply by the 1,000 constant. For example, 175 (power factor) divided by 185 (bullet weight in grains) times 1,000 equals a required velocity of 946 fps.

A competitor who uses a load with a Minor power factor of 125 to 174.9 earns five points for all shots inside the A zone of the standard IPSC cardboard target, three points for B and C zone hits, and one point for each hole in the D zone. A competitor who shoots a Major caliber (175 or higher power factor) receives the same number of points for A zone hits, but earns one additional point for each shot into the other zones. For example, if a Minor caliber shooter has one hit in each of the four designated zones on the target, he earns a total of 12 points whereas the Major caliber shooter earns 15 points for the same number of shots in the four zones.

The power factor requirement is why cartridges with maximum power levels from the 9mm Luger on down are not popular among USPSA competitors while the .45 ACP, .38 Super, CP 9x21mm Super, .40 S&W, and 10mm are.

554

Todd Jarrett and friend. *(Front Sight photo)*

To compensate for the many factors that cause velocity variations in handloads (which can cause the host club's chronograph to ruthlessly downgrade your Major loads to Minor), most competitors load their ammunition to exceed the minimum by 5 to 10 percent. I personally prefer to load to a power factor of 185 or a bit higher, as do most competitors.

For the benefit of those who wonder how the present minimum power factor of 175 for Major was arrived at, I'll flip the calendar back to the infancy of IPSC. In those pre-affordable chronograph days, only the big ammunition manufacturers had equipment for measuring bullet velocity. Consequently, clubs who were members of IPSC were furnished plans for building an inexpensive ballistic pendulum. When a suspended steel plate on the device was struck by a bullet, it arched rearward and pushed a pointer around a protractor. On a properly calibrated pendulum, a Major caliber was one that pushed the pointer to 150 degrees or more. Any load that failed to swing the arm to 150 degrees was classified as Minor.

In a January 1978 bulletin to IPSC members, Jeff Cooper recommended that all clubs calibrate their pendulums for each match by shooting them with a commercial match hardball load (230-grain bullet at an advertised 850 fps) fired in a Star PD with a 3.8-inch barrel. He went on to explain that since any production autoloader in .45 ACP should be able to compete as a Major

Walt Bodie dropping an empty magazine and reaching for a full one on the run. (Front Sight *photo*)

556

power gun, club pendulums should not be calibrated by firing military hardball in a Government Model with 5-inch barrel. When the first USPSA rule book was published in 1983, the more readily available Colt Commander became the official pendulum calibrating instrument.

Once affordable chronographs became available and clubs began to abandon the ballistic pendulum, it was discovered that in the short barrels of the Star PD and Colt Commander, Federal's 230-grain match load would average around 775 feet per second. Using today's method of calculating the power factor of a load, that comes out at 178. IPSC eventually settled on a round figure of 175, decreased it to 170, and then raised it back to 175.

Incidentally, the power factor floors for rifles are 160 for Minor and 340 for Major.

The Shooter Classification System

When a fledgling shooter decides to try his hand at most competitive sports, he is thrown to the wolves so to speak and must compete head-to-head against those who have been in the game for years. It used to be that way in USPSA competition, but not anymore. In 1991 my article on a Greenville, South Carolina, club called the Carolina Practical Shooting League (CPSL) was published in *Handgun Quarterly* magazine. One of the oldest practical pistol clubs in the country, the CPSL utilized the standard USPSA classification system, but had an additional class called Unclassified. Its purpose was to enable a beginner to compete against other beginners until his or her scores indicated a need to be moved to a higher class. In contrast, clubs that followed USPSA classification guidelines to the letter required a beginner to compete against A or Master class shooters until being classified. That often took six months or more and new competitors with zero experience got hammered at every match by the best in the club. Embarrassment and bruised pride caused many to become discouraged and drop out before giving the sport a fair shake whereas CPSL's Unclassified classification kept them on board until the hook was deeply set.

Whether or not that writeup on CPSL got some attention in the right places, I can't say, but in early 1992 the USPSA announced the adoption of a new classification called Unclassified.

When joining the organization and competing in matches held by a USPSA-affiliated club, you become eligible to participate in the National Classification System by shooting classifier stages designed, sanctioned, and sent to all clubs each quarter by USPSA. At the end of each quarter, club officials forward your scores to USPSA headquarters where they are gobbled up by a giant computer.

Kippi Boykin wows the crowd with her fast and accurate shooting from a rather awkward position. *(*Front Sight *photo)*

Once you have fired six classifier stages, your combined scores are weighed against those of all other participating USPSA members across the country who fired identical stages during the same time frame. Based on how your score compares with those of other members, you are classified as D, C, B, A, or Master. The important thing to remember about this sport is, regardless of your level of skill with a handgun, you compete only against other shooters with the same classification. This is why Unclassified and D class shooters take home about as much gold as those Master class hotshoes.

The National Range Officer's Institute

Instructors from the National Range Officer's Institute travel to various parts of the country to conduct training and certification classes for volunteer USPSA range officers. I am aware of no other shooting organization that offers such a valuable service. When I step to the firing line at a match held by a USPSA-affiliated club, it is most comforting to know that my safety as well as the safety of all other competitors is Job One to a group of professionally trained match officials.

USPSA Club Finder Service

Membership information is available by sending your name and address to USPSA, Box 811, Sedro Wooley, WA 98294. If you need assistance in locating a practical shooting club in your area, enclose a note indicating the largest town or city near you. The information will be forwarded to the USPSA-affiliated club or section coordinator nearest you and you should be contacted within a few weeks. As an active member, you will also receive a subscription to *Front Sight*, the USPSA's official magazine.

The Equipment vs. Talent Experiment

Among practical pistol competitors, two schools of thought have long existed on the question of raw talent vs. the evolution of equipment in club-level competition. One side is firmly convinced that the most talented shooter will win even if he is somewhat handicapped in the equipment department. The opposing team is equally convinced that given enough edge in equipment, a less-talented but good shooter can beat the hotshoe. Recently I was involved in an experiment that may not have completely answered the question, but might serve as a bit of food for thought.

This is a true story about two USPSA/IPSC shooters who compete at the same club. One is a Master class shooter rather young of age, the other is a considerably older B class shooter. When the Master class shooter was using an open-sighted compensated racegun in .38 Super and the B class shooter used the same type of gun in .45 ACP, they were miles apart at the finish line. The youngster was simply too fast for the oldster. When the B class shooter switched to a .38 Super comp gun, he closed the gap considerably, but still ate a lot of Master class dust at every match. When the B class shooter had a red-dot sight installed on his Super, he started nipping at the Master's heels, but his scores were still lower. Then the Master class shooter decided to switch to a Minor caliber Limited class gun. At that point the two were no longer competing in the same class, but here's the interesting part— their scores were virtually the same.

The moral to this story? I'll let you decide.

Who Is Mr. Pepper Popper?

I'll close this chapter with a bit of trivia that I wrote for one of the magazines some time back and am including it here, not because it is all that important, but because I received so many favorable letters from readers when doing it the first time. The information won't help your shooting, but it may win you a cup of coffee next time you're chewing the fat with your buddies.

In USPSA/IPSC competition, the cardboard target with its A through D scoring zones, the steel plate, and the Pepper popper are the most common victims of competitors' bullets. Vaguely humanoid in shape, the Pepper popper is a 42-inch tall reactive steel target sometimes described by Minor caliber shooters as the immovable steel lollipop. It is not uncommon to see a number of these targets in one or more stages of a match. Just prior to the match, each Pepper popper is placed into position and adjusted by range officials so it will topple over when struck on or near its calibration line by a 9mm Parabellum Minor power factor load.

Originally called the J. P. Ballistic Target, it was named in honor of its designer, IPSC member John Pepper of Maryland. In my files is a copy of the original drawing and specification package submitted by Pepper to IPSC officials for approval. The documents are dated December 22, 1978.

Pepper poppers often are called immovable steel lollipops by Minor caliber practical pistol competitors.

25

The Practical Belt Holster

A fine custom gun deserves nothing less than the best belt holster. Many excellent designs are available for the Government Model and its variations. Different styles are out there for the choosing and all fit neatly into what I prefer to describe as practical and competition classifications. The former is what most handgunners either own or are seeking. The latter is covered in Chapter 26.

Holster quality ranges from poor to excellent with most companies offering one or the other, but not both. Cheap holsters usually consist of inferior materials put together with shoddy workmanship around a poor design. Companies that specialize in such merchandise offer the exact same designs year after year and manage to stay in business only because their prices are low. The product looks attractive while hanging on the rack in a gun shop, but a bit of hard use soon reveals to its new owner that a penny saved is not always a penny earned. You get exactly what you pay for in a holster.

A good holster is made of the best materials available. It holds its shape during years of wear, is extremely durable, its workmanship is top drawer, and it represents the latest in design. On top of that it looks as good as it is. The better holsters are also user-friendly and when hanging at the waist feel like they were designed and made by people who actually wear their product. A top-quality holster designed for concealed carry hugs the gun snug against the body. It also will hang onto the gun while its wearer runs, jumps, falls down, or whatever, and yet will release the gun smoothly without excessive resistance during the draw. It will do this when it's five days old and it will do this when it is five years old.

The more progressive holster companies seldom rest on their laurels and constantly improve their line of existing products or introduce new and innovative ideas. They also keep a sensitive finger resting on the pulse of consumer demand, back up their products with an excellent warranty, and prove it by breaking a leg to keep a customer happy. The size of the company has nothing to do with the product's quality. Some of the best holsters in the world are turned out by large firms like Safariland, DeSantis, and Bianchi, and by small one- or two-man shops like Milt Sparks.

The Hard Synthetic Holster

There was a time when all the better holsters were made entirely of leather, but synthetic materials are biting off an increasingly larger share of the market each year. Like music, synthetic holsters are divided into two groups. Among members of the hard group are multilayered laminated designs like those made of Safari-Laminate by Safariland. The Safariland holster is constructed of a stiff layer of polyvinylchloride sandwiched between an extremely tough Porvair outer shell on the outside and a soft natural suede leather lining inside next to the gun. The combination is tougher than dirt on one side and kind to the finish of a gun on the other.

From a distance, Safari-Laminate with the brown color option looks exactly like natural leather. When it comes to strength, durability, shape retention, and the ability to shed moisture, the hard synthetic holster is superior to leather. On average, it also is considerably lighter and usually a bit less expensive. All of these features plus an aggressive marketing program probably are what have enabled Safariland to capture a lion's share of the law enforcement market.

The Soft Synthetic Holster

Holsters in the soft group consist of a thin layer of padding sandwiched between a skin of extremely tough Cordura® nylon on the outside and a smoother fabric liner on the inside. The better grades are chemically treated to shed moisture. On the positive side, this type of holster usually is the least expensive available. It also can be lighter in weight and a bit less bulky than other types, a characteristic of which some lawmen who carry a gun concealed are quite fond. Some models are, however, considerably more bulky than some of the extremely lightweight leather holsters. One exception is the Super Belt Slide from Michaels of Oregon. The one for Colt's Commander (No. 8601-0) weighs a mere two ounces, is extremely thin, and represents a lot of holster at minimal cost.

A Super Belt Slide synthetic holster for the Officer's ACP from Michaels of Oregon.

Many soft holsters lack rigidity and must rely on a strap to retain the gun, whereas those made of stiffer materials allow the utilization of other retaining system designs. The mouth of some soft holsters tends to collapse when the gun is removed, making reholstering difficult. The more expensive holsters have a semirigid track inside to prevent wearing the finish from the front sight, and some even have a tension screw-type retention device in addition to the strap. Any snaps, buckles, and rivets on the better holsters are installed in a manner that prevents scratching the gun while the bargain basement grade will ruin the finish on a nice gun in short order. The edge binding on a top-quality synthetic holster is tightly stitched and lies flat. Top-of-the-line holsters of this type often have an adjustment screw designed to enable tension on the gun to be varied.

The combination of synthetics and leather is becoming popular. I believe all of the Safariland Safari-Laminate designs are lined with extremely soft suede leather. Bianchi's No. D4500 Ranger Black Shadow is constructed by sandwiching foam padding between an inside layer of ballistic weave nylon on the outside and an extremely soft fine-grain leather inside. It is a great holster and extremely comfortable to wear, but could be improved a bit if its belt loops were located similar to the true pancake design.

Leather

From a practical point of view, a leather holster is inferior in some ways to its synthetic competitors. From a traditional and purely cosmetic point of view, no other material even approaches leather when it comes right down to complimenting the appearance of a handsome custom gun. Nothing else looks, feels, or smells as good.

The better leather holsters are made of full-grain cowhide with the thickness of the layer(s) of leather used varying according to design. For example, three of my concealed-carry Commander holsters are what I classify as flyweight, medium weight, and heavy weight. The thickness of the leather used in constructing them is .130, .200, and .300 inch, respectively. Incidentally, the terms full-grain and top-grain are used rather loosely among holster manufacturers, but are supposed to indicate that the leather was tanned with the grain (or hair) side of the hide left intact. Examination of the leather with a magnifying glass reveals whether it is or isn't. If you see irregular pores that once contained hair, it is full-grain leather. If not, the leather has been sanded before the finish was applied.

I could go on and on about such things as stitching, laminating, finishing, and why extra layers of leather are used in the welt areas of top-quality holsters, but the fact of the matter is, the really good companies don't make a leather holster of inferior quality. Some models cost more than others, but when buying a holster made by a reputable firm, you can safely bet you're getting your money's worth. The biggest question shooters face when choosing a top-quality holster from among the reputable companies is not which brand is best, but which do I like best?

Weights

Lots of folks look long and hard at weight when buying a pistol for concealed carry, but often overlook the same characteristic when shopping for its holster. You can buy a lightweight Commander at 27½ ounces, add half a pound for its holster, and end up at the same weight as the standard Commander. Or you can start with the steel frame Commander and end up with almost a quarter pound more heft than the Government Model. Top-quality holsters of the same basic style and quality made of the same materials differ considerably in heft.

Of several holsters I have for the Commander, the Bianchi PRD (Pinch Retention Device) weighs eight ounces, the Sparks No. 1AT (Adjustable Tension) weighs 5¾ ounces and the DeSantis No. 19 Mini Scabbard weighs a mere three ounces. The difference in weight between the lightest and heaviest is about the same as that of eight rounds of Remington's .45 ACP +P load.

Covered VS. Open Trigger Guard

Some holster styles cover the trigger while others leave it exposed. Contrary to what was once popular opinion, an exposed trigger does not increase the speed of the draw simply because the finger should never enter the trigger guard until the muzzle of the gun is out of the holster and pointed in the target's direction. Those who think an exposed trigger makes the draw quicker should attend a practical pistol match and watch competitors snatch their guns from Safariland 008 and Ernie Hill Fas-Trac holsters and place a bullet dead center of the target in less than one tick of the clock. When a gun rests in either of those holsters its trigger and trigger guard are completely covered.

Lined vs. Unlined

A holster lined with extremely soft leather is easier on the finish of a gun, especially blued steel. On the other hand, a lined holster usually is a bit heavier and more bulky than the unlined variety.

The Clip-On

Most holsters are the belt loop-type, but some companies offer other designs as well. One is an easy-on, easy-off, holster that simply clips onto

Made of top grain cowhide, the DeSantis Mini Scabbard holster weighs a mere three ounces.

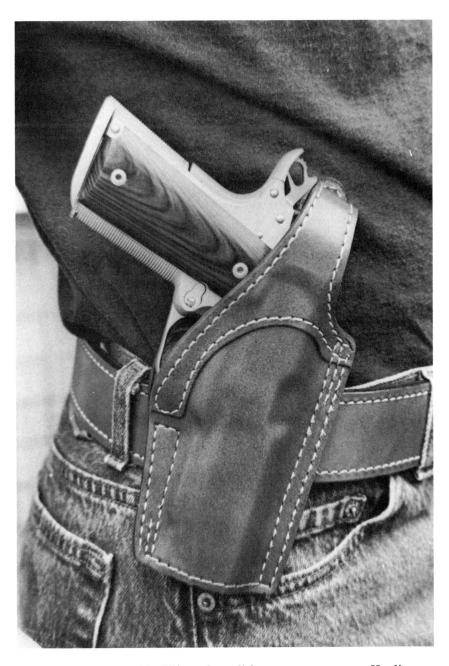

The Safariland No. 530 "Klipspringer" is an easy-on, easy-off, clip-on holster made of Safari-Laminate lined with soft glove leather. The Commander version weighs 3¾ ounces.

the belt or waistband of the pants. The Safariland No. 530 Klipspringer with its stainless steel spring is a good example. Another is the Bianchi No. 119 Talon.

I have a salesman friend who travels throughout his state while calling on customers. Sometimes he is on the road deep into the night. When stopping to call on a customer, he leaves his Officer's ACP in the car. When stopping at a rest area along the highway late at night, he simply attaches the snub-nose .45 and its Safariland Klipspringer to his belt before stepping out of the car. Incidentally, he does have a permit which enables him to legally carry a pistol concealed. The important thing to remember when shopping for a holster of this type is to choose one that will hang onto the belt or waistband and not come loose when the gun is drawn. In other words, when you draw the pistol in a hurry you don't want it to come out still wrapped in its holster.

Paddle-Type

The paddle holster is not as quick to put on and take off as the clip-type, but is quicker than the belt loop-type. It has two other advantages: it requires no belt and the large surface area of the paddle distributes weight over a large surface area of the body rather than on the belt. This makes a gun feel about half as heavy as it is. This type is very popular among plainsclothes officers who wear dress pants with no belt loops. The better ones are designed to resist moving upward as the gun is drawn. Among those I've tried, the DeSantis No. 13 (leather) and Safariland 5118 (laminate) are the most impressive. The latter also can be converted to a belt loop-type holster with the No. 518BL accessory. To me, this style of holster, when properly designed, is more comfortable to wear than any other type, but body heat does have a tendency to build up beneath the paddle when it is worn during hot weather.

The Pancake

The pancake holster was designed to hold a pistol extremely close to the body. For this reason, it has become relatively popular among plainsclothes lawmen who wear concealed firearms. It once stood alone in that department, but some of the extremely thin belt loop-types now snug the gun just as close to its wearer. Its primary disadvantage is that of weight.

Inside-the-pant

Inside-the-pant (ITP) style holsters are extremely popular and almost every company offers at least one. It presses the gun extremely close to the body for concealed carry. Thousands of people swear by this type of holster, but

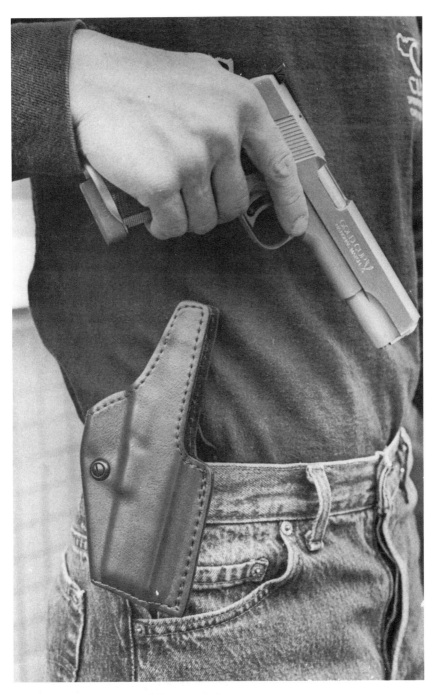

Safariland No. 5118 paddle-type holster.

Constructed of Safari-Laminate lined with soft suede leather, this Safariland No. 5118 paddle-type holster is easy to put on and take off. The one illustrated is for the Glock 17 and weighs five ounces.

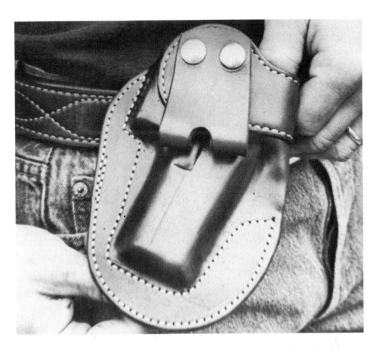

This Milt Sparks inside-the-pant leather holster for the Government Model weighs 5½ ounces.

I've yet to find one that's comfortable. This style works fine for me when I carry a Government Model .380, but carrying a larger pistol in one is another matter entirely.

Open- vs. Closed-End

I prefer an open-end holster because it usually is a bit lighter than a closed-end type. It also is more versatile. My DeSantis No. 19 Mini Scabbard was made for the Officer's ACP, but in a pinch, will also work with the Commander and Government. The muzzle of the Government Model protrudes from the end of the holster quite a bit, but whan a Commander is in the holster, only about a quarter inch of its muzzle shows.

The Crossdraw

The crossdraw style of holster has both advantages and disadvantages. On the positive side, some find it quicker to draw a concealed gun from since the weak hand can be used to pull aside the coattail with the weak hand while the gun is being drawn by the strong hand. A gun also is more easily drawn with either hand from the crossdraw style than from the strongside style. On the negative side, the crossdraw holster is not quite as concealable because it cannot be worn as far to the rear as a strongside holster.

Gun Retention Designs

A number of police officers have lost their lives in the line of duty when their handgun was snatched from its holster by an assailant. I doubt if it is possible for any manufacturer to come up with an absolutely snatchproof retention design, but they keep trying. Safariland was first in the industry to classify duty holsters on the basis of their ability to hang onto a gun when unauthorized hands are attempting to remove it. As Safariland literature describes the three classifications, Level I is moderate retention, Level II is optimum retention, and Level III is maximum retention. Of course, the more difficult the gun is for an assailant to remove from the holster, the more time it takes for the person wearing it to do the same.

As a rule, a holster designed for concealed wear does not have an elaborate retention system simply because it is usually worn out of sight and made relatively snatchproof by clothing worn over it. At the very most it is a simple thumb-released retaining strap. Examples of this type are the Safariland No. 28 Pancake, Bianchi No. 7L Shadow, DeSantis No. 1 Thumb-Break Scabbard, and the DeSantis No. 13 Paddle. A lot of concealment holsters don't even have a retaining strap. The Safariland Nos. 14-ITP, 21-ITP, 027 Waistband J-Hook, 527 Stealth, and 5181 Paddle are good examples.

When Judy Woolley wears a carry gun in competition, its holster must have an adequate retention system. *(*Front Sight *photo)*

Some holsters have a mechanical device designed to hold the gun securely in place and yet release it without a great deal of resistence during the draw. An excellent example of what is often described as an indirect retention system is on Milt Sparks' No. 1AT. When its brass tension screw is turned clockwise, it increases the holster's grip on the gun's muzzle. You can't get much less complicated or more troublefree than that. As the holster wears over the years, simply tighten the screw a bit to keep its tension on the gun the same. This is an old idea in retention designs and one of the best because it is as simple as dirt and never wears out. A number of Safariland holsters also have this feature.

Another type of mechanical retention device is what I prefer to describe as a direct retainer. It usually consists of a device that grasps the trigger guard of a gun, but releases it during the draw. Perhaps the most ingenious of such devices is Safariland's tension block which is described in great detail in Chapter 26. The trigger guard latch in the Bianchi PRD holster is similar in concept, but totally different in design.

The simplest and perhaps the most expensive way to retain a gun in a holster is to forego all straps, snaps, and latches and form the leather so it follows every line and contour of the gun. In other words, when you look at this

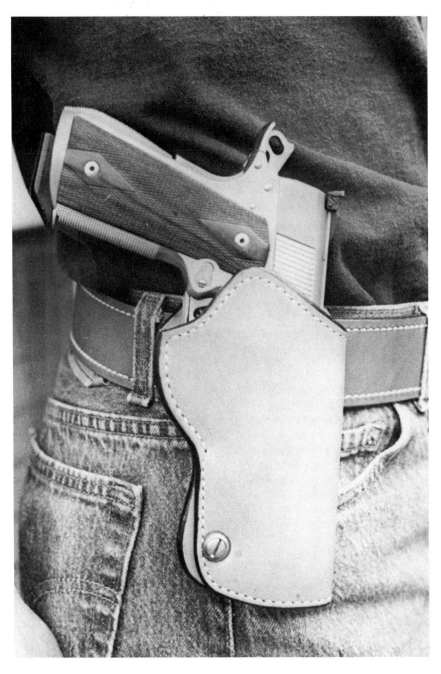

This Milt Sparks holster has a brass tension screw for adjusting the grip on the gun.

type holster, you can see the gun's features molded into its leather. I've yet to see any other company execute this style of holster as well as DeSantis.

At the end of this chapter you will find an article reprint written by Bill Rogers in December 1991 on the weapon retention designs of various styles of holsters. The report deals mainly with revolver holsters, but Rogers went on to assist Safariland in the design of new duty holsters for autoloaders as well. As this book is written, seven different models are available for auto-loaders, including the Nos. 2, 200, and 2005 (Level I Retention); 295 and 2955 (Level II Retention); and SSIII and 0705 (Level III retention). (Rogers' report is reprinted with the permission of Safariland Ltd., Inc.)

The Belt

Like holsters, belts vary considerably in quality. The two basic types of leather belts are lined and unlined. The former will maintain its shape longer, but is heavier than the latter. Most companies offer styles that suit uniformed law enforcement personnel quite well. The same goes for plainclothes officers who wear extremely casual dress such as khakis or jeans. Strangely enough, none that I'm aware of offer styles designed specifically for wear with more dressy clothing.

Two of the best heavy-duty leather belts I've tried are Milt Sparks' Model 1B and the Bianchi B21. Both are slightly less than 1¾-inches wide. Made from extremely heavy cowhide, they retain their initial stiffness during hard usage, yet are extremely comfortable to wear even when sitting down. This is due to their contoured cut, an option offered by few beltmakers. In addition to being more comfortable, a contoured shape prevents the belt from becoming folded or creased by the rear pant loop, a common occurrence with straight-profile belts.

The Sparks 1B features a narrow strip of Velcro® sewn inside which mates with the same material sewn into the belt loop of various models of Sparks holsters. Rather than utilizing the common metal snaps on the folded end of the belt for retaining the buckle, Sparks skins the cat by using removable slotted-head brass screws. The Bianchi Model B21 has foam padding stitched between its two layers of leathers, an excellent design for competitive use, but a bit thick for casual wear.

Magazine Pouches

Various styles of magazine pouches are available in both the clip-on and belt loop-types. As synthetic pouches of the former type go, the one from Michaels of Oregon is tough to beat for the money. It has a sturdy clip for

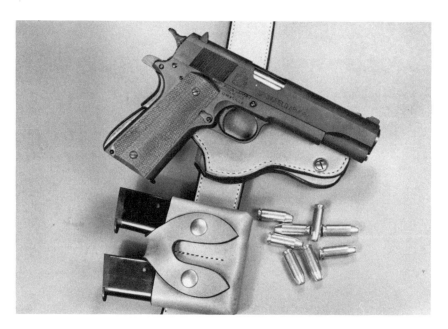

Milt Sparks belt, carry holster, and magazine pouch are made of top-quality leather.

This synthetic clip-on magazine pouch from Michaels of Oregon is lightweight and inexpensive.

slipping over the belt and a flap replete with Velcro® fastener. It also is light-weight and extremely compact. For those who prefer leather, several single and twin magazine models are available from Milt Sparks, DeSantis, Bianchi, and others. In the vertical pouch lineup, I particularly like the Safariland No. 23. An inside-the-pant, clip-on type, it is made of suede leather.

Safariland seems to come up with more new ideas in magazine pounches than any other company. One of the latest is the No. 276 Mag-in-the-box. When the snap-type flap is released, a spring-loaded plate in the bottom of the pouch pushes the magazine upward for easy grasping. It is available in vertical and horizontal carry styles. If I had to pick out a favorite among the entire bunch, it would have to be the Safariland No. 123. It holds the maga-zine in a horizontal position and attaches to the belt with a Velcro® loop which makes it quick and easy to put on and take off. Made of extremely thin Safari-Laminate, it is extremely comfortable to wear and one of the lightest pouches available.

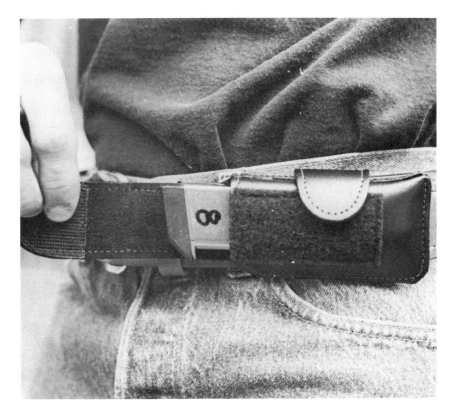

This quick-detach Safariland horizontal-carry magazine pouch attaches to the belt with a Velcro® strap.

Holsters Designed for Weapon Retention
by
William H. Rogers
(December 1991)
(Reprinted Courtesy of Safariland Ltd., Inc.)

In the late 1960s and early 1970s, holsters using a front opening design were made popular by Safety Speed, Hoyt, Bianchi, and Rogers Holster Company. Most of those designs were similar to the Berns-Martin concept of a clamshell capturing a revolver and preventing it from being drawn straight up by locking on the back of the trigger guard. The majority of uniformed law enforcement officers were using a "Border Patrol" type holster which retained the weapon only by a strap behind the hammer. The country was experiencing civil unrest unlike it had ever faced before. The rioting, looting, and burning of Watts in Washington, D.C., in Chicago, and in several other major cities, coupled with violent protests on most college campuses, had increased the concern over weapon retention by police officers.

During this same period of time, the Uniform Crime Reports showed an increase from 8 to 11 percent of police officers killed with their own weapons. This increase, however, did not show the full picture. Hundreds of officers lost their weapons during this peroid without anyone being shot. The author believes that most of the weapons simply fell out of the holsters without their owners even being aware of the problem. The retaining strap on the border patrol-type holster could be easily released accidentally by the wearer without his knowledge. With the strap released, simply falling down or getting out of a car was sufficient force to cause the revolver to fall out of the holster. The front opening holsters all used some means to maintain pressure against the revolver even if a retaining strap had been removed. They were, therefore, more secure if their straps were released.

A popular theory of the time was that officers were more likely to be attacked, unaware, from behind. Because the weapons could not be drawn straight up and out from the front opening holsters, officers attacked from the rear would have a better chance to retain their weapons. Departments switching to the front-opening-designed holsters immediately decreased the incidence of lost weapons. This was primarily because the weapons were not accidentaly falling out of the holster during a scuffle. These immediate results caused departments throughout the United States to move away form the "Border Patrol" style holster toward the "Front Break" design.

By the late 1970s and early 1980s, every holster company in the U.S. offered a "Front Break" design. Some of the models picked up the title of security or safety holster. These titles implied that the officer involved in a fight was more likely to retain his weapon. The theory that officers were more likely to be attacked unaware from behind had never been established by any study, nor had it been refuted. It is the belief of this author that the theory was, and still is, unfounded. Police officers are unlikely to have someone sneak up behind them without reacting to the threat. In the mid-1980s, the Uniform Crime Report showed an increase from 11 to 15 percent of the number of officers killed with their own weapons. The increase during this period of time is significant because during this same time, most, if not all academies and departments had included a course in weapon retention in their curriculum.

In 1983, two separate incidents in which officers were shot with their own weapons prompted this author to make a more complete study of weapon retention. In both of the aforementioned incidents, the officers were wearing a front break holster of the author's design called "The Boss." It was determined that in both cases the main securing strap had been released inadvertently by the officer or by the assailant during a brief encounter and in both cases the assailants pulled the weapon through the front of the holster while they were moving away from the officer or the officer was pulling away from them. The end result was that the officers were disarmed so quickly they could not react in time to defend themselves. Over a period of about six months some 25 similar cases were reviewed by the author. Some of the incidents went back several years and a variety of holsters were included. None of the other incidents reviewed included any of the author's holsters. The task was difficult because most of the synopses of the cases did not include enough information. It was necessary to talk to the investigating officer or to the survivor to find out how the weapon was lost. In all the cases studied, a common denominator was found.

No matter what type of holster, no matter how many subjects were involved or from what direction the attack originated, the end result was the same. The weapon was lost always from the adjacent side or the front of the officer, not from the rear. In most cases, it was believed that the holster was secured prior to the attack and it was usually one violent thrust that resulted in weapon loss. This one violent grab and pull was so quick and forceful that the officer was unable to react in time to prevent a takeaway.

This author designed a series of tests for uniform holsters based on the study. A holster to be tested was mounted on a new uniform belt and secured to an average-sized male volunteer by the use of an under belt and keepers. An unloaded weapon was then secured in the holster.

In Test No. 1, the assault was limited to a single violent force in seven different directions. This force was as much as the attacker could exert in the direction he was pulling. The directions of force were straight forward, straight backward, straight sideward, straight up, forward and up, backward and up, sideward and up. The assailant was directed to use both hands and to wear leather gloves to protect his hands and also to maintain a more positive grip on the weapon. He, however, was not allowed to touch any part of the securing strap or straps. The entire force was directed at the weapon. The victim was not allowed to resist and was required to hold his ground instead of relaxing and giving in the direction of the attack. The direction that the assailant pulled and the result was noted. The holster was checked for integrity and resecured if necessary. The assailant was directed to do the same test from a different direction. This process was continued until all seven directions of attack had been tried.

After Test No. 1 was completed, the wearer of the holster was required to release the primary security device, usually the hammer strap, and required to perform three movements without touching the holster or weapon. In this test, the wearer was required to do a forward somersault, a rearward somersault, and to jump over a 20-inch obstacle with a 180-degree mid-air turn. If the weapon remained secure through Test Nos. 1 and 2, the holster was declared to have a Security Level of I and was further tested.

With the primary securing device released, Test No. 1 was repeated. If the holster was able to retain the weapon from any one of the seven directions of attack, it was rated at a Level II. Then the secondary retaining device of the holster was released and Test No. 1 repeated. If the holster was capable of retaining the weapon from any of the seven directions, it was rated as Security Level III.

In 1983 and 1984, the author tested every major holster company's uniform holster line, including his own company's holsters. Many of the holsters could not survive Test No. 1. The holster body would shear off of its belt attachment. Some of the front-break models would release the weapon on the first thrust and be so badly sprung that the weapon could not be resecured for a second attempt. Holsters made entirely of leather softened and quickly stretched out of shape. The metal components, spring wire, and belt-piece shanks bent easily and allowed the holster to fail. Holsters with stitched front or back welts either tore open at their welts or stretched the stiches so that the holster was just a loose-fitting bag.

The direction of force that was most devastating was when the attacker faced the victim, offset slightly toward his holster side, and pulled forward and up with one motion. This appeared to be consistent with the findings of the real-life incident studies. The front-break models that used a strap around the front of the holster instead of over the hammer usually failed Test No. 1, even though the strap remained secure. The models that had a strap over the hammer could not withstand the force forward because that was the direction in which the holster opened. The snap would simply release or shear off.

Only three holster models were able to rate a Security Level I. Those same three models also were able to meet the requirements of Level II because they could withstand a straight back and straight up pull with the retention strap released. It should be noted that even though those three front break models passed the Levels I and II tests, they could only pass with certain revolvers. Colt revolvers and the Smith & Wesson Military and Police model failed in most cases while the S&W revolvers with adjustable sights performed the best. It also should be noted that when the same test was performed on the same model of holsters that had been in use for several years, they could not pass the Level I test. This was due to the fact that the holsters had loosened up, the retention straps had stretched, and certain retaining surfaces had been burnished by constant use.

Another observation, which was later determined to be critical, was the location and direction of release of the primary securing device. The standard high profile thumb release strap was many times released inadvertently by the attacker as he reached for the handle of the weapon from the front direction. This occurred when the attacker, as instructed, tried to not hit the release. In the case of the front-break holster which the attacker had only to pull forward after releasing the retention strap, even the fastest reaction time by the officer was not quick enough to avoid losing the weapon.

Based on the retention test results, the following conclusions were made:

1. The most devastating force was delivered by an attacker who approached from the front and pulled forward and upward with all his strength and weight. The officer, in an effort to retain his balance and to break away from the attacker, automatically pulled back and down with all of his strength and weight. The combination of the two forces is severe.

2. Holsters manufactured entirely of leather, or with stitched-on belt mounts, metal inserts, or with front or back stitched welts, are not strong enough to survive the possible forces. This is especially true if the holster is used for several years and exposed to the elements.

3. Because its front side is allowed to open or give in the direction of the most devastating force, the front-break is inherently the weakest design.

4. If the primary retention device of a holster is released either by the wearer or the assailant, the easiest design to snatch a weapon from is the front-break.

5. The primary retention device must be designed in such a way that it would be difficult to release by an assailant during the action of reaching for the weapon.

With these conclusions in mind, the author designed and patented a holster made from a synthetic laminate with a leather lining. The holster was designed in such a way as to increase its grip on the weapon when the weapon was pulled forward and upward. The design used two securing straps each of which could pass the Level I retention test. The straps were designed so they would be difficult to release by an assailant, but at the same time be in a natural position for the wearer to release quickly. The holster used no welts and the back attachment was bolted in place. The holster was able to pass all tests for a Security Level III and, hence, was named SSIII. The front-break holster called "The Boss" was dropped from the Rogers literature and replaced with the SSIII.

In 1985, the author sold his company to Safariland Ltd., Inc., of Ontario, California, and agreed to continue to consult and design holsters for them. Safariland sold the SSIII as the Model No. 070 and adopted similar testing procedures under the author's previous guidelines. A research and development team consisting of the author and several employees of Safariland and the old Rogers Holster Company was formed to redesign the entire uniform holster line. At that time, the only holster that would pass a Level I retention test was the Rogers SSIII and the Safariland No. 070. Safariland's No. 275 front-break was a popular holster at the time, but it had a stitched back welt. It was redesigned to eliminate the welt and redesignated No. 275-2. My laminated process for holster material was given the trademarked name of "Safari-Laminate."

In 1987, Safariland discontinued the No. 275-2 holster and all customers who were using it were advised to test the No. 070 and the new No. 200 holsters for possible replacement. Like the No. 070, the No. 200 could pass a Level I retention test. In 1989, Safariland discontinued all uniform holsters that could not pass the Level I test. All models were dropped except the Nos. 070, 200, and 295 for semiautomatics. The No. 200 is rated at a Security Level I, and the No. 070 is rated at Level III. More recently, a Level II holster for revolvers was designed and is presently undergoing testing and evaluation.

Safariland has done an admirable job of informing dealers, law enforcement departments, and individual end users of its security rating system for holsters. The system is presently used only by Safariland and has not been officially recognized by any orginization. The system is easy for law enforcement agencies to use in conducting their own test on holsters made by Safariland as well as by other companies. However, as always, each department must conduct its own tests and determine its own standard of performance.

26

The Competition Rig

ANY holster design that complies with the USPSA rules and regulations can be used in practical pistol competition, but the pure competition holster is designed to be used for no other purpose. Without doubt, this book covers some items that eventually will become obsolete, some quicker than others. I'm not sure this will hold true for competition holsters as they seem to have evolved about as far as they can go from a practical point of view. I'm sure other brands and designs will be introduced, but I doubt if they will be greatly superior to the two that absolutely dominate practical pistol competition as this chapter is written.

Just as the Government Model pistol almost totally dominates all levels of USPSA/IPSC competition, so it goes with Ernie Hill's Fas-Trac and Safariland's 008 Final Option holsters. Both are available for autoloaders and revolvers. Overall, the two holsters once appeared to be about neck-to-neck in popularity, but the Final Option now seems to be leading the race by about a five to one margin. In alphabetical order, here's an up-close and in-depth look at the two rigs more shooters are wearing in practical pistol competition than all others combined.

Ernie Hill's Fas-Trac

The Fas-Trac holster from Ernie Hill Speed Leather is constructed of 18-gauge steel sheeting sandwiched between two layers of extremely heavy 8-ounce cowhide. The belt loop is made of the same materials except its steel stiffener plate is 16 gauge. The layer of steel in those areas retains the

584

**The author shooting a C. W. Custom Colt Double Eagle "Plus"
compensated gun in competition.**

original shape of the holster even after thousands of draws during practice
and competition. It also makes the rig relatively heavy, a characteristic I like
very much in a competition holster. Top-quality leather with its natural finish
makes the Fas-Trac too magnificent to describe with mere words. All stitching is heavy nylon.

With the exception of a narrow strip of leather extending low around its
toe, the entire front of the Fas-Trac holster is open. You simply lift the pistol
a mere one inch and its muzzle is clear of leather. The best way I know to
describe how it feels to draw a pistol from this holster is to say it is as close
as you can get to snatching the gun from thin air without being illegal for
competition. Even when the tension screws at the muzzle and trigger guard
are adjusted to hold the gun firmly in place for running, jumping, or climbing
during competition, the Fas-Trac exerts little resistance to the draw. In large
part this is due to its muzzle stabilizing system.

Inside the toe of the Fas-Trac is a molded synthetic insert held in place
by a steel retaining screw through the rear fold of the holster and a brass
muzzle tension screw through its side panels. The insert serves triple duty
as a sight track, a muzzle peg, and a muzzle stop. When a gun is holstered,
its front sight glides into the track as its muzzle slides over the tapered peg

585

Ernie Hill's Fas-Trac holster is available for optical-sighted Government Model pistols.

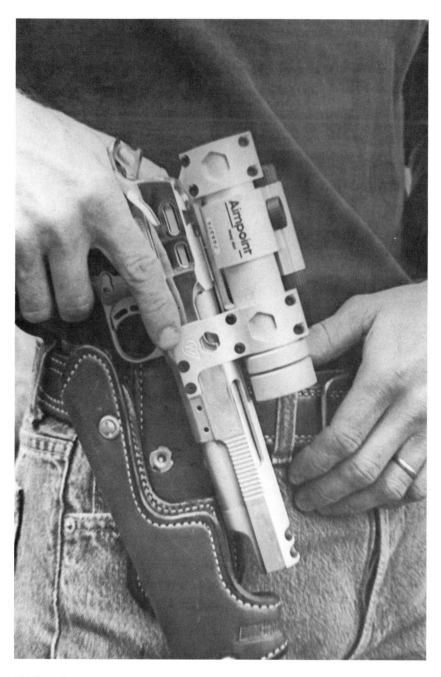

Lifting the gun about an inch clears its muzzle of leather when drawing from the Ernie Hill Fas-Trac holster.

This practical pistol competitor has one magazine in his gun and four
on his belt.

and comes to rest against the forward end of the insert. The amount of tension exerted on the gun's muzzle by the sides of the holster is adjusted by turning the brass screw with a coin.

Farther up is a second brass tension screw with its exposed shank inside the holster enclosed by a nylon sleeve. It serves as a stop against which the front of the trigger guard rests and can be used to vary the amount of tension exerted on the sides of the trigger guard by the holster. When using the Fas-Trac in competition, I prefer to leave the top screw only snug and place more holster tension on the muzzle of the gun with the bottom screw.

Opinions among IPSC competitors differ on the exact angle a holstered gun should hang from the belt during competition. Some like for it to be held perfectly vertical while others prefer muzzle-forward positions with the muzzle angled away from vertical by varying degrees. With competition holsters of yesteryear, you had two choices, either have one custom built with the exact angle you wanted or live with what the larger makers had to offer. Ernie Hill changed that with the introduction of his Fas-Trac holster and its dial an angle capability.

Rather than being integral with the holster, the belt loop of the Fas-Trac is a separate part joined to the body of the holster by Hill's adjustable Angle-Loc device. Secured to the back of the holster is a tough synthetic disc with

Ernie Hill's Fas-Trac holster, belt, and magazine pouch with a custom Springfield Armory compensated gun in .45 ACP.

deep serrations or teeth around the perimeter of its flat surface. An identical disc is fastened to the back of the belt loop. A heavy brass screw extends through the back of the belt loop and holds the discs together with their teeth engaged. When the screw is loosened enough to allow the teeth of the discs to disengage, the holster is free to swivel 360 degrees. Simply pick the angle you prefer, tighten the screw, and you're ready for competition.

The Fas-Trac is available for numerous autoloaders with barrel lengths ranging from 5- to 7-inches, including those made by Colt, Glock, Smith & Wesson, SIG/Sauer, Taurus, Beretta, Browning, and the various CZ-75 clones. It also is available for various Ruger, Colt, and S&W double-action revolvers. Optional finishes are natural hand-rubbed oil (my favorite) or black basketweave. When placing an order, you must specify the brand and model of your gun, its barrel length and caliber, whether it has open or optical sights, and the finish desired.

To increase the versatility of my Fas-Trac, I ordered it with a .45 caliber insert installed and an extra insert with a muzzle peg of smaller diameter. They are easily interchanged. Doing so enables me to use one holster with various Government Model comp guns (all with the same barrel length) in calibers .45 ACP, 10mm Auto, .38 Super, and 9x23mm Super. The same holster also fits my Warner custom Double Eagle comp gun perfectly.

Angelo Spagnoli has just snatched his compensated gun from an Ernie Hill Fas-Trac holster. *(Front Sight photo)*

590

Safariland's 008 Final Option

With the exception of its thin leather lining and steel screws, the 008 Final Option is made entirely of synthetic materials. The use of synthetic laminates enables Safariland to make an extremely durable yet exceptionally light holster. Bearing a slight resemblance to leather, the outer layer is a highly damage-resistant, urethane-based material called Porvair. To add shape-retaining stiffness to the holster, the middle layer is PVC. Inside next to the gun is a layer of sueded leather.

During fabrication, the layers of Porvair, PVC, and leather are sewn together with heavy nylon thread. A casting shaped like the pistol for which the holster is being made is placed inside and the entire works goes into a mold where it is heated to an extremely high temperature. After it is allowed to cool, out pops an extremely durable, uncommonly stiff, and totally dependable Final Option Holster.

A pistol is held in the Final Option by an adjustable retaining device described by Safariland as a trigger guard tension block. An injection molding, the retaining block is held to the inside surface of the holster's rear fold by two hexhead screws. The trigger guard latch eventually will wear out, requiring replacement of the entire block, but a new one available from Safariland is easily installed with a small hex wrench. The part number is 008-1.

When a gun is inserted into the Final Option, the bottom of its trigger guard slides into a track inside the block and comes to rest with its front surface resting against the sleeved shaft of a transverse tension screw. Pushing down and slightly rearward on the grip of the pistol forces the bottom of its trigger guard against the beveled edge of a spring-loaded latch, forcing it to retract into the righthand wall of the block. As the bottom of the trigger guard comes to rest against the track, the latch springs from its cavity with its end protruding inside the trigger guard. The trigger guard is now held captive between the flat bottom surface of the latch and the track's top surface.

Once latched into the Final Option, a pistol cannot rock forward and out the open front of the holster during competition. In fact, when the tension screw is adjusted to maximum, you can do handstands or cartwheels and the holster won't lose its grip on the gun. How the holster can hold a gun so securely and yet release it smoothly during the draw can be seen by closely examining the shape of the latch. When the gun is lifted vertically, the front inner surface of its trigger guard is forced against the beveled front surface of the latch, causing it to retract back into its cavity in the block.

The Final Option holster can be used with belts other than the original Safariland Model 023 (black basketweave) or 095 (brown stitched), but doing

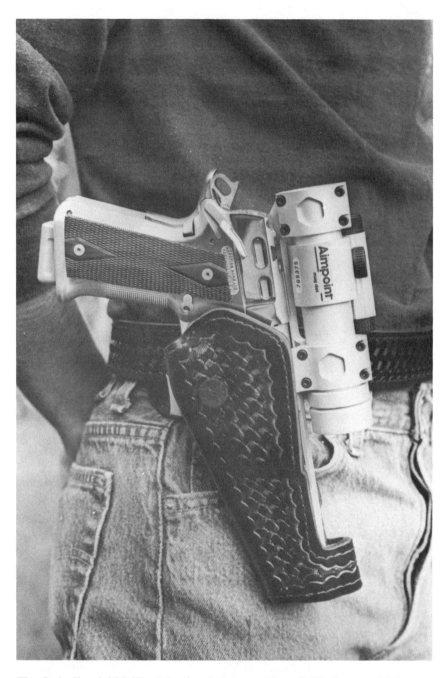

The Safariland 008 Final Option holster with a C. W. Custom high-capacity .38 Super built around the Caspian frame and slide.

A practical pistol competitor caught in the act of drawing his compensated pistol from a Safariland 008 Final Option holster.

Debbie James making her compensated Government Model in .38 Super sing its song. *(Front Sight photo)*

so defeats the intent behind one of its design features. Also fabricated of synthetic laminates, the belt is fully lined with Velcro® which mates with the same material inside the belt loop. Since the tunnel inside the loop is considerably wider than the 1½-inch wide belt, the holster can be swiveled to a shooter's preferred angle where it is held firmly in that position by the Velcro®. Once the Velcro® has welded (and I do mean welded), the belt and holster are extremely difficult to separate.

Safariland offers a similar competition holster called the Cup Challenge, but the Final Option is available for the Government Model pistol with three barrel lengths only, standard 5-inch (A), and two for compensated barrels of 5¾- to 6¼-inches (B) and 6½- to 7-inches (C). Since the end of this holster is open, barrel length is noncritical as long as the barrel is not shorter than the minimums listed in the three available holster lengths. For example, a gun with a 5-inch barrel won't work in holster length B, but a gun with a 6½-inch comped barrel will work in holster A. The muzzle of the longer gun will extend beyond the end of the holster and by doing so increase the distance the gun must be lifted before it clears the holster. In other words, if you start competing with a Government Model pistol with 5-inch barrel and the A length holster, and later install a 6½-inch comped barrel on the gun, you can get by with the same holster, but your speed is likely to suffer a bit until you spring for the size C holster.

I am extremely impressed by the speed, durability, and clever design of Safariland's latest, but using it in competition takes a bit more getting used to than other holsters. With practice, you learn to insert the muzzle of a pistol into the holster's toe until the front of the trigger guard stops against the shank of the transverse tension adjustment screw and then push the trigger guard firmly against the latch. When wearing ear protection you can't hear the latch click into engagement with the trigger guard of the gun, but you can feel it through its grip.

Even if you miss the latch when reholstering, it is unlikely that the gun will roll forward through the open front of the holster and end up in the mud. If the trigger guard is not engaged by the latch, the open-end design simply allows the gun to sink deeper into the Final Option where it is loosely retained by the narrow strip of material around the holster's toe.

The only custom modification commonly made to the Government Model pistol that is not compatible with the Final Option is checkering on the bottom of the trigger guard. The lock block in the holster will accept a trigger guard so modified, but the sharp checkering will chew up its latch in short order. Checkering on the front of the trigger guard works fine because that area does not make contact with the latch.

Due to the tremendous gripping power of the mating Velcro® linings, your first attempt at pushing the Safariland belt through the loop on the Final Option holster probably will end in total frustration unless you employ a little trick most owners of this rig have had to learn the hard way. First, insert a strip of paper approximately eight inches long and two inches wide into the belt loop of the holster and against its Velcro® liner. This prevents the Velcro® inside the belt from engaging its mate while the belt is being pushed through the loop. With the holster positioned on the belt where you want it and adjusted to the desired angle, remove the paper and the holster will stay in position until the cows come home.

Rather than fighting the Velcro® grip before each match, I find it best to leave the Final Option permanently attached to its belt. When strapping on the rig for competition, I remove the buckle from the belt and feed that end through the loops on my trousers, beginning at my right rather than my left side. Before installing the buckle, magazine pouches are slid over that end of the belt.

I mention all of this only because thousands of the original models 023 and 095 belts are still in use throughout the world. Safariland introduced an even better way to skin an already good cat in 1992. When combined with the Model 029 underbelt, the Models 028 (black basketweave) and 098 (plain brown) buckleless belts represent one of the greatest ideas in competition rig design. This setup lets you peel off the outer belt after a match without removing the holster and magazine pouches. Great idea.

Magazine Pouches

You can get by with a couple of extra magazines when shooting some stages of some matches, but you will need quite a few on others. I remember shooting a 100-round match in which one stage required the expenditure of 38 rounds of ammunition. On that stage I needed a minimum of five, eight-round magazines for my Colt .45 ACP comp gun, but a mandatory reload at one point required that I have six. On the other hand, had I been shooting that stage with a high-capacity gun in 9x23mm Super, two of its magazines would have sufficed.

Regardless of how many extra magazines you need during a match, the only satisfactory way to carry them is in holders or pouches hanging from the belt. They are available from several companies for various types of magazines, from the single-column Government Model styles to the wider staggered-column magazines for the various high-capacity guns.

Some shooters prefer to carry all magazines in the vertical position. Others prefer to carry the front magazines horizontally or at their favorite angles between horizontal and vertical. When worn in that position, the magazines don't stab you in the breadbasket when you bend over. The most popular magazine holders available are made by Safariland and Ernie Hill Speed Leather. Other companies make them, but for serious competitive use they position magazines too close to the body therefore making them slower to use in a speed match.

The most handsome magazine holders around are those available from Ernie Hill in single-, double-, and triple-pocket styles. Each pocket has its own brass tension screw. Depending on the model number, they hold magazines in a variety of positions ranging from horizontal to vertical and several angles in between. For example, my Model 2FDM holds two magazines in the vertical position; my Model 3FDM holds the same number of magazines angled slightly above the horizontal position. As we have come to expect from Hill, these beauties are made from extremely heavy, top-quality cowhide.

The Safariland holders are extemely versatile due to their almost unlimited angle adjustment capability. Made of extremely durable and ridged synthetic laminates, they have individual tension screws and are fastened to a thin PVC bar with two screws each. Two screws also hold the bar to a molded PVC belt loop. The bar and the holders each have 45 degrees of angle adjustment which enables the shooter to wear extra magazines in about any practical position or combination of positions imaginable.

Ron Griffin is wearing a triple-pocket Ernie Hill holder that positions
the magazines at about a 45-degree angle.

This twin-pocket leather holder from Ernie Hill has tension screws
and positions magazines on the belt in a vertical position.

Safariland 008 Final Option holster, belt, and magazine pouches with a Wilson Super Grade in .38 Super.

These magazine holders are designed specifically for the Safariland synthetic belts and naturally work best with them. They can be used with other belts as long as maximum width does not exceed 1.70 inches and the belt is not over .200-inch thick. On the negative side, the sharp edges on the plastic belt loops will absolutely ravage the smooth finish of your beautiful leather belt.

The Limited Class Holster

Members of the United States Practical Shooting Association who consider a compensated pistol with an optical sight a bit less than practical got their way in 1992 when the organization adopted a new Limited classification for handguns. In a nutshell, if a gun does not have a compensated barrel or optical sight, it is a Limited class gun. If it has either or both, it is an Unlimited class gun.

The majority elected to allow the continued use of pure competition holsters like the Safariland Final Option and Ernie Hill's Fas-Trac. If common sense prevails, and I'm sure it will, that particular rule will remain unchanged. Although those holsters are not practical in the true sense of the word, they are much safer to draw from because they hold the gun away from the body rather than snugged closely against it as most other types do. In addition, they position the gun with its muzzle pointed either straight down (toward the ground) or angled slightly forward. Some carry or duty holsters angle the muzzle to the rear and I for one wouldn't want to be standing directly behind a competitor who is wearing one when the buzzer sounds. If it ever does come to pass that holsters used in Limited class competition must be as practical as the guns, those who make the rules will surely take this into consideration.

27

Into the Twenty-first Century

I N the year 2011, the Government Model pistol will be 100 years old and still very much alive and kicking. Few other firearms can boast of such a track record. The Winchester Model 94 deer rifle is still around, and Colt's custom shop occasionally turns out a single action revolver or two. A few companies still make the 1898 Mauser rifle in its original form, and I believe the Luger pistol is still being built in small quantities in Europe. The 1899 Savage lever action rifle is still with us, but only barely.

Each new year brings more new guns competing for a place in the hearts of handgunners, but they have yet to dethrone the Government Model as America's favorite centerfire autoloader. There are several reasons for this. For one, John Browning's old gun is still made of good, solid steel parts rather than a combination of metal stampings and synthetic materials. This makes it look like a gun one would be proud to own. Nostalgia and tradition also continue to contribute to the ever-growing popularity of the Government Model. Last, but certainly not least in importance, no other autoloading pistol responds so well to custom work. For this reason, thousands of handgunners consider a custom Government Model pistol the most handsome handgun in the world.

The American shooter is rather a whimsical creature and predicting how long into the twenty-first century the Government Model pistol will maintain its great popularity is a tough job, but it probably will depend on the application. With this in mind, I'll gaze deep into my crystal ball and make a few predictions.

Bullseye competitors are likely to stick with custom Government Model pistols on into the twenty-first century.

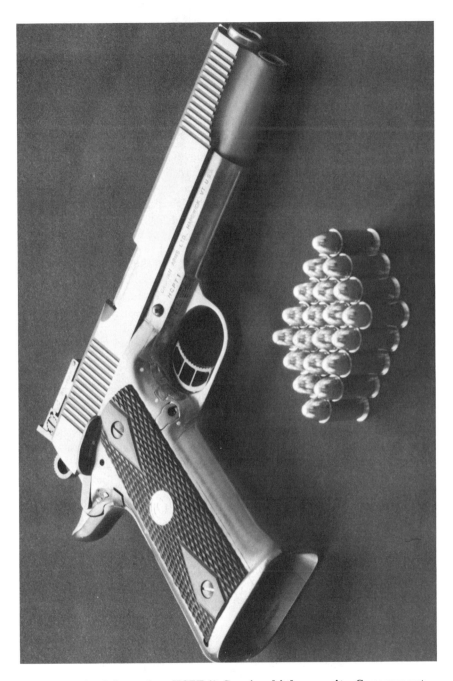

Prototype (serial number HCPT-1) Caspian high-capacity Government Model in .38 Super. *(Paul Hantke photo)*

Personal Defense

In law enforcement circles, the Government Model pistol has lost the race to high-capacity guns in 9mm Luger and .40 S&W. Those same guns also are becoming the first choice among private sector citizens who use factory guns. The Government Model and its variations will continue to have a stronger following among those who have custom guns built simply because John Browning's old gun seems more deserving of the effort than any other centerfire autoloader. There also are those who believe seven to eight rounds of .45 ACP punch is all the firepower one needs. Practically speaking, I personally can't imagine why any private citizen would need more than a Government Model, an Officer's ACP, or perhaps a lightweight Commander with its magazine filled with Remington's 185-grain +P load for home defense use, but such an opinion is not as popular today as it once was.

I'll have to admit, a high-capacity gun does solve the problem of how best to carry extra ammunition. When I holster my Glock 22 in .40 S&W, its magazine has 15 rounds on tap. This is one round of firepower more than my C. W. Custom Officer's ACP and I have to tote an extra "+1" magazine with it. Building a high-capacity custom gun around the Caspian aluminum frame solves the extra ammo problem, but it does become somewhat cumbersome for a carry gun.

Competition

I don't see any handgun dethroning the Government Model pistol among bullseye shooters for many years. I say this because no other autoloading pistol offers an equal level of accuracy, reliability, and durability. Some of the other autoloaders are as accurate, some are as reliable, and a very small number are as durable, but not a single one is all three.

In USPSA/IPSC competition, smaller autoloaders in 9x21mm have presented somewhat of a threat to Government Model supremacy, but all is not roses in River City. When subjected to the pounding dished out by thousands of heavy Major-power loads each year, those guns are nowhere near as durable simply because they are not designed to withstand the strain. As it now stands, you have two choices: buy a custom 9mm Luger-size competition rig and replace it every year or so, or pay the same price for a custom Government Model and shoot it until the cows come home. Regardless of the gun or who builds it, nothing comes close to withstanding the pounding of Major-power loads like a Government Model pistol. The same goes for trigger quality—nothing else comes close in this department to a highly tuned Government Model pistol.

Like most serious practical pistol competitors, Debbie James is
switching to a high-capacity gun. (Front Sight *photo*)

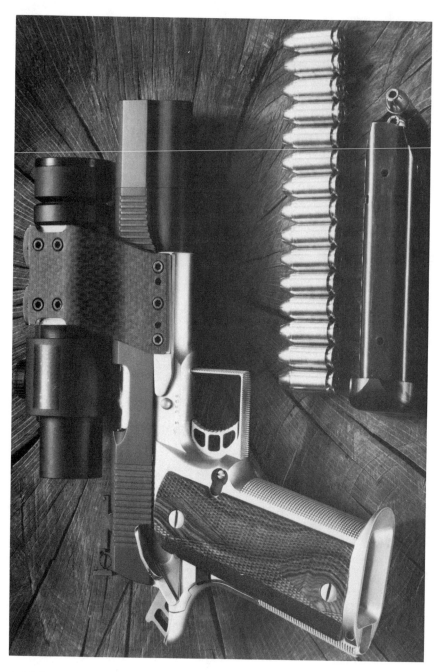

A high-capacity compensated competition gun in .40 S&W built
around a Para-Ordnance frame and Caspian slide by Bill Laughridge.

Mike Yorke reloads his optical-sighted .38 Super while on the run.
*(*Front Sight *photo)*

Todd Jarrett was the first to win a major practical pistol tournament with a high-capacity Government Model in .38 Super on the Para-Ordnance frame. (Front Sight *photo*)

If not for the introduction of new high-capacity frames from Caspian, Para-Ordnance, and CMC, the Government Model may have eventually lost out in popularity to the 9mm Luger-size competition guns. As I now see it, the only reason anyone will be shooting anything other than an optical-sighted, high-capacity Government Model pistol in .38 Super or CP 9x23mm Super in Unlimited class practical pistol competition is because they are being paid to do so.

The Government Model pistol may have a tougher row to hoe among some Limited class practical pistol competitors. I say this because as the USPSA rules now stand, the .40 S&W is the minimum acceptable Major power cartridge. High-capacity guns such as the Glock, the Taurus, and the Springfield Armory P9 in that caliber will likely become the first choice of those competitors who choose to shoot factory guns. On the other hand, since most of the really serious competitors are likely to shoot custom guns, high-capacity Government Model pistols will take home their share of Limited class gold. As these words are written, Bill Wilson and Chuck Warner are already cranking out high-capacity Limited class guns in .45 ACP and 10mm Auto built around the steel Para-Ordnance frame. Warner also is building guns around the Para-Ordnance aluminum frame that weigh less than a standard-capacity Government Model with a steel frame. His aluminum-framed gun has Bob Krieger's ACC-U-RAIL system, the Heinie-designed steel recoil block, and a Caspian slide. His plans are the same with Caspian's high-capacity aluminum frame. I expect to see other pistolsmiths follow suit.

Cartridges

The .45 ACP is a remarkable cartridge. Despite the fact that it now has much more competition from other autoloading cartridges than in years past, its popularity continues to grow. Here's an example of what I'm talking about. One of our major manufacturers of autoloading pistols hopped aboard the .40 S&W bandwagon just as that cartridge was riding the crest of its huge wave of publicity. Eventually, the same basic gun also was offered in .45 ACP. Within less than six months, that manufacturer had sold more .45 caliber autoloaders than will be sold in .40 S&W in several years.

The .45 ACP is yielding to the firepower rage in law enforcement circles, but I don't see it losing much ground in personal defense guns among the private sector. A Government Model in .40 S&W holds one more round of ammunition, but the majority of handgun owners believe that pales to insignificance when its bullet diameter is compared to the .45 ACP. The introduction by Remington of a +P factory load with its 185-grain jacketed hollowpoint bullet at 1140 fps has definitely transformed the .45 ACP into a twenty-first century cartridge.

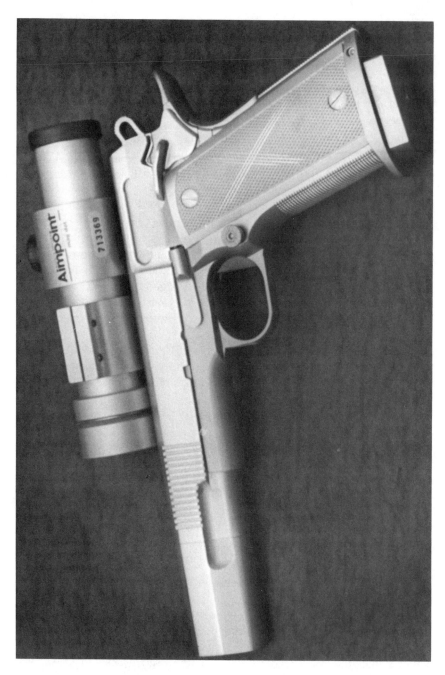

Left-side view of a Chuck Warner high-capacity Para-Ordnance in .38 Super with a lightened slide and his full-profile compensator.

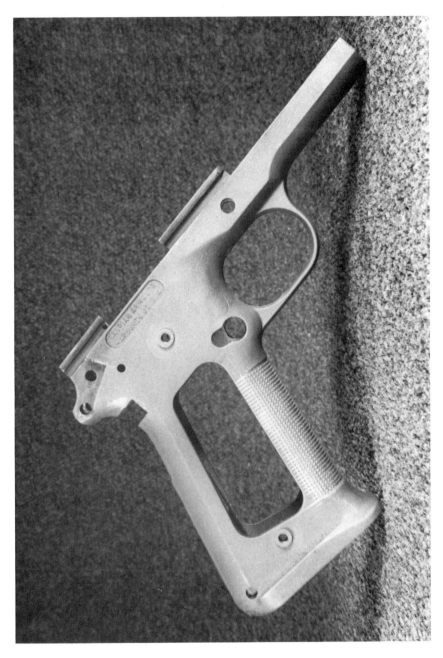

This Caspian high-capacity aluminum frame weighs five ounces, or
nine ounces less than a standard-capacity Colt steel frame.

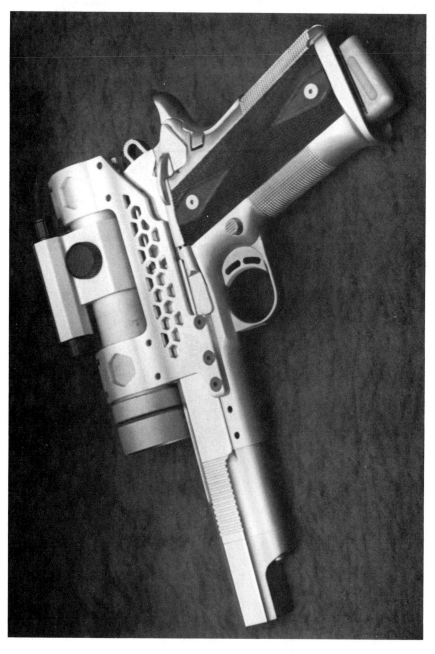

Left-side view of a Chuck Warner high-capacity .38 Super built around a Caspian frame and a lightened and shortened Caspian slide.

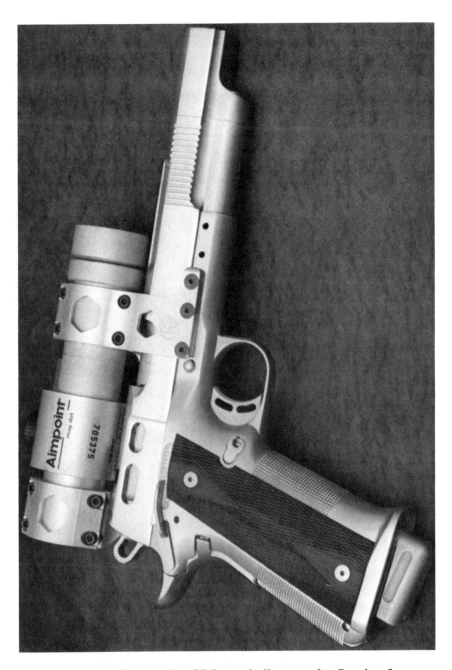

Chuck Warner high-capacity .38 Super built around a Caspian frame
and slide wearing a fat-dot Aimpont in a Weigand Stabilizer mount.
(Cecil Hare photo)

Right-side view of a Chuck Warner high-capacity Para-Ordnance in .38 Super with a lightened slide and his full-profile compensator.

Steve Woods high-capacity Para-Ordnance in .38 Super with his compensator, scope mount, and lightened Colt slide. *(Stephen Longley photo)*

Rick Bowerman shooting a 20-shot .38 Super built on the Caspian frame by Glades Gunworks.

Called the Burner, this 20-round .38 Super is one of the first three built by Bill Wilson on the McCormick-Tripp frame. The 48-ounce gun was built to the author's specifications for use in the 1992 USPSA National Championships.

Named after Jerry Barnhart, the 20-shot Burner in .38 Super and built on the McCormick-Tripp frame represents Bill Wilson's first entry in the IPSC Unlimited class high-capacity race. Barnhart won the 1992 USPSA National Championship with a similar gun.

Don Fraley
D&J Custom Gun Shop
426 Ferry Street
Russell, KY 41169
(606) 836-2663

Jim Garthwaite
Jim Garthwaite Pistolsmiths
Rt. 2, Box 310
Watsontown, PA 17777
(717) 538-1566

Richard Heinie
Richard Heinie Products
323 West Franklin
Havana, IL 62464
(309) 543-4535

Bill Jarvis
Jarvis Gunsmithing, Inc.
Box 173
Hamilton, MT 59840
(406) 961-4392

J. D. Jones
SSK Industries
721 Woodvue Ln.
Wintersville, OH 43952
(614) 264-1076

Ben Jones
Kim Stroud
Gun Craft, Inc.
2403 21st Ave. S.E.
Ruskin, FL 33570
(813) 645-3828

Bob Krieger
Bob Krieger, Inc.
2271 Star Court
Rochester Hills, MI 48309
(313) 853-6171

Dave Lauck
D&L Sports
P.O. Box 651
Gillette, WY 82717
(307) 686-4008

Bill Laughridge
Cylinder and Slide, Inc.
P.O. Box 937
Fremont, NE 68025
(402) 721-4277

Glenn Martin
Shooter's World
3828 N. 28th Ave.
Phoenix, AZ 85017
(602) 973-4640
(602) 226-0170

Steve Nastoff
Nastoff's .45 Shop
P.O. Box 446
12288 Mahoning Ave.
North Jackson, OH 44451
(216) 538-2977

Dave Pegram
Triad Custom Handguns
620 South Elm St., Ste. 167
Greensboro, NC 27406
(919) 370-0571

Irving Stone, III
Bar-Sto Precision Machine
P.O. Box 1838
29 Palms, CA 92277
(619) 367-2747

Jim Stroh
Alpha Precision
2765 Preston Rd.
Good Hope, GA 30641
(404) 267-6163

George Vais
Vais Arms
6611-2 Chimney Rock
Houston, TX 77081
(713) 664-6961

Tom Volquartsen
Volquartsen Custom Ltd.
Rt. 1
Carroll, IA 51401
(712) 792-2542

Chuck Warner
C. W. Custom
4E Dudley
Southport Industrial Park
Robuck, SC 29376
(803) 576-8557

Jack Weigand
Weigand Combat Handguns, Inc.
341 South Main Road
Mountaintop, PA 18707
(717) 474-9804

Neil Wiggans
The Shooters Shop
Route 2, Box 154A
Atlanta, MO 63530
(816) 239-4346

Bill Wilson
Ron Phillips
Wilson's Gun Shop, Inc.
Rt. 3, P.O. Box 578
Berryville, AR 72616
(501) 545-3618

Steven P. Woods
Woods Pistolsmithing
3840 Dahlgren Ct.
Ellicott City, MD 21043
(301) 465-7979

Appendix II

Other Contributors

These people and companies also assisted in the preparation of this book and the author is forever grateful.

Steve Alexander
SA Shooting Accessories, Inc.
P.O. Box 835790
Richardson, TX 75083
(214) 231-6084

Charles Bane
Carter Jones
Bull-X Incorporated
P.O. Box 183
Farmer City, IL 61842
(309) 928-2574

Burt Bastian
Storm Lake Machine
177700 147th St. SE
Monroe, WA 98272

L.L. Baston Company
P.O. Box 1995
El Dorado, AR 71731
(800) 643-1564

Wayne Bergquist
Glades Gunworks, Inc.
4360 Corporate Square
Naples, FL 33942
(813) 643-2922

Betty Bell
Protective Optics, Inc.
1320 W. Winton Ave.
Hayward, CA 94545
(800) 77-OPTIC

Horace Booth
Checkmate Custom Gun
    Refinishers
8232 Shawn Road
Brooksville, FL 34602
(904) 799-5774

Hope Bianchi
Bianchi International
100 Calle Cortez
Temecula, CA 92390
(714) 676-5621

Behn's Bullets
208 N. 27th Ave.
St. Cloud, MN 56303
(612) 253-8653

W. E. Birdsong
Black-T
P.O. Box 9549
Jackson, MS 39206

Frank Brownell III
Brownells, Inc.
Route 2, Box 1
Montezuma, IA 50171
(515) 623-5401

Pat Connors
The Shooter Shop
514 N. Main
Butte, MT 59701
(406) 723-3842

Dave Corbin
Corbin Manufacturing
P.O. Box 2659
White City, OR 97503
(503) 826-5211

Mike Dillon
Dillon Precision Products, Inc.
7442 E. Butherus Dr.
Scottsdale, AZ 85260
(602) 948-8009

Frank Garcia
B.A.T. Products
P.O. Box 55-8266
Miami, FL 33255
(305) 688-0262

Paul Hantke
23642 Via Chiripa
Misson Viejo, CA 92691

Scott Helmer
Tasco Sales, Inc.
7600 Northwest 26 Street
Miami, FL 33122
(305) 591-3670

Kim Hendon
Aimpoint
580 Herndon Parkway
Suite 500
Herndon, VA 22070
(703) 472-6828

Janet Herriott
Centaur Systems, Inc.
1602 Foothill Dr.
Kalispell, MT 59901
(406) 755-8609

Ernie Hill
Ernie Hill Speed Leather
4507 North 195th Ave.
Litchfield Park, AZ 85340

Don Jeckell
Safariland
3120 E. Mission Blvd.
Ontario, CA 91761
(714) 923-7300

Kerry R. Kinder
Hesco-Meprolight
2821 Greenville Rd.
LaGrange, GA 30240

Sheila Koenig
Tru-Flight Bullets
421 N. Pennsylvania Ave.
Wilkes Barre, PA 18702
(717) 821-5644

Stephen "Steve" Longley
2224 N. Charles St.
Baltimore, MD 21218
(301) 467-4185

David Manson
Clymer Chamber Reamer Co.
1645 W. Hamlin Rd.
Rochester Hills, MI 48309
(313) 853-5555

Michael's Of Oregon
P.O. Box 13010
Portland, OR 97213
(503) 255-6890

Betty Millett
Millett Sights
16131 Gothard St.
Huntington Beach, CA 92647
(714) 843-5575

Milt Sparks Holsters
605 E. 44th St.
Boise, ID 83714
(208) 377-5577

Rebecca Nill
Trijicon, Inc.
P.O. Box 2130
Farmington Hills, MI 48333
(313) 553-4960

Ken Oehler
Oehler Research
P.O. Box 9135
Austin, TX 78766
(512) 327-6900

John Ricco
C.P. Bullets
1814 Mearns Rd.
Warminster, PA 18974
(215) 956-9595

Joe Scurto
DeSantis Holster & Leather
149 Denton Ave.
New Hyde Park, NY 11040
(516) 354-8000

Gary Smith
Caspian Arms, Ltd.
14 N. Main St.
Hardwick, VT 05843
(802) 472-6454

Dave Stanford
U.S. Practical Shooting Assn.
(*Front Sight* Magazine)
P.O. Box 811
Sedro Wooley, WA 98284
(206) 855-2245

Dave Wayland
Wayland Precision Wood
    Products
Box 1142
Mill Valley, CA 94942

Walter Wolff
Wolff Gun Spring Co.
P.O. Box I
Newtown, PA 19073
(800) 545-0077

Zediker Publishing
P.O. Box 426
Clifton, CO 81520
(303) 434-5305

Appendix III

Spring Rates

Factory Standard Spring Weights

Pistol	Weight (Pounds)
Government Model recoil spring, 9mm Luger	14
Government Model recoil spring, .38 Super	14
Government Model recoil spring, .40 S&W	20
Government Model recoil spring, 10mm Auto	23
Government Model recoil spring, .45 ACP	16
Government Model hammer spring (mainspring)	23
Government Model magazine spring (10mm)	10
Government Model magazine spring (.45 ACP)	9½
Government Model magazine spring (9mm Luger)	7
Government Model magazine spring (.38 Super)	7
Commander recoil spring, 9mm Luger	16
Commander recoil spring, .38 Super	16
Commander recoil spring, .45 ACP	18
Commander hammer spring (mainspring)	23
Commander magazine spring	*
Officer's ACP recoil spring, .45 ACP	23
Officer's ACP hammer spring (mainspring)	23
Officer's ACP magazine spring	*
Colt ACE, recoil spring, .22 Long Rifle	14

*Same as Government Model

NOTE: The factory standard recoil spring rates for the Double Eagle and its variations are the same.

Recommended Recoil Spring Rates

Pistol	Caliber	Type Load	Compensated Barrel	Spring Rating *(Pounds)*
Officer's ACP	.45 ACP	+P	No	24
Officer's ACP	.45 ACP	Hardball	No	22
Officer's ACP	.45 ACP	Target	No	18.5
Commander	.45 ACP	+P	No	22
Commander	.45 ACP	Hardball	No	18.5
Commander	.45 ACP	Target	No	14
Commander	.38 Super	Factory	No	16
Commander	9mm Luger	Factory	No	16
Government Model	.45 ACP	Pin loads	No	22+
Government Model	.45 ACP	+P	No	20
Government Model	.45 ACP	+P	Yes	18.5
Government Model	.45 ACP	Hardball	No	16
Government Model	.45 ACP	Hardball	Yes	14
Government Model	.45 ACP	IPSC(1)	No	18.5
Government Model	.45 ACP	IPSC(1)	Yes	15
Government Model	.45 ACP	Target	No	12
Government Model	.45 ACP	Target	Yes	10
Government Model	.45 ACP	Bullseye(2)	No	8
Government Model	10mm Auto	Factory	No	23
Government Model	10mm Auto	Factory	Yes	19
Government Model	10mm Auto	IPSC(1)	No	20
Government Model	10mm Auto	IPSC(1)	Yes	17
Government Model	10mm Auto	Subsonic	No	15
Government Model	.40 S&W	(Same as for 10mm Auto)		
Government Model	.38 Super	Factory	No	14
Government Model	.38 Super	Factory	Yes	10
Government Model	.38 Super	IPSC(1)	No	16
Government Model	.38 Super	IPSC(3)	Yes	12
Government Model	.38 Super	IPSC(4)	Yes	10
Government Model	.38 Super	Steel(5)	Yes	9

Pistol	Caliber	Type Load	Compensated Barrel	Spring Rating *(Pounds)*
Government Model	9x23mm Super	(Same as for .38 Super)		
Government Model	9x21mm +P	(Same as for .38 Super)		
Government Model	9mm Luger	Factory	No	14
Government Model	9mm Luger	Subsonic	No	12

(1) Major power loads for USPSA/IPSC competition.
(2) 200-grain bullet at 650 to 700 fps.
(3) Major power loads with 147-grain and heavier bullets.
(4) Major power loads with bullets lighter than 147 grains.
(5) 115-grain bullet at 1,000 to 1,050 fps for steel plate competition.

NOTE: These recommended spring rates are to be used only as a guide or starting point. Some gun and load combinations will require the use of springs heavier or lighter than the rates shown.

Wolff Spring Selection

Government Model

Type Spring	Weights Available *(Pounds)*
Recoil (standard-rate)	7, 8, 9, 10, 11, 12, 13, 14, 15, 16, 17, 18.5, 20, 22, 23, 25, 26
Recoil (variable-rate)	5, 6, 7, 8, 9, 10, 11, 12, 13, 14, 15, 16.5, 17, 18.5, 20, 22, 23, 24, 26
Hammer (mainspring)	17, 18, 19, 20, 21, 23, 25, 26, 28, 30, 34
Magazine catch	1, 2, 3, 4
Firing pin (extra-power)	About 15 percent stronger than factory standard
Plunger tube	Factory replacement
Firing pin block	Factory replacement

Type Spring	Weights Available *(Pounds)*
Magazine (.45 caliber)*	6, 7, 8, 9.5, 10, 11
Magazine (.38 caliber)*	6, 6.5, 7, 7.5, 8
Magazine (9mm caliber)*	6, 6.5, 7, 7.5, 8

Commander

Recoil (standard-rate)	12, 13, 14, 15, 16, 17, 18, 20, 22, 24, 26, 27
Recoil (variable-rate)	7, 8, 9, 10, 11, 12, 13, 14, 15, 16, 17, 18, 19, 20, 21

Officer's ACP

Recoil (standard-rate)	18.5, 20, 22, 24
Hammer (mainspring)	20, 21, 22, 23, 24, 25

Wolff Recoil Calibration Spring Kits

Kit	Springs Included
Ultra-Light Pak**	5, 6, 7, 8, 9
Reduced-Power Pak**	11, 12, 13, 14, 15
Extra-Power Pak**	18.5, 20, 22, 24
Reduced-Power Pak Variable**	9, 10, 11, 13, 14, 15
Extra-Power Pak Variable**	17.5, 18.5, 20, 22
Master Calibration Pak***	9, 10, 11, 12, 13, 14, 15, 17.5, 18.5, 20, 22

*For Government Model and all other variations of this caliber.
**Also contains three extra-power firing pin springs.
***Also contains five extra-power firing pin springs.

Weights in Grains of Wolff Recoil Springs*
(Progressive-weight)

Energy Rating (Pounds)	Weight (Grains)
5.0	68.7
6.0	72.4
7.0	80.3
8.0	86.4
10.0	96.1
11.0	98.3
12.0	104.7
13.0	107.6
14.0	111.9
15.0	115.5
16.5	121.5
17.5	128.3
18.5	129.0
22.0	140.8

*Springs were weighed on an RCBS electronic powder scale, but may vary slightly in weight from lot to lot.

Appendix IV

Factory Load Velocities

9mm Parabellum (Luger)

Load	Advertised* Velocity (fps)	Actual Velocity (fps) 4.25" Barrel	5" Barrel
MagSafe 60-gr. EES	1,900	1,911	1,951
MagSafe 68-gr. EES	1,730	1,724	1,772
Remington 88-gr. JHP	1,500	1,528	1,563
Hornady 90-gr. JHP-XTP	1,360	1,372	1,411
Hornady 100-gr. FMJ-RN	1,220	1,184	1,206
Cor-Bon 115-gr. JHP +P	1,350	1,312	1,331
Remington 115-gr. JHP +P	1,250	1,274	1,286
Black Hills 115-gr. JHP-XP	1,250	1,227	1,238
Winchester 115-gr. STHP	1,225	1,171	1,202
Hornady 115-gr. JHP-XTP	1,155	1,210	1,229
Speer Lawman 115-gr. JHP	1,155	1,118	1,133
CCI Blazer 115-gr. JHP	1,155	1,191	1,252
Cor-Bon 124-gr. JHP +P	1,250	1,241	1,268
CCI Blazer 124-gr. TMJ	1,155	1,109	1,146
CCI Blazer 124-gr. TMJ-LF	1,155	1,172	1,210
Remington 124-gr. FMJ-RN	1,110	1,152	1,183
Hornady 124-gr. FMJ-FN	1,110	1,107	1,129

Load	Advertised* Velocity (fps)	Actual Velocity (fps)	
		4.25" Barrel	5" Barrel
Remington 140-gr.			
SJHP-SUB	935	951	960
Cor-Bon 147-gr. JHP +P	1,100	1,122	1,142
Winchester 147-gr.			
STHP-SUB	1,010	1,044	1,058
Speer Lawman 147-gr.			
JHP-SUB	1,000	968	974
CCI Blazer 147-gr. TMJ	1,000	1,014	1,036
Remington 147-gr. JHP-SUB	990	1,010	1,024
Winchester 147-gr. JHP-SUB	990	1,003	1,019
Winchester 147-gr.			
FMJ-TCM**	990	988	1,018
Black Hills 147-gr. JHP	975	966	809

*In 4-inch barrels
**Target load

.38 Super

Load	Advertised* Velocity (fps)	Actual Velocity (fps)		
		4.25" Barrel	5" Barrel	5.50" Barrel
Remington 115-gr. JHP +P	1,300	1,192	1,241	1,283
Winchester 125-gr. STHP +P	1,240	1,178	1,210	1,259
Winchester 130-gr. FMJ +P	1,215	1,156	1,198	1,244
Remington 130-gr. FMJ**	1,040	961	1,017	1,033

*In 5-inch barrels.
**Remington no longer loads the 130-grain FMJ bullet in the .38 Super. This is the .38 ACP load which is still available.

.40 Smith & Wesson

Load	Advertised* Velocity (fps)	Actual** Velocity (fps)
Cor-Bon 150-gr. JHP	1,200	1,251

Load	Advertised* Velocity *(fps)*	Actual** Velocity *(fps)*
Winchester 155-gr. STHP	1,205	1,152
Hornady 155-gr. JHP-XTP	1,180	1,171
Black Hills 155-gr. JHP	1,150	1,167
Remington 155-gr. JHP	1,140	1,168
Winchester 155-gr. FMJ-TCM***	1,125	1,088
Cor-Bon 180-gr. JHP	1,050	1,061
CCI Blazer 180-gr. PHP	1,000	1,022
Winchester 180-gr. JHP	990	954
Winchester 180-gr. JHP-SUB	990	941
Remington 180-gr. JHP	985	1,010
Black Hills 180-gr. JHP	950	966
Hornady 180-gr. JHP-XTP	950	965
Hornady 180-gr. FMJ-FN	950	970

*In 4-inch barrels
**5-inch barrel
***Match load

10mm Auto

Load	Advertised* Velocity *(fps)*	Actual** Velocity *(fps)*
MagSafe 96-gr. EES	1,780	1,765
Cor-Bon 150-gr. JHP	1,300	1,366
Hornady 155-gr. JHP-XTP	1,410	1,310
Black Hills 155-gr. JHP	1,250	1,228
Winchester 155-gr. FMJ-TCM**	1,125	1,068
Winchester 175-gr. STHP	1,290	1,184
Hornady 180-gr. JHP-XTP	1,265	1,219
Remington 180-gr. JHP	1,240	1,210
Cor-Bon 180-gr. JHP	1,175	1,231
CCI Blazer 180-gr. PHP	1,150	1,108
Remington 180-gr. JHP-SUB	1,055	1,027
Winchester 180-gr. JHP-SUB	990	1,010
Black Hills 180-gr. JHP	950	972
Hornady 180-gr. JHP-XTP-SUB	950	1,015

Load	Advertised* Velocity (fps)	Actual** Velocity (fps)
Remington 200-gr. FMJ-FN	1,160	1,210
Hornady 200-gr. JHP-XTP	1,150	1,053
Hornady 200-gr. FMJ-FN	1,150	1,114
CCI Blazer 200-gr. TMJ	1,050	1,018

*In 5-inch barrels
**Match load

.41 Action Express

Load	Advertised* Velocity (fps)	Actual** Velocity (fps)
Speer Lawman 180-gr. PHP	1,000	977
IMI UZI 170-gr. JHP	1,200	1,114
IMI Samsom 200-gr. FMJ	1,000	910

*In a 5-inch Bar-Sto barrel

.45 ACP

Load	Advertised* Velocity (fps)	Actual Velocity (fps) 3.50" Barrel	4.25" Barrel	5" Barrel
Cor-Bon 185-gr. JHP +P	1,150	1,024	1,085	1,131
Remington 185-gr. JHP +P	1,140	1,047	1,083	1,134
Remington 185-gr. JHP	1,000	834	889	947
Winchester 185-gr. STHP	1,000	873	916	968
Black Hills 185-gr. JHP	975	911	924	963
Hornady 185-gr. JHP-STP	950	829	893	931
Remington 185-gr. FMJ-SWC**	770	684	717	735
Winchester 185-gr. FMJ-SWC**	770	663	702	751
CCI Blazer 185-gr. FMJ-SWC**	770	702	754	810

Load	Advertised* Velocity (fps)	Actual Velocity (fps)		
		3.50" Barrel	4.25" Barrel	5" Barrel
Cor-Bon 200-gr. JHP +P	1,050	952	977	1,038
Speer Lawman 200-gr. JHP	975	816	851	919
CCI Blazer 200-gr. JHP	975	822	864	947
Black Hills 200-gr. JHP	900	867	903	989
Hornady 200-gr. JHP-XTP	900	818	882	928
Hornady 200-gr. FMJ-SWC**	800	668	710	755
Black Hills 230-gr. FMJ-RN	850	776	810	838
Federal 230-gr. JHP-HS	850	758	809	855
Winchester 230-gr. JHP-SUB	850	762	803	841
Hornady 230-gr. FMJ-FN	850	805	831	865
CCI Blazer 230-gr. FMJ-RN	845	811	810	861
Remington 230-gr. FMJ-RN	835	792	821	846
Winchester 230-gr. FMJ-RN	835	763	788	804

*From 5-inch barrels
**Target load

Legend

EES:	Epoxy-encapsulated shot
FN:	Flat nose
FMJ:	Full-metal-jacketed
HS:	Hydra-Shok
JHP:	Jacketed hollowpoint
L:	Lead
LF:	Lead free
PHP:	Plated hollowpoint
RN:	Roundnose
STHP:	Silvertip hollowpoint
SJHP:	Semijacketed hollowpoint
SUB:	Subsonic
SWC:	Semiwadcutter
TCM:	Truncated cone match
TMJ:	Totally-metal-jacketed (plated)
XTP:	Extreme terminal performance

Appendix V

Actual Jacketed Bullet Diameters*

Manufacturer	Bullet Number	Weight (Grains)	Style	Diameter (Inch)
Nominal 9mm, .38 Caliber				
Hornady	3552	100.0	FMJ	.3547
Hornady	35700	110.0	JHP-XTP	.3578
Hornady	35540	115.0	JHP-STP	.3548
Hornady	3556	124.0	FMJ-FP	.3547
Hornady	35710	125.0	JHP-XTP	.3579
Hornady	35730	125.0	JHP-XTP	.3565
Hornady	3559	147.0	FMJ-RN-BT	.3546
Hornady	35580	147.0	JHP-XTP	.3545
Hornady	35780	158.0	FP-XTP	.3566
Hornady	35750	158.0	JHP-XTP	.3568
Hornady	3572	160.0	JTC-SIL	.3566
Nosler	42050	90.0	JHP	.3549
Nosler	42059	115.0	FMJ	.3548
Nosler	43009	115.0	JHP	.3546
Nosler	42055	125.0	JHP	.3566
Nosler	44839	150.0	IPSC	.3567
Nosler	42058	180.0	NE-SIL	.3563
Sierra	8105	95.0	FMJ	.3549
Sierra	8115	115.0	FMJ-TM	.3550

Manufacturer	Bullet Number	Weight *(Grains)*	Style	Diameter *(Inch)*
Sierra	8325	140.0	JHC	.3565
Sierra	9335	150.0	FPJ-TM	.3558
Sierra	8350	170.0	FMJ-TM	.3566
Sierra	8370	180.0	FPJ-TM	.3566
Speer	4000	88.0	JHP	.3548
Speer	4001	95.0	TMJ	.3548
Speer	3996	115.0	JHP	.3549
Speer	3995	115.0	TMJ	.3545
Speer	4004	124.0	TMJ	.3551
Speer	4006	147.0	TMJ	.3553
Tru-Flight	–	115.0	TCJ	.3547
Tru-Flight	–	125.0	TCJ	.3555
Tru-Flight	–	130.0	TCJ	.3564
Tru-Flight	–	135.0	TCJ	.3561
Tru-Flight	–	147.0	TCJ	.3563
Bull-X	–	125.0	JSN	.3553

Nominal .40 Caliber, 10mm

Manufacturer	Bullet Number	Weight *(Grains)*	Style	Diameter *(Inch)*
Hornady	40000	155.0	JHP-XTP	.3998
Hornady	40050	180.0	JHP-XTP	.3996
Hornady	40041	180.0	FMJ-FP	.3995
Hornady	4007	200.0	FMJ-FP	.3996
Hornady	40060	200.0	JHP-XTP	.3993
Nosler	44838	135.0	JHP	.4001
Nosler	44849	150.0	JHP	.4000
Nosler	44844	170.0	JHP	.3998
Nosler	44837	180.0	JHP	.3996
Sierra	8430	150.0	JHP	.3997
Sierra	8480	180.0	FPJ	.3998
Sierra	8480	190.0	FPJ	.3997
Speer	4401	180.0	PHP	.4001
Speer	4403	190.0	TMJ	.4003
Tru-Flight	–	180.0	TCJ	.4005

Manufacturer	Bullet Number	Weight (Grains)	Style	Diameter (Inch)
Nominal .41 Caliber				
Hornady	41000	210.0	JHP-XTP	.4101
Hornady	4105	210.0	JTC-SIL	.4097
Nosler	43012	210.0	JHP	.4098
Sierra	8500	170.0	JHC	.4000
Sierra	8520	210.0	JHC	.4099
Speer	4420	210.0	TMJ	.4096
Nominal .45 Caliber				
Hornady	45100	185.0	JHP-XTP	.4509
Hornady	4513	185.0	FMJ-SWC	.4507
Hornady	45140	200.0	JHP-XTP	.4509
Hornady	4515	200.0	FMJ-C/T	.4508
Hornady	45160	230.0	JHP-XTP	.4508
Hornady	4517	230.0	FMJ	.4506
Sierra	8800	185.0	JHP	.4514
Sierra	8810	185.0	FPJ	.4512
Sierra	8825	200.0	FPJ	.4513
Sierra	8815	230.0	FMJ	.4512
Sierra	8820	240.0	JHC	.4513
Speer	4473	185.0	SWC-TMJ	.4503
Speer	4475	200.0	SWC-TMJ	.4507
Speer	4477	200.0	JHP	.4509
Speer	4479	225.0	JHP	.4507
Speer	4480	230.0	FMJ	.4508
Speer	4481	260.0	JHP	.4507
Nosler	42062	185.0	JHP	.4511
Nosler	42064	230.0	FMJ	.4513
Nosler	43013	250.0	JHP	.4509
Tru-Flight	–	185.0	TCJ	.4514
Tru-Flight	–	200.0	SWC-TCJ	.4511
Tru-Flight	–	230.0	TCJ	.4511
Tru-Flight	–	250.0	TCJ	.4513

*Five each of the various bullets were randomly selected and measured with a micrometer.

NOTE: Bullets will vary slightly in diameter from lot to lot, even the same weight and style from the same manufacturer.

Appendix VI

The Cover Gun

The custom gun on the cover of this book was built by Chuck Warner of C. W. Custom. Since the author and C.P. Bullets received Clymer chamber reamers for the CP 9x23mm Super on the same day in early March of 1992, the high-capacity competition rig may be the very first gun built in that caliber. Completed long before 9x23mm cases became available, the gun has a C. W. Custom 5¼-inch heavy fluted barrel with TCP compensator, a titanium full-length recoil spring guide rod, and a T-Bone slide grasping handle. Kim Stroud of Gun Craft contoured the top of the compensator for a perfect match with the integral rib of the shortened Colt Gold Cup .38 Super Elite slide. The slide races smoothly over an Acc-U-Rail system installed by Bob Krieger on a swiss-cheesed Para-Ordnance steel frame. Also there are a Brown ambidextrous thumb safety and beavertail grip safety, Wilson titanium firing pin, C. W. Custom lightweight trigger, CMC titanium hammer and hammer strut, and Gun Craft steel magazine release with a Cylinder and Slide extended button. The magazine well funnel also is from Gun Craft. The Aimpoint 5000 electronic sight is held in place by a Woods frame-attached Competitor mount. Full-coverage 30-line checkering wraps around the recontoured and extended frontstrap. The bottom of the trigger guard and the heel of the slide have 40-line checkering. The blued and hard chrome finishes are by Horace Booth of Checkmate Custom Gun Refinishers. The checkered bocote grip panels are from Dave Wayland. The brass magazine bumper is from Wayne Bergquist.